The Dream Adventure

The Dream

Adventure

Edited with an introduction by Roger Caillois

The Orion Press
New York

All rights reserved
First printing
© 1963 by Roger Caillois
Library of Congress Catalog Card Number: 63-9524
Designed by Wladislaw Finne
Manufactured in the United States of America

The Editor has made every effort to trace the ownership of all copyrighted material. In the event of any question arising as to the use of any selections the Editor, while expressing regret for any error he may have made, will be pleased to make the necessary correction in future editions of this book. Thanks are due to the following authors, publishers, publications and representatives for permission to use the selections indicated:

The first, third, and fourth selections from Lieh Tzu are reprinted by permission from Lionel Giles' *Taoist Teachings from the Book of Lieh Tzu,* published by John Murray in their Wisdom of the East Series.

The selection from Shen Chi-chi is taken from *Traditional Chinese Tales* translated by Chi-Chen Wang and is reprinted by permission of the translator.

The second selection from P'u Sung-ling is taken from *Chinese Ghost and Love Stories,* copyright Rose Quong 1946, and is reprinted by permission of Rose Quong.

The selection from Ts'ao Hsueh ch'in is taken from Arthur Waley's preface to Chi-Chen Wang's translation of *Dream of the Red Chamber* and is reprinted by permission of Chi-Chen Wang.

The selection from Jean Lorrain is reprinted by permission of the Société des Gens de Lettres de France.

The selection from H. G. Wells is taken from *Collected Short Stories of H. G. Wells,* and is reprinted by permission of his Executors.

The selection from Oliver Onions is reprinted from *Widdershins* by permission of Willis Kingsley Wing and Berta Oliver.

The selection from W. Somerset Maugham is taken from *The Mixture As Before* by W. Somerset Maugham. Copyright 1939 by W. Somerset Maugham. Reprinted by permission of Doubleday & Company, Inc., the author, and William Heinemann Ltd.

"A Visit to the Museum" by Vladimir Nabokov. © Esquire, Inc. First published in Esquire Magazine.

The selection from Louis Golding is © "Pale Blue Nightgown" by Louis Golding from *A Book of Tales* under the title: *Pale Blue Nightgown,* published by Hutchinson & Co. Ltd, London, 1944. It appears by permission of Robert Harben.

The selection from Henry Kuttner and Catherine L. Moore is copyright 1953 by Ballantine Books Inc.

The selection from Luisa Mercedes Levinson is from *La Palida Rosa de Soho* and is reprinted by permission of the author.

The selection from Jorge Luis Borges is copyright 1961 by the University of Texas from *The Texas Quarterly,* Winter 1961, Vol. IV, No. 4.

The selection from Julio Cortazar is from *Bestiario* and is reprinted by permission of the author.

Contents

THE DREAM IN LITERATURE

CONCLUSION

Some there are who dream of feasting and when they waken they weep; others, who weep in their dreams yet when they waken go ahunting. Still, all of them when they dream know not that they dream, and at times they dream that they are engaged in dreaming: only at the moment that they waken do they know they have but dreamed. It is only at the Great Awakening that one knows that All has been only a Dream. The ignorant rabble believes itself awake and would distinguish the Prince from the shepherd. What presumption! Ch'iu and thou are nothing but dreams and when now I tell thee that thou dreamest, I too am dreaming my dream.

(*Chuang Tzu,* Ch. 2.)

Introduction

There are two types of problems concerning dreams that have always puzzled men's minds. One problem concerns the actual meaning or significance of the dream; the other, the relationship between the dream and the waking world or, one might say, the degree of reality that one may attribute to the dream.

Since time immemorial visions in dreams have seemed to man to disguise a meaning that is both mysterious and yet open to understanding, so that seemingly a competent interpreter should be capable of elucidating them. From this have stemmed innumerable "dream books" and "dream guides" whose purpose it is to decipher the strange and disconcerting messages of the dreams. One of the earliest of these collections goes back to ancient Egypt of the period of the Twelfth Dynasty (that is to say, to the eighteenth or twentieth century B.C.). In the Indian *Atharva Veda* which is usually attributed to the fifth century B.C., the Parishishtas of the sixty-eighth verse-chapter is called "Treatise on Dreams." This is based on a more ancient work which bears the same title and which catalogues the various omens foretold in dreams. Leo A. Oppenheim has published and translated a neo-Babylonian dream guide, part of the library of Assurbanipal (669-626 B.C.), which was discovered at Nineveh. Another dream guide is the one of Artemidorus of Daldis, which has been frequently adapted and reprinted. The whole literature of dream guides seems singularly lacking in variety.

A dream abounds in images and impressions; it is confused and entangled. By necessity then, a dream guide can deal with only isolated elements from the dreams, but they soon become wearying collections of formulas. The Babylonian dream guide, opened at random, offers the following example: "If he eat of the flesh of a bear, it signifies rebellion; if he eat of the flesh of an ape, he will acquire something by the use of force; if he eat of more common meat he will have peace of mind; if he eat asphalt he will have sorrow; if he eat naphtha he will have anxiety of mind." And so the list continues *ad infinitum.* Then come other headings, each of them with enumerations: "If he be given . . . If he should cut . . . If he should hold . . . If he should carry . . ." Once the principle is adopted, there is no stopping.

The other dream guides, no matter their culture of origin, hardly deviate, either in inspiration or in presentation from a tradition that may be considered almost immutable. I shall give one more example, this time taken from the Indian *Sushruta Samhita* of the fourth century A.D. Being an extract from a voluminous medical work, it bears more resemblance to psychoanalytic material than to the long subject lists that make up the dream guides usually peddled by hawkers.

DREAMS THAT PORTEND DEATH

I shall speak of dreams that have a bearing on death and on health, of the dreams of a friend of the sick man as well as those of the sick man himself: The one who, with his body smeared with oil, turns southwards with elephants or beasts of prey, asses, wild boars, or buffaloes,

the one who, tied up, is dragged away southwards by a black woman, dressed in red, snickering, disheveled, and jerky,

the one who is lured away southwards by his friends or is surrounded by dead persons while walking about,

the one who is roughly seized by men with disfigured faces and the feet of dogs, the one who drinks honey or oil, the one who is sitting in a puddle or the one who, with his body spattered with mud, gesticulates or breaks into laughter,

the one who, without any clothes, wears on his head a red garland or the one from whose belly sprouts a reed, a bamboo shoot, or a palm tree,

the one who is swallowed by a fish or who enters into his mother, the one who falls from a mountain or into a gloomy ravine,

the one who is carried away by a water course, the one who loses his Brahmin belt, the one who is surrounded and tied up by these crows or other birds of misfortune, all these are lost.

The one who sees the falling of stars or other heavenly bodies, extinguishes a lamp or gouges out an eye, the one who sees the trembling of the images of gods or the trembling of the ground,

the one who vomits, who is purged or whose teeth fall out, the one who climbs into a cotton-tree or into various other trees in full bloom, who climbs on an ant hill, on a funeral pyre, or on a sacrificial stake,

the one who receives or eats cotton, oil-cake, iron, salt, sesame or baked foods or drinks alcohol, all these if they are well shall fall ill; if ill they will die.[1]

The human mind seems strangely conservative on these topics. I suppose it is so by necessity for it is the very problem of the dream which is inherent in human nature. There is nothing that is too absurd, too miraculous, or too contradictory of which one may not dream, and it is almost impossible that any more than a very small portion of these dreams will ever be realized. Therefore, it is necessary in order to interpret dreams, to first reduce to a small number the events likely to occur to everyone in the course of a short life: a meeting, an illness, a loss or a gain, success or defeat, fortune or ruin, a voyage, falling in love, and the ultimately inevitable—death. Every science of divination—palmistry, astrology, or any other type one may imagine, even the interpretation of dreams itself—is forced to pass through this narrow door, reducing the infinite possibilities, limited only by the imagination, into a round dozen dramatic events. This procedure is bound to succeed for, at the first coincidence, everyone is dazzled by the skill of the interpreter who has been able to read into the puzzling riddles the forecast of an unexpected event that nothing—except, it is true, the law of averages—has enabled him to foresee. It is a fact, in any case, that for approximately four thousand years lists of the relation between dream-images and their meaning have met with resounding success. In our

1. "Les songes et leur interprétation," *Sources orientales* II (Paris: Le Seuil, 1959), pp. 223-224.

own days, in a rather more flexible form and with the help of scientific jargon, the interpretations of psychoanalysis continue the tradition, satisfying the same immemorial need.

The Bible is full of dreams that are explained by the prophets and others, such as the dreams of Pharaoh and Nebuchadnezzar. In post-Biblical literature the idea was put forward that the dream itself was unimportant and that it was the interpretation that counted, becoming itself the effective forecast and thereby forcing reality to follow suit. A quotation from the *Mishnah (Berakhot,* 55b) illustrates this: "There were twenty-four interpreters of dreams in Jerusalem. Once I had a dream and went to everyone of them and what any one interpreted, none of the others interpreted in the same way, and yet all of them were fulfilled. This is in pursuance of the saying: *The dream follows the mouth* (of the one who interprets it)."[2]

Various examples point out the truth of this doctrine and indicate the theological premise on which it is based. A story from the *Midrash* commenting on Joseph's interpretation of dreams excellently illustrates this:

THE DREAM OF THE BROKEN ROOF-BEAM

A certain woman came to Rabbi Eliezer and said to him: "I saw in a dream that the roof-beam of my house was broken." He said to her: "You will give birth to a male child and it will survive." She went away and it happened to her as he had prophesied.

She came another time to ask him and found his disciples in the house of study but the Rabbi was not with them and she said to them: "Where is your master?"

They said to her: "Tell us what you wish to ask and we shall tell you." She said to them: "I saw in a dream that the roof-beam of my house was broken."

Then they said to her: "You will bury your husband."

Upon leaving she began to weep. Rabbi Eliezer heard her lamentations and asked his disciples: "What did you say to the woman who came to me earlier?"

They told him that she had come to ask a question and when Eliezer asked what she had said, they told him the details. Thereupon Rabbi Eliezer said to them: "Behold, you have destroyed this man, for is it not written: And it came to pass, as he interpreted to us, so it was? (Genesis, *41:13*) *And was it not said by Rabbi Yohan-*

2. *Midrash (Berakhot* 55b), cited by Georges Levitte and Guy Casaril, "Les rêves et leur interprétation dans les textes post-bibliques," *Evidences,* No. 82, March, 1960 (Paris: American Jewish Committee).

nan: Everything [*every dream*] happens in accordance with the interpretation?"[3]

If we believe that fleeting, incoherent dream visions may come true, then we must suppose that they can either announce or control the unpredictable future. If, however, we believe that it is the interpretation that eventually comes true, then, in order to admit and understand this, it is enough to remember that men are credulous and easily influenced; furthermore men are vain, for it is flattering to imagine oneself the object of prophecy or of supernatural warnings. Similarly, it is possible that the disclosures of psychoanalysis in modern times impose themselves in parallel fashion on the analyst.

The second type of problem relative to the dream deals with the possible interpenetration (in the consciousness) of the waking and dreaming states, their opposition, the order of their importance, the possibility of their working together. The question to be asked here relates not only to the significance of the vision seen in the dream, but also to the significance of the act of dreaming itself. If the world of the dream is considered as a separate universe, is it then more real, equally real, or less real than the waking world?

What, on the other hand, actually happens in a dream? The sleeper's personality is usurped by that of a double whom he can observe living beyond his own control, in complete independence, but in a way that is bound to involve him to a certain extent. At times this actor steps into the dreamer's role, extending his personality, partaking of his sorrows, his fears and his lusts, baffling and sometimes dumbfounding him. Sometimes the dreamer feels himself in the very skin of his nocturnal double, perceiving with his double's eyes, or touching with his hands the other characters in the dream. Sometimes he watches this reflection of himself developing among the others, watching—with horror or perhaps even indifference—his gestures which are being performed outside of himself, as if they were being shown on a screen or happening on the other side of a mirror.

Another approach involves the possibility of bringing back from the world of dreams some object—a scar, a mark, a token—which will be proof of the dream's reality, something solid and tangible which will survive after the illusions of the dream have faded away,

3. *Midrash (Bereshit Rabba* LXXXIX, 8), cited by Levitte and Casaril, op. cit.

to attest to the unimpeachable existence of the world from which it has been brought.

Someone, in a dream, wakes up—or rather believes that he has awakened, although he continues to dream—and now lies expecting another awakening, which may this time be real but may also be as illusory as the first. In this way he will be transported from one dream to another, from one awakening to another, without ever being absolutely certain whether he has finally arrived at the true awakening, the one that will restore him to the world of reality.

The universe of daytime existence sometimes appears to be simply a duplication of the world of dreams. The sleeper who surrenders himself to the belief that his dream-images truthfully portend the future, will see in them the unfolding of future events that reality is soon obliged to reproduce or to imitate. After a delay of shorter or longer duration, the waking world will have to follow, to obey, and to conform with his dream. Inevitably, inexplicably, implacably, it will faithfully repeat the scenes that were earlier observed in the course of the dreams, as if these images had been only temporarily postponed, to reappear later, inevitably, but in their good time: delayed and vainly rebellious reflections.

At times it is necessary to wait so long for the dream's realization that it is almost forgotten. Then suddenly reality makes a noticeable digression and, at the most unexpected moment, all the episodes that had been revealed earlier only in the fleeting illusions of the dream fall into place and are brought to life—this time in the world of reality.

Nothing is more personal than a dream, nothing else so imprisons a person in irremediable solitude, nothing else is as stubbornly resistant to the possibility of being shared. In the world of reality everything is susceptible to universal test. The dream, on the other hand, is an adventure that only the dreamer himself has experienced and which only he can remember; it is a water-tight, impenetrable world which precludes the least chance of cross-checking. The temptation now arises to believe that two or more persons (or even a whole multitude) may at times have the same dream or have dreams that are parallel or complementary. The dreams would thus be corroborated, fitting together like the pieces of a puzzle and, by acquiring in this way the solidity and stability possessed by the perceptions of the waking world, would become verifiable like them and, even better, would create certain bonds between the dreamers—secret, narrow, restricted and imperious bonds.

Finally, since at every moment of the dream the sleeper is unaware of the fact that he is dreaming and is even convinced that he is awake, it is clear that there can never be a moment in which a person who believes himself to be awake does not have to entertain the suspicion of a doubt that he might perhaps at that time actually be dreaming.

Here are the elements of a problem that has from early times disquieted sensitive personalities. Religious beliefs, for instance, have always been the most easily inclined to the view that dreams might pave the way to the realm of the divine. Thus a papyrus of the fourth century B.C. relates a dream of Pharaoh Nectanebo in the course of which the god Onuris complains to Isis that his temple stands uncompleted. Nectanebo orders an inquiry and learns that no inscription has yet been carved on it. He asks for the best sculptor of hieroglyphics to be brought and orders him to finish the work in the shortest possible time. And Artemidorus mentions dreams which he calls "politic"—those that occur on the same night to all the inhabitants of a city and deal with events that concern that town. The Babylonian *Talmud* (*Ta'anith,* 21b) also alludes to this type of dream. While in Mesopotamia, Assurbanipal recounts:

THE DREAM OF ASSURBANIPAL

The army saw the river Idid'e, a rushing torrent, and feared to cross it. The goddess Ishtar who dwells at Arbel sent a dream in the middle of the night to my army in which she told them: "I shall march before Assurbanipal, the king whom I have begotten!" The army believed this dream and crossed the river without hindrance.[4]

This dream is authenticated because it was experienced simultaneously by a large number of sleepers. It might just as easily have been authenticated if the revelation which it brought could have been precisely identified, that is to say, if reality would have confirmed the message of the dream, perhaps as in the following example taken from Plutarch and told also by Tacitus.[5]

THE DREAM OF PTOLEMY

Ptolemaeus Soter saw in a dream the colossus of Pluto that stood at Sinope (although he knew it not, nor had ever seen what shape it was of) calling upon him and bidding him to convey it speedily

4. Quoted by Leo A. Oppenheim, "The Interpretation of Dreams in the Ancient Near East with a Translation of an Assyrian Dream-Book," *Transactions of the American Philosophical Society,* New Series, Vol. 46, part 3 (Philadelphia: 1956).

5. Plutarch, *De Isis et de Osiridis* 28, quoted by Oppenheim, op. cit. Also refers to similar text of Tacitus, *Historiae* IV, 83-84.

away to Alexandria. And as he was ignorant and at a great loss where it should be found, and was telling his dream to his familiars, there was found by chance a certain fellow that had been a general rambler in all parts (his name was Sosibius) who affirmed he had seen at Sinope such a colossus as the king had dreamt of. He therefore sent Soteles and Bachus thither, who in a long time and with much difficulty, and not without the special help of a Divine Providence, stole it away and brought it to Alexandria. When therefore it was conveyed thither and viewed, Timothy the Expositor and Manehto the Sebennite, concluding from the Cerberus and serpent that stood by it that it must be a statue of Pluto, persuaded Ptolemy it could appertain to no other god but Serapis.

Classic antiquity knew of one proof that was even more convincing of the truth of a dream: the token that was received in the course of a dream, which the sleeper finds next to himself on awakening. Pindar related the dream of Bellerophon in which Phallas brings him a magic bridle, rather like a golden diadem in appearance, with the help of which Bellerophon will be able to subdue Pegasus. Bellerophon wakes up and immediately grasps the "supplementary" supernatural object which the divinity has laid next to him.[6] This theme recurs frequently, notably in ancient Nordic literature.

More subtly, the proof left behind by the vanishing dream is at times not material, but is as volatile, ambiguous, and intangible as the dream itself. A short Chinese tale tells of the young Liu of P'eng-ch'eng who dreams of going to a brothel where he becomes intoxicated together with the girls. Each dream takes him back to the same scene of debauchery. He wonders, however, whether his dreams were perhaps not real for the perfumes of the women continue to permeate his clothes even when he is awake.[7] Upon occasion the dream precedes reality; it may announce it or foreshadow it with uncanny precision. The dream may be insistent and meticulous while reality, coming later, docile and servile, will seem to be only a hallucinated repetition of the earlier dream. I shall give two examples based on this theme, one ancient and one modern, both distinguished by the fact that they have been offered as authentic. Worlds separate them—time, distance, differences of culture. Nevertheless, each of the two affirms, almost in the same way, that life is at times only a reproduction of the vision of dreams, the newly arrived present being a delayed and

6. Pindarus, *Olympic Odes* XIII, 65 ff.
7. "Liu Tao-chi," in *T'ai P'ing Kuang Chi*, Ch. 282.

perhaps obscured reflection of the dream. The first account is taken from a Chinese collection which relates the strange events that happened during the T'ang dynasty. It tells of a young scholar, Liu Tao-chi who, while staying at the monastery of Kuo Ch'ing on Mount T'ien T'ai in the year 899 A.D., dreamed of a young girl whom he saw in a certain garden, under a window, near a leaning cypress surrounded by sunflowers. He dreamed of going through the marriage ceremony with her and frequently he came back to see her—always in his dreams. Time passed. One day, while staying in another monastery, the young scholar recognized the same garden, the same window, the same cypress, and the same sunflowers. A passing guest at the monastery had an attractive daughter, still single, who had recently fallen ill. She was the girl whom the young scholar had married and had regularly gone to visit—in his dreams.[8]

J. O. Austin, a justice of the peace from Middletown, New York, in a letter to Camille Flammarion dated June 25th, 1901, tells of an adventure—similar in a way to the previous account—that happened to him in his youth. Flammarion unhesitatingly accepted this account as true and treated it with courteous respect. He used it later in the second edition of one of his works in place of another story, by Alexandre Berard, which he had meanwhile learned to have been purely fictitious.

THE DREAM OF THE SCHOOLMASTER

I was about twenty years old and principal of a public school. Being very absorbed in my duties, I thought of them at night in my dreams no less than by day during my hours of work. One night I dreamed that I was in the class room and had just finished the opening exercises, when I heard some taps on the door. I opened it and saw a man with two children, a little girl of eleven and a boy of eight years. The visitor came in and explained to me that, as a result of the Civil War, he had left his home in New Orleans and had brought his family to the district where my school was. He wished to entrust his children to my care for their education and their instruction. He further asked me which books were necessary and I gave him a list which he took away. The next day the children were accepted as my pupils.

The dream stopped there but it had impressed me vividly and the picture of this father and these two children had been so strongly photographed on my mind that I would have been able

8. "Liu Tao-chi," loc. cit.

to recognize them anywhere, even in the population of Paris or London.

How great then was my astonishment when the day after this dream I heard the same knocks on the door that I had heard in my dream and, going to open, I saw before me this same visitor and his two children. The rest follows: we held the same conversation that we had held in my dream.

I will add that this man was an absolute stranger to me. New Orleans is 1350 miles or 2000 kilometers from here and I have never been further than 100 miles or 160 kilometers from my home.[9]

It can also happen that a dream is experienced, told, and interpreted, all in the dream. The dream of the neo-Babylonian King Nabonidus (556-539 B.C.) has been carved on a stele. (The most indestructible stone being used to record the most fleeting of visions!) The monarch saw in his dream a disturbing conjunction of the stars and planets. A man stood up by his side and told the king: "This conjunction does not hold any evil portents." Then, still in the same dream, as the inscription relates in precise detail, Nebuchadnezzar appeared to him, accompanied by a servant. The servant said to Nebuchadnezzar: "Speak to Nabonidus so that he may tell you the dream that he has dreamed." Nebuchadnezzar ordered Nabonidus to tell him the dream and Nabonidus did so. In all likelihood his royal predecessor thereupon interpreted the dream for him but the stele is unfortunately damaged at this point.

The case of a dream related and then interpreted in the same dream is dealt with in the *Talmud* (*Berakhot,* 55b). It is similarly mentioned in the collection of dreams of the library of Assurbanipal. "If he should dream a dream inside a dream and (in his dream) he relates his dream . . ."

The ancient Indians were interested in the mystery of parallel dreams in which two persons, unaware of each other, had a common destiny announced to them. In the *Kathasaritsagara* or *Ocean of Rivers of Tales,* Somadeva, a twelfth-century author, tells how King Vikramaditya saw in a dream, in a country unknown, a young girl with whom he fell in love. He dreamed that he was embracing her, when his happiness was suddenly interrupted by the cry of the night watchman. At the same time, in a distant country, Princess Malayavati, who usually had a great horror of men, dreamed that she saw a great personage emerging from a

9. Camille Flammarion, *L'inconnu et les problemes psychiques,* (2d ed.; Paris: Flammarion, 1929), Vol. II.

monastery. She married him and was tasting with him the joys of love on the nuptial couch when she was awakened by her chambermaid. After many vicissitudes the two heroes eventually meet, recognize each other and are united in matrimony as they earlier were in their dreams.

Complementary dreams represent a higher degree of complexity. Now it is no longer a matter of simple symmetry, but of a more delicate relation which causes a second dream to become the clue to the first. The most striking example of this is perhaps the one found in *The Arabian Nights.*

THE RUINED MAN

There lived once in Baghdad a wealthy man and made of money, who lost all his substance and became so destitute that he could earn his living only by hard labor. One night he lay down to sleep, dejected and heavy-hearted, and saw in a dream a Speaker who said to him, "Verily thy fortune is in Cairo; go thither and seek it." So he set out for Cairo; but when he arrived there, evening overtook him and he lay down to sleep in a mosque. Presently, by decree of Allah Almighty, a band of bandits entered the mosque and made their way thence into an adjoining house; but the owners, being aroused by the noise of the thieves, awoke and cried out; whereupon the Chief of Police came to their aid with his officers. The robbers made off but the Wali entered the mosque and, finding the man from Baghdad asleep there, laid hold of him and beat him with palm-rods so grievous a beating that he was well-nigh dead. Then they cast him into jail, where he abode three days; after which the Chief of Police sent for him and asked him, "Whence art thou?" and he answered, "From Baghdad." Quoth the Wali, "And what brought thee to Cairo?" and quoth the Baghdadi, "I saw in a dream One who said to me, Thy fortune is in Cairo; go thither to it. But when I came to Cairo the fortune which he promised me proved to be the palm-rods thou so generously gavest to me." The Wali laughed till he showed his wisdom teeth and said, "O man of little wit, thrice have I seen in a dream one who said to me: 'There is in Baghdad a house in such a district and of such a fashion and its courtyard is laid out gardenwise, at the lower end whereof is a jetting fountain and under the same a great sum of money lieth buried. Go thither and take it.' Yet I went not; but thou, of the briefness of thy wit, hast journeyed from place to place, on the faith of a dream which was but an idle galimatias of sleep." Then he gave him money saying, "Help thee back therewith to thine own country." The Baghdadi took the money and set out upon his homewards journey. Now the house the Wali had described was the man's own house in Baghdad; so the wayfarer returned thither and, digging underneath the fountain in his garden, discovered a great treasure. And thus Allah gave him abundant fortune.[10]

A popular Hassidic tale gives a less elaborate version of the same tale:

TWO OTHERS WHO DREAMED

A man one day went to consult the Rabbi of Kotzk to ask him if he should leave his native town where nothing had gone right for him, in order to try his fortune elsewhere. The Rabbi replied by quoting the following tale: A Jew from Cracow had dreamed repeatedly that a treasure had been buried near a certain mill. He got up one fine morning and went to the mill and started to dig all around it; but in vain. The miller asked him what he was digging for and the man explained his purpose. The miller, fully astonished, then related that he himself had repeatedly dreamed that a treasure had been buried in the courtyard of a certain man in Cracow and he mentioned the name of the man—who happened to be none other than our treasure seeker himself. The man from Cracow went straight home, dug up his courtyard, and found a treasure.[11]

In these two stories, a man discovers a treasure as a result of a dream which has been dreamed by another but which he himself can better interpret. Japanese folklore has a curious variation on the same theme based on the hero who buys or "steals" the revealing dream. In one such story, a man sees a gadfly flying away from the nostril of his sleeping friend, then flying back, entering and leaving the nostril a few more times. The sleeper awakes and recounts his dream: A gadfly came to rest in the garden of a very rich man on the Island of Sado, under a camellia bush laden with white blossoms. The gadfly told the dreamer to dig, which he did, finding there a vessel full of gold coins. The hero immediately begs his friend to sell him his dream and the friend agrees. The buyer then goes to the Island of Sado, takes up service in the household of the rich man, digs up the treasure from under the white camelia, and requests his discharge. After this he lives happily ever after in his own village.[12]

10. Richard Burton, *Arabian Nights,* 351st night.
11. Levitte and Casaril, "Kotzker Maayoth 105," op. cit.
12. *Sources orientales* II, op. cit., pp. 311-312.

Another Hassidic tale with numerous variations in the folklore of various countries shows how many different episodes of a life can be unfolded in the short duration of one dream:

A DESTINY IN A DREAM

There was once a very hospitable man who never stopped asking: "Oh, my worthy guest, am I not the most hospitable of men?" The Baal Shem-Tov sent one of his disciples to him, Rabbi Ze'ev Kitzes. The man having once more asked his customary question, Rabbi Ze'ev said to him: "We shall see," and the man fell asleep. Rabbi Ze'ev pressed a finger on the man's forehead and the man started dreaming. He dreamed that a great noble had stopped at his house and, after drinking some wine, had fallen down dead at a stroke. The most hospitable of all men thereupon fled the scene and became a carrier of water. The buckets were heavy, he stumbled and fell and broke his leg. The broken leg gave him so much pain that he woke up. He related his dream to Rabbi Ze'ev who told him: "You have been given the privilege of contemplating what will be your lot if you continue to sustain Satan with the arrogance which compels you to solicit compliments for your hospitality." And the man promised to return to the paths of humility.[13]

The most remarkable dream of this type is the one related by Don Juan Manuel, the Infante of Castile (1284-1348), a dream probably inspired by an earlier Arab tale. In this, the whole of a contingent destiny, encompassing an entire career, is concentrated into a few hallucinated minutes:[14]

THE SORCERER WHOSE REWARD WAS NOT FORTHCOMING

There was once in Santiago a dean who had a mind to learn the art of magic. He was informed that there was no one else who knew so well that art as did Don Yllan of Toledo. He went therefore to Toledo.

The very day of his arrival he directed his way to the house of Don Yllan whom he found reading in a secluded chamber. Don Yllan received him with kindness and asked him to remain for the noontime meal so that he might later reveal to him the purpose of the visit. He showed him into a very pleasant room and told the dean he was much delighted to make his acquaintance. After the

13. Levitte and Casaril, "Maayoth hagedolim hechadash 44," op. cit.

14. Translation based on Juan Manuel, Infante of Castile, *El libro de los Exiemplos del Conde Lucanor et de Patronio,"* No. XI.

meal the dean revealed to his host the purpose of his visit and prayed him for instruction in the magic sciences. Don Yllan replied that he conjectured that his guest, being now a dean, was a man of fine position and of great future, but that he feared that he might later be forgotten by him. The dean promised and swore that he would never forget the favor rendered by Don Yllan and that he would always remain in his debt to him. An arrangement was then reached and Don Yllan explained to his guest that the magic arts could be taught only in a secluded location. Taking him by the hand, Don Yllan led the dean into an adjoining room, on the floor of which could be seen an enormous ring of iron. First, however, Don Yllan ordered his servant to prepare partridges for the evening meal, stipulating that the partridges were not to be put on the spit to roast until the order had been given. Don Yllan and the dean then lifted the ring and descended by a well-constructed stone staircase to such a depth that it seemed to the dean that the bed of the River Tagus must already be over their heads. At the foot of the stairway was a cell with a library, as well as a workshop of sorts fitted out with the instruments of magic. While they were looking at some of the books two men entered bearing a letter for the dean. The letter had come from the bishop, the dean's uncle, and informed him that the bishop lay very ill and that the dean must hasten if he wished to find his uncle still alive. This news vexed the dean most seriously, in part for the illness of his uncle and in part because it might become necessary for him to interrupt his studies. He chose, therefore, to write a letter of excuse which he sent to the bishop.

Three days later other men dressed in mourning arrived carrying other letters for the dean in which he was informed that the bishop was now dead, that the bishop's successor was about to be chosen and that it was hoped, by the Grace of God, that the dean himself might be chosen. He was told, furthermore, that he should not put himself to the trouble of coming for it might be more advantageous that he be elected in his absence.

Ten days later two equerries arrived, richly habited, who presented themselves, falling on their feet and kissing his hand, and greeted the dean as the new bishop. When Don Yllan saw this he addressed himself happily to the new prelate and told him of how he thanked the Lord for learning of such joyful news. Then he requested the office now vacated by the dean for one of his sons. The new bishop informed him that he had reserved the position for his own brother but that, having decided to grant Don Yllan a special favor, they would leave together for Santiago.

The three of them made their way to Santiago where they were received with many honors. After six months the bishop received envoys from the Pope who offered him the archbishopric of Toulouse and left to his disposition the choice of nominating his successor. When Don Yllan learned of this he reminded the former dean of his promise and asked for the vacant title for his son. The archbishop, however, informed Don Yllan that he had reserved the bishopric for his uncle, but that, having decided to grant Don Yllan a special favor, they would leave together for Toulouse. Don Yllan had no choice but to agree.

They left for Rome, all three, and there they were received with great respect, with masses in their honor and with processions. The Pope died at the end of four years and our cardinal was elected by unanimous vote to the papacy. Learning of this, Don Yllan kissed the feet of His Holiness, reminding him of his former promise, and requested a cardinal's hat for his son. The Pope threatened him with prison, saying that he knew full well that Don Yllan was nothing but a sorcerer who had once taught magic in Toledo.

The unfortunate Don Yllan replied that he would in that case return to Spain and begged for something to eat on the way. The Pope refused.

At this Don Yllan, in a resolute voice, said, "It seems I must then eat by myself the partridges that I had ordered prepared for this night." The servant made his appearance and Don Yllan ordered him to roast the partridges. Upon these words the Pope suddenly found himself back in the underground cell in Toledo, once again the dean of Santiago and so ashamed of his ingratitude that he did not cease begging for Don Yllan's pardon. Don Yllan told him, however, that the test had sufficed. He gave him no part of the partridge but accompanied the dean as far as the street where he wished him good-bye and very courteously took his leave.

It may happen that one dreams in a dream that one has wakened from a dream while in actual fact the same dream continues to be unfolded. The sleeper draws nothing from this decisive change except the misleading assurance that he is now awake. He generally passes through a state in which his reason so mingles with illusion that both soon become inextricable from one another. An historical example of this is furnished by the *Memoirs* of Shah Tahmasp I (1514-1576) who dreamed on the nineteenth of Safar in the year 961 of the Hegirah that he had seen a verse of the Koran written in the sky, saying: "Allah will provide for you against them: He understands and He knows." After this he dreamed that he awakened and found himself in his summer encampment at Khoy, fearing the approach of a storm and making the necessary precautions to evacuate his household in case the tents should be carried away. The wind, however, turned aside at the last moment, but in the cloud of dust that it raised could be seen a herd of rams and antelopes.

Then, still in a dream, Tahmasp saw his sister arranging cushions on which fine ladies reclined. They wore neither ornament nor finery and were Georgian women of perfect beauty. Among them was the sister of the vizir whom, however, he could not recognize, her features having changed. He woke up for a moment (or dreamed he had) while he recited the verse from the Koran that he had seen written in the sky. He then fell asleep once more (or dreamed he did) falling once more into the same dream and reciting the same verse. Now suddenly he realized that the verse had signified the defeat of his enemies.[15]

India, which may well be considered the center of asceticism and mental disciplines, has invested the dream with other powers again. The recluse, carried away by his meditation, gives a material existence to the images of his dreams, if he can only succeed in sustaining them with sufficient intensity. The dream then becomes lucid, deliberate, and creative; it becomes, in fact, a consciously willed effort which will be realized provided only that it is diligently pursued. The story of the poet Tulsidas, who earlier had composed an epic devoted to Hanuman and his army of apes, illustrated this belief. A few years later, Tulsidas was imprisoned by a despot in a stone tower. The poet set himself to dreaming, to meditating, to dreaming again, to rallying all the resources of a mind that had been sharpened and trained to the solitary life, and out of his dream he managed to recreate Hanuman and his army of apes, who thereupon overran the kingdom, seized the tower, and set the poet free.

All these themes, or nearly all of them, are to be found in the almost inexhaustible literature of China, which seems to have explored the problems posed by dreams in a systematic manner. By carefully choosing stories to illustrate these problems, it would be possible no doubt to outline the basic principles of the dream. Some of them would illustrate familiar problems; others would invent and refine hitherto unknown complications with extravagant and tyrannical logic. Examples might include the cyclical dream of Pao-Yu; the story of the man who in his dream becomes part of a real fresco; the story of a man who while awake becomes a character in the dream of another but who, by his own brutal actions, inter-

15. "Tazkarat," p. 65, Kaviani, and H. Massé, *Antologie Persane* (Paris: Payot, 1950.)

rupts the sleeper in whose dream they occur, thereby putting an end to the dream and to himself; and lastly such a dream as the story of the legal impasse which occurs when the hide of a deer is discovered, a deer a peasant believes to have killed in a dream.

I believe that a grouping of such tales is of interest. These stories from China deal convincingly with the powers of the dream and contrast interestingly with the way in which the dream is ordinarily used by occidental writers. At times, Western writers make use of the dream as a convenient explanatory device as Plato did with the dream of Er of Pamphylia, and Cicero with the dream of Scipio: these are metaphysical hypotheses in disguise. However, other writers use edifying dreams as a device to make profligate sinners repent of their ways or to avert the punishments of the Hereafter. (It must be admitted that Buddhism, too, is not ignorant of this use of the dream.)

Romanticism has tended to transform the dream into a literary device in which lyricism finds easy scope. Jean-Paul, whose novels are liberally sprinkled with rhetorical dreams, is perhaps the most frequently quoted example of this. Later writers were, on the other hand, satisfied with noting down their dreams and presenting them as poetic material in the rough, unpolished state, in the hope of beguiling the reader when awake after they had overcome the author while asleep.

Very frequently the dream remains a fairy tale which is dispelled by the awakening and to which at times an encumbering allegorical value is attributed; it has nothing in common with the intellectual complications of oriental dreams as literature presents them. "It was only a dream," the sleeper cries out upon waking, occasionally disappointed, occasionally relieved, all according to whether the dream gratified or oppressed him. It is never more than an illusion, which may have been pleasing or distressing and it is sufficient for the subject to open his eyes to send his dreams back into nothingness.

Descartes wondered what would happen to a sleeper who had continuous, coherent dreams, if he were transported in dream to varying and dissimilar locations, waking each time in a bewildering environment without links to either the preceding environment or to the one following. The dream might well acquire the permanence of reality, while reality would acquire the improbability, the instability, the evanescence, and the kaleidoscopic character of the dream.

The founder of the Isma'ili sect, Hassan-i-Sabbah is traditionally credited with having used the philosopher's theoretical conjecture some centuries before him, employing it in the gardens of Alamut to fanaticize the Assassins. Hassan gathered his youngest and most ardent disciples in his inaccessible retreat, The Eagle's Nest, a precipitous and arid stronghold in the heart of the desert where it seemed impossible that the least vegetation might flourish. A secret spring, however, transformed a hidden ravine into a remarkable orchard that abounded with fruit and flowers. Hassan plied his guests with Indian hemp and while they were under the influence of the drug he had them brought into his incredible garden. They woke up there in a bewildering setting where ravishing young creatures, perfumed and dressed in transparent veils, invited the young men to pick the flowers and fruit for themselves. They were offered refreshing drinks and were invited to partake of the pleasures of love. Then, satiated and drowsy, the young men were taken back to their dusty, stifling cells. Awakening, they could glimpse through narrow slits only the endless sand and stone of an inhospitable region. They were told that they had been dreaming and that their dreams had given them a foretaste of the Paradise to which they would be admitted if they died in carrying out the orders of the Prophet. As many times as was considered necessary, they were led back between two periods of sleep into the unsuspected garden of delights: each time they regained consciousness they were more convinced than the previous time that they had been dreaming.

Marco Polo and a manuscript of the fourteenth century now kept in the Vienna Library[16] both attest to this frightening subterfuge. The ruse runs directly counter to the accepted opinions on the subject of dreams which consider it perfectly normal that a dream may—just for a moment—be taken for reality but that reality is never—certainly not for any length of time—taken for a dream. So much so in fact that tradition soon found itself altered and the "hallucinations" were attributed to hashish. Old Hassan Sabbah, more realistically, did not think that he could rely entirely on drug-induced hallucinations and thought it wiser to confirm their effects with real fruit, authentic flowers, and young girls who were anything but immaterial.

There is also a Christian version of this oriental tale of fantasy, *Life Is a Dream,* a play by Pedro Calderón de la Barca (1600-1681). An intrigue is recalled: since childhood, Sigismond has been imprisoned by his father, the king of Poland, in an isolated tower. His father makes him drink a certain drug which puts him to sleep. He is then carried into the royal palace where he wakes up luxuriously dressed and, by order of his father who wishes to put him to the

16. Marco Polo, Chapters XLI-XLII, ms. 107 of the Vienna Library. Here quoted after Hammer by Jacques Bolle, *Les séductions du communisme de la Bible à nos jours* (Paris: Morgan, 1957), pp. 186-187.

test, is treated as a sovereign by all the courtiers. Sigismond at first wonders whether he is not perhaps dreaming; then, taking confidence, he quickly shows himself to be brutal and headstrong, cruel and tyrannical. The proof is conclusive: the young man—being given once more the same narcotic—finds himself that same day back in his prison, dressed in his accustomed rags. His warder has no difficulty in persuading him that he has only dreamed the miraculous interlude. A popular uprising later sets him free and for the second time he is given unlimited power. However, he believes that now for the second time he is only experiencing a dream, that the glittering show will vanish away, and he will find himself once more in his dungeon. This time, of course, nothing of the sort is true, but now Sigismond knows that all of life is only a dream and dreams themselves are also dreams. The lesson to be learned here is metaphysical rather than religious. I do not know to what extent the Polish ruse as dramatized by Calderón was inspired by the Persian stratagem as described by the Venetian traveler. Possibly there was no influence at all, which would make the coincidence even more remarkable.

The study of dreams increased from the second half of the nineteenth century onwards. Among the most remarkable of these studies were the works of two scholars who were—perhaps not entirely by chance—almost exactly contemporaneous, both of them being also professors at the Collége de France. The first of them, the historian and archaeologist Alfred Maury (1817-1892) published his work, *Le sommeil et les rêves* (Slumber and Dreams), in 1861. The other, the Marquis d'Hervey de Saint-Denis (1823-1892), in 1867 published a more ambitious and more significant work whose title, *Les rêves et moyens de les diriger* (Dreams and Means of Controlling Them), reveals its basic conception. Under the double influence of classical and Chinese antiquity (so one may presume) the study of dreams in a systematic manner began. The influence of the dream was measured, its students submitted to its delusions or extolled them, and the pitfalls of the dream were charted.

The dream no longer appeared in literature only as an edifying fable, as a rhetorical device or as a fantasy deliberately freed from having to conform to the laws of logic or reality. It now became the motivating element of the plot, either complicating it or resolving it. It was used to transform the personality of the characters, to trouble their reasoning, and to modify their conduct. At times the dream was used as an omen or as the announcement of an extraordinary destiny; it heralded the disclosures of implacable fate. Charles Nodier's *Smarra* remains a learned exercise—to my mind a detestable one—of ridiculous pomposity, whose pedantry, concerned with giving the impression of a nightmare, represents a misunderstanding that is almost grotesque. *Aurélia,* the disclosure of the agonies and obsessions that destroyed the sanity of Gérard de Nerval, goes beyond being a literary game: it is an upsetting and confusing document rather than the calculated construction that this work is in other respects. In this domain, in fact, in which the dream takes important new forms and adopts new "tactics," setting snares and ambushes for the unwary, madness takes on the precision and skill of an architectural system, hiding its speculations under the obliging mask of panic-stricken frenzy. At any rate these stories of inconsistent literary value have at least endowed the dream with a new importance and, so to speak, with the stamp of literary nobility; they have started the dream off on a remarkable new career.

In the main, the old problem of the dream made its reappearance now, not, however, under the schematic aspect which had invested its unresolved enigmas in the past with the indescribable allure of the axiomatic or of mathematical paradox. Now the problem fostered a psychology delighting in the depiction of the human mind as lying in wait for premonitions, responsive to the coincidences and the ambiguous persistance of chance, vulnerable to the assaults of the unseen—an alert recipient of messages and warnings from the Beyond, from and to which only dreams have access.

The gradual convergence of dreams and fantasy is inevitable, for the dream—mysterious at all times—readily becomes terrifying. In it, the dreamer can imagine himself introduced into a supernatural world or, conversely, something from a forbidding world may seem to him to be forcing its way into his consciousness. In an earlier anthology devoted to the phantasm of terror, I collected a number of tales that could all have found their place in this collection, but I have decided not to reproduce them here simply in order to avoid duplication. On the other hand, I have rejected parables or straightforward descriptions presented in the form of dreams, true dreams that have been consciously transcribed on wakening, and the sort of dreams that in pious tales bring on the conversion of the sinner. I have preferred to collect the stories which build up—in the best of examples with clockwork precision—a delicate structure in which the dream furnishes the decisive "spring" in one way or another. Some of the others, which are purely anecdotal, have been included for their entertainment value or because they occupy an important historical position. As a general rule I have found it better to retain those stories that depend on a particular vision or a state of hallucination, stories which, although they cannot properly be called dreams, convey nevertheless the same atmosphere and play the same role as does the dream; this has been more useful than to include those digressions or fantasies styled "dreams" by pure convention and by rhetorical artifice when do they not, in fact, possess the least of the insiduous ambiguities peculiar to The Dream.

At times, the tales in this collection elaborate a given age, illustrating timeless cares. The bridle that Bellerophon found next to him on waking is a token of the same kind as the poem found in the sleeve of the hero of a Chinese tale of the T'ang period, as the cloudy opal of Leslie Charteris' hero in *Aurora,* or as the key to the tomb in *Vera,* a story by Villiers de l'Isle-Adam.

The sudden tragedy in the *Pale Blue Nightgown* by Louis Golding, the obsessive warnings imagined by Ksaver Sandor Gjalski in *The Dream of Doctor Mišić* and by W. Somerset Maugham in *Lord Mountdrago,* extend and romanticize with frightening vividness the long-held conviction—or perhaps the occasional experience, generally explicable by the illusion of *deja vu*—that dreams have the power to "create" the future by anticipating it.

This type of story, in a manner, replaces the adventures that befell the young scholar, Lieou, at the monastery of Kwo Tsing in earlier days or, in the past century, the account of J. O. Austin, the American justice of the peace. These last two selections, which are really documents, are dry, but they achieve their purpose. To draw dramatic effects from them needs only the skill and inventiveness of the writer.

Kipling's *The Brushwood Boy,* a story of parallel dreams experienced by a young Englishwoman and a soldier in the Indian Army independently of each other, before both meet, recognize each other, finally to marry, furnishes a modern version of the parallel dreams of King Vikramaditya and Princess Malayavati.

Tulsidas, in giving form to the army of apes which sets him free, foreshadows the ascetic who, in *The Circular Ruins* by Jorge Luis Borges, solely by the power of his dream created a being, indistinguishable from a living person except for the fact that neither fire nor water has any effect on him. Absorbed in concentration, the ascetic suddenly finds his retreat on fire, but the flames do not harm him; he realizes then that he himself is a fictitious creature in someone else's dream. A touching variant of the same theme inspired a short story by Giovanni Papini, *The Last Visit of the Sick Cavalier,* in which the hero defines his precarious state in the following terms: "I exist because there is a man who dreams me, a man who sleeps and dreams and sees me acting and living and moving and who is dreaming at this moment that I am speaking to you just as I am doing. When he started to dream, my existence began. When he wakes up I shall cease to be. I am a figment of his imagination, a creation of his mind, a guest of his long nocturnal fantasies. The dream of this someone has so much stability and duration that I have become visible even to those who are awake."

Tchuang-tseu, driven to despair by the debate within himself as to whether he is a philosopher who has dreamed that he is a butterfly or whether he is a butterfly dreaming that he is a philosopher, has his occidental counterpart in the short story by Théophile Gautier, *The Dead Leman.* The story ends unfortunately with the banal tale of a vampire, after our expectations have been raised, having heard Romuald declare earlier: "Sometimes I fancied myself a priest who dreamed every night he was a gentleman, at other times a gentleman who dreamed he was a priest. I could no longer distinguish between dreaming and waking, and I knew not where reality began and illusion ended."

However, despite this ambiguity, the story still deals with one man, the same man living alternately in two different environments, by turns pious and debauched. Our literature returns again to the contrast between insect and man in a science-fiction story, *A Wild Surmise,* told with singular daring by Henry Kuttner and Catherine L. Moore. In clinics on two distant planets, a man and an insect live dreams and dream lives that are complementary and inextricable. The contrast between the two stories on a single theme is striking and shows admirably how the given data of a problem can be ramified to produce divergent solutions. In Gautier's story, for example, the perplexed hero living a split life cannot tell the dream from the reality. In the Kuttner-Moore tale, an insect in its dream lives a human existence; the man in his dream lives the life of the insect, complete with faceted eyes, six legs, and an annulated abdomen. It is no longer a question of a single consciousness powerless to distinguish between illusion and reality, but of two beings from two different realms; each while asleep dreams the daytime life of the other, due to daily transpositions that recur endlessly.

The list of divergencies or persisting elements of this sort is certainly not complete, but I imagine that these examples will be sufficient to catch a glimpse of the powers of which a dream may dispose, powers that can delude the mind or lead it astray. It might be convenient perhaps to add here a word in conclusion to explain the probable origin of the powers that are so obstinately attributed to something which is, after all, only a disordered succession of empty images.

The mystery of the dream originates from the fact that this phantasmagoria over which the sleeper has no control is at the same time entirely a product of his imagination. When it is unfolded before him without his consent, he can hardly believe himself responsible. On the other hand, it is difficult for him not to persuade himself that this shifting series of images is addressed to him. He postulates a meaning for this rarely explicit message which, were it not so enigmatic, would not be so troubling. The sleeper likes to flatter himself that the dream does not come from himself, rather from some external power which is superior, inaccessible, auspicious or ominous—it does not really matter which. At the same time he does not doubt that he is the privileged recipient of something solemn and occult. He experiences the dream as a dictation in which the one who dictates (perhaps knowing neither that he is dictating nor what he is dictating), the one who (like a scribe with neither initiative nor control) docilely takes down those despotic words he hears, and the one who, quite astonished, reads the text back (a text he does not know but which seems nevertheless to bring back memories)—are all one person: he himself. Throughout his dream, as principal or as witness, he participates or looks on by proxy. A fraternal effigy takes his place, an agent without instructions, but for whom he nevertheless must answer, somewhat like the novelist who remains responsible for the characters he has sent out into the world, although their sayings and actions should not honestly be imputed to him.

The spell that dreams cast stems on the one hand from the strange phenomena connected with them: the feeling of obsession, of being possessed, of the change of personality—to all of which the dream has kinship. It stems, furthermore, from the expectation of a sign from the Beyond and from the hope of receiving an unimpeachable revelation. On the other hand, it is also due to the way a dream approaches the quality of a literary creation, although a literary creation requires the highest degree of vigilance and care—neither of which are directly compatible with the passivity and surrender of the dream.

The dream remains the common property of the sleeper who has dreamed it and of the waking person who remembers it; in an analogous sense the novel fulfills itself with a meditation between the writer who has created it and the reader who is introduced for a brief instant, for an interlude, as a supernumerary character into a fictional world, no doubt a deceptive and inconsistent world, but a world to which one must resort so long as one delights in literature.

I shall go further: Is it possible that without fantasies, visions, and dreams, an individual could emerge or exist, I mean a being who is someone or something without being Everything?

The inference is so commanding that the most rugged of theologians, in every period and of every persuasion, those who have dared to venture to the brink of the dizzy precipice of metaphysics, those who are mathematically cool and precise, have all agreed in assuming (one might say unanimously) that the relation between God and the world is like that which an all-powerful Spirit—a Spirit that has no need to use its power, that scorns to impose its will, absent-minded, impish, overgenerous—has with its Dream (solely through an excess of excellence), without even being aware of it. The Dream is the unfathomable, the inscrutable Universe that He lets emanate from Himself, a heedless and needless fantasy, perhaps.

While engaged in the collection of material for a *problématique* of the dream, I have been guided in my choice by a very precise criterion.

I have established that the dream has been used only recently in the literary process.

Recorded dreams and interpreted dreams are both old and plentiful; invented dreams are relatively recent. Narratives in which one discovers at the end that the events recounted were dreams and not real, or which contain dreams told so as to give the reader the same feeling of reality that the dream gives to the dreamer, are rare and date from only yesterday, if not from today. It is works such as these that I have preferred to use in this collection. Only they can make me experience the impression of dreaming, that is to say, when I close a volume of such stories or otherwise interrupt my reading, I experience an impression analogous to that which I feel on waking from a dream. Most of the other stories of dreams have the serious fault of being presented as such at the outset, thereby spoiling everything.* Can it still be a dream if one has been warned in advance that it is one? It will lack the particular attribute of a dream which is to persuade.

Certain works were too lengthy for this anthology: Gérard de Nerval's *Aurélia,* Kafka's *The Trial* and *The Castle,* Victor Segalen's *René Leys,* Sadegh Hedayat's *The Blind Barn Owl.* For other reasons I had to reject certain stories which appeared in an earlier anthology of "fantastic" tales. This is the case with Jorge Luis Borges *The Circular Ruins* and Julio Cortazar's *The Night Turns to the Skies,* both of which I was able to replace with other stories by the same authors. I was unable to do this with Giovanni Papini's

* See the author's *L'incertitude qui vient des rêves* (The Doubt Which Stems from Dreams) Paris, 1956, especially the section "Rhétorique du Rêve" (The Rhetoric of the Dream) pp. 132-149.

The Last Visit of the Sick Cavalier or with Turgenev's *The Dream*. The dimensions of this volume forced me to sacrifice Balzac's *The Two Dreams,* Sylvain Latour's *The Slave Market of Vevy,* and *The Sailor's Last Letter* by Georges Eekhoud. I particularly regretted being unable to include the Leslie Charteris' labyrinthic *Aurora* or *The Semiramis Affair* in which A. E. W. Mason makes ingenious use of the particular quality of the unconscious memory. These two contributions from the realm of detective literature (at first glance so unexpected, but on later reflection so obvious) lack the attributes of the dream which would permit their inclusion in this collection. I would equally have liked to include one of Jacques Sternberg's tightly written, fast-moving pieces, but this proved to be impossible. I have indicated authors and titles here so that anyone interested may fill in the gaps from which this anthology, like all such works, suffers.

ROGER CAILLOIS
Translated from the French by Michael Bernet

Chinese Dialectics

Tso-ch'iu Ming

FIFTH CENTURY B.C.

Nothing is known of Tso-ch'iu Ming except that he wrote the Tso Chuan (The Chronicles of Tso), *which survives as a "Commentary" on the* Ch'un Ch'iu (The Spring and Autumn Annals) *of Confucius covering the period from 722 to 481* B.C. *He was not only the first Chinese historian worthy of that name but has also been hailed as the "Father of Chinese Prose." The* Kuo Yü (Narratives of the States), *which covers roughly the same period, is also attributed to him.*

THE DREAM OF THE DUKE OF CHIN

The Duke of Chin saw in a dream a great demon with disheveled hair reaching to the ground, who beat his breast and stamped his feet and said, "You have unjustly executed my descendants and I have permission from the Supreme Deity to take vengeance." The demon then advanced upon him, breaking down successively the outer and inner gates. The Duke retreated into his chamber but the demon also broke down the chamber door. At this point the Duke awoke. He summoned the witch of Sang-t'ien and the latter told him everything he had dreamed. "What does it mean?" asked the Duke. "You will not taste the new wheat," she replied.

After this, the Duke became very ill and asked the state of Tsin to send a physician, whereupon the Duke of Tsin sent the physician Huan. While the latter was on his way, the Duke dreamed that his disease had turned into two boys, one of whom said, "The man is a good physician; he will do us harm. How can we escape him?" Then the other said, "If we place ourselves below the heart and above the diaphragm, what can he do to us?" When the physician arrived, he said, "Nothing can be done for this disease. It is located below the heart and above the diaphragm; it cannot be attacked directly[1] and it cannot be reached with medicine. There is nothing to be done for it." "He is a good physician," the Duke said, rewarded him generously and sent him back to Tsin.

In the sixth month, on Ping-wu, the Duke wished to taste of the new wheat and had some presented by the superintendent of his fields. While the cook was getting the wheat ready, the Duke summoned the witch of Sang-t'ien, showed her the wheat and had her put to death. But as the Duke was about to taste the new wheat, he felt a distension in his abdomen. He hurried to the privy and there he fell into the pit and died. Among his servants there was one who had that morning dreamed that he had carried the Duke on his back and ascended to heaven with him. Now at the noon hour, he was the one who carried the body of the Duke out of the privy. He was consequently buried alive with the Duke.

Tso Chuan, Ch'eng 10
Translated from the Chinese by Chi-Chen Wang

1. Here the text is obscure, but acupuncture is probably meant.

Lieh Tzu 450-375 B.C.?

The Book of Lieh Tzu *is traditionally attributed to Lieh Yü-k'ou, about whom even less is known than other philosophers of ancient China. As it has come down to us, the work consists mostly of a mixture of myth, legend and fable. Though generally considered a forgery of a much later period (some place it as late as the fourth century* A.D.*), it may well contain material dating back to Lieh Yü-k'ou's time. Whatever its true vintage, it remains one of the most widely known of the Taoist classics.*

KING MU OF CHOU

In the time of King Mu of Chou, there was a magician who came from a kingdom in the far west. He could pass through fire and water, penetrate metal and stone, overturn mountains and make rivers flow backwards, transplant whole towns and cities, ride on thin air without falling, encounter solid bodies without being obstructed. There was no end to the countless variety of changes and transformations which he could effect; and, besides changing the external form, he could also spirit away men's internal cares.

King Mu revered him as a god, and served him like a prince. He set aside for his use a spacious suite of apartments, regaled him with the daintiest of food, and selected a number of singing-girls for his express gratification. The magician, however, condemned the King's palace as mean, the cooking as rancid, and the concubines as too ugly to live with. So King Mu had a new building erected to please him. It was built entirely of bricks and wood, and gorgeously decorated in red and white, no skill being spared in its construction. The five royal treasuries were empty by the time that the new pavilion was complete. It stood six thousand feet high, overtopping Mount Chung-nan, and it was called Touch-the-sky Pavilion. Then the King proceeded to fill it with maidens, selected from Chêng and Wei, of the most exquisite and delicate beauty. They were anointed with fragrant perfumes, adorned with moth-eyebrows, provided with jewelled hairpins and earrings, and arrayed in the finest silks, with costly satin trains. Their faces were powdered, and their eyebrows pencilled, their girdles were studded with precious stones. All manner of sweet-scented plants filled the palace with their odours, and ravishing music of the olden time was played to the honoured guest. Every month he was presented with fresh and costly raiment; every morning he had set before him some new and delicious food.

The magician could not well refuse to take up his abode in this palace of delight. But he had not dwelt there very long before he invited the King to accompany him on a jaunt. So the King clutched the magician's sleeve, and soared up with him higher and higher into the sky, until at last they stopped, and lo! they had reached the magician's own palace. This palace was built with beams of gold and silver, and incrusted with pearls and jade. It towered high above the region of clouds and rain, and the foundations whereon it rested were unknown. It appeared like a stupendous cloud-mass to the view. The sights and sounds it offered to eye and ear, the scents and flavours which abounded there, were such as exist not within mortal ken. The King verily believed that he was in the Halls of Paradise, tenanted by God Himself, and that he was listening to the mighty music of the spheres. He gazed at his own palace on the earth below, and it seemed to him no better than a rude pile of clods and brushwood.

It seemed to the King as if his stay in this place lasted for several decades, during which he gave no thought to his own kingdom. Then the magician invited him to make another journey, and in the new region they came to, neither sun nor moon could be seen in the heavens above, nor any rivers or seas below. The King's eyes were dazed by the quality of the light, and he lost the power of vision; his ears were stunned by the sounds that assailed them, and he lost the faculty of hearing. The framework of his bones and his internal organs were thrown out of gear and refused to function. His thoughts were in a whirl, his intellect became clouded, and he begged the magician to take him back again. Thereupon, the magician gave him a shove, and the King experienced a sensation of falling through space.

When he awoke to consciousness, he found himself sitting on his throne just as before, with the selfsame attendants round him. He looked at the wine in front of him, and saw that it was still full of sediment; he looked at the viands, and found that they had not yet lost their freshness. He asked where he had come from, and his attendants told him that he had only been sitting quietly there. This threw King Mu into a reverie, and it was three months before he was himself again. Then he made further inquiry, and asked the magician to explain what had happened. "Your Majesty and I," replied the magician, "were only wandering about in the spirit, and, of course, our bodies never moved at all. What essential difference is there between that sky-palace we dwelt in and your Majesty's palace on earth, between the spaces we travelled through and your Majesty's own park? You are accustomed to being permanently in the body, and cannot understand being out of it for a while. Can any number of changes, or successive intervals of fast and slow, fully represent the true scheme of things?

The King was much pleased. He ceased to worry about affairs of State, and took no further pleasure in the society of his ministers or concubines.

Translated from the Chinese
by Lionel Giles

THE COUNTRY OF KU MANG AND OTHERS

In the southern corner of the Extreme West there is a country called Ku Mang, whose boundaries are unknown. Because the Male and

Female Principles do not meet here, there is no distinction of summer and winter; because the sun and moon do not shine here, there is no distinction of day and night. Its people partake of no food and wear no clothes. They spend most of their lives in sleep, from which they wake up only once in fifty days, and they take what they do in their dreams as real and what they see while awake as illusory.

The area bounded by the four oceans is known as the Central Country. It straddles the north and south banks of the Yellow River and spreads over the east and west sides of the Mount Tai, to an extent of over ten thousand *li*. Here the Male and Female Principles are evenly divided; hence there is summer and winter. Here the distinction of light and darkness is clear; hence there is day and night. Among its people there are those who are wise and those who are foolish. Here things are produced in great abundance and the arts and crafts are practiced in all their diversity. The people are ruled over by princes and their ministers and are restrained by laws and rules of conduct. It is impossible to recount all the things they say and do. They stay awake and sleep by turns and they take what they do in the former state as real and what they see in the latter state as illusory.

In the northern corner of the Extreme East there is country called Fu Lo. Its soil and air remain uniformly warm, being shined upon by the surplus light[1] of the sun and moon. The precious grains do not grow here; the people live on roots and fruits only, and they know not the art of cooking with fire. Their nature is violent and the weak are oppressed by the strong. They esteem advantage over others instead of justice. They are always dashing about and rarely stop to rest; they are always awake and never indulge in sleep.

Translated from the Chinese
by Chi-Chen Wang

MR. YIN AND HIS SERVANT

Mr. Yin of Chou was the owner of a large estate who harried his servants unmercifully, and gave them no rest from morning to night. There was one old servant in particular whose physical strength had quite left him, yet his master worked him all the harder. All day long he was groaning as he went about his work, and when night came he was reeling with fatigue and would sleep like a log. His spirit was then free to wander at will, and every night he dreamt that he was a king, enthroned in authority over the multitude, and

1. The indirect light of the sun and moon?

controlling the affairs of the whole State. He took his pleasure in palaces and belvederes, following his own fancy in everything, and his happiness was beyond compare. But when he awoke, he was a servant once more. To some one who condoled with him on his hard lot the old man replied: "Human life may last a hundred years, and the whole of it is equally divided into nights and days. In the day-time I am only a slave, it is true, and my misery cannot be gainsaid. But by night I am a king, and my happiness is beyond compare. So what have I to grumble at?"

Now, Mr. Yin's mind was full of worldly cares, and he was always thinking with anxious solicitude about the affairs of his estate. Thus he was wearing out mind and body alike, and at night he also used to fall asleep utterly exhausted. Every night he dreamt that he was another man's servant, running about on menial business of every description, and subjected to every possible kind of abuse and ill-treatment. He would mutter and groan in his sleep, and obtained no relief until morning came. This state of things at last resulted in a serious illness, and Mr. Yin besought the advice of a friend. "Your station in life," his friend said, "is a distinguished one, and you have wealth and property in abundance. In these respects you are far above the average. If at night you dream that you are a servant and exchange ease for affliction, that is only the proper balance in human destiny. What you want is that your dreams should be as pleasant as your waking moments. But that is beyond your power to compass." On hearing what his friend said, Mr. Yin lightened his servant's toil, and allowed his own mental worry to abate; whereupon his malady began to decrease in proportion.

Translated from the Chinese
by Lionel Giles

WHOSE DEER WAS IT?

A man was gathering fuel in the Chêng State when he fell in with a deer that had been startled from its usual haunts. He gave chase, and succeeded in killing it. He was overjoyed at his good luck; but, for fear of discovery, he hastily concealed the carcass in a dry ditch, and covered it up with brushwood. Afterwards, he forgot the spot where he had hidden the deer, and finally became convinced that the whole affair was only a dream. He told the story to people he met as he went along; and one of those who heard it, following the indications given, went and found the deer. On reaching home with his booty, this man made the following statement to his wife: "Once upon a time," he said, "a wood-cutter dreamt that he had got a deer, but couldn't remember the place where he had put it. Now I have found the deer, so it appears that his dream was a true dream." "On the contrary," said his wife, "it is you who must have dreamt that you met a wood-cutter who had caught a deer. Here you have a deer, true enough. But where is the wood-cutter? It is evidently your dream that has come true." "I have certainly got a deer," replied her husband; "so what does it matter to us whether it was his dream or mine?"

Meanwhile, the wood-cutter had gone home, not at all disgusted at having lost the deer. But the same night, he saw in a dream the place where he had really hidden it, and he also dreamt of the man who had taken it. So, the next morning, in accordance with his dream, he went to seek him out in order to recover the deer. A quarrel ensued, and the matter was finally brought before the magistrate, who gave judgment in these terms: "You," he said to the wood-cutter, "began by really killing a deer, but wrongly thought it was a dream. Then you really dreamt that you had got the deer, but wrongly took the dream to be a reality. The other man really took your deer, which he is now disputing with you. His wife, on the other hand, declares that he saw both man and deer in a dream, so that nobody can be said to have killed the deer at all. Meanwhile, here is the deer itself in court, and you had better divide it between you."

The case was reported to the Prince of the Chêng State, who said: "Why, the magistrate must have dreamt the whole thing himself!" The question was referred to the Prime Minister, but the latter confessed himself unable to disentangle the part that was a dream from the part that was not a dream. "If you want to distinguish between waking and dreaming," he said, "only the Yellow Emperor or Confucius could help you. But both these sages are dead, and there is nobody now alive who can draw any such distinction. So the best thing you can do is to uphold the magistrate's decision."

Translated from the Chinese by Lionel Giles
(All four selections from *Lieh Tzu,* Book III)

Chuang Tzu 369-286 B.C.?

The Chuang Tzu, *which ranks with the* Tao Te Ching *as one of the most important classics of Taoism, is unique in that it rejects the social and political realities, which other ancient Chinese philosophers accept as frameworks upon which they must base their theories, in favor of imaginative flights of the spirit. The paragraph included here is from one of the "inner" chapters, generally regarded as authentic works by Chuang Chou.*

CHUANG CHOU AND THE BUTTERFLY

Once Chuang Chou dreamed that he was a butterfly. He fluttered about happily, quite pleased with the state he was in, and knew nothing about Chuang Chou. Presently he awoke and found that he was very much Chuang Chou again. Now, did Chou dream that he was a butterfly or was the butterfly now dreaming that he was Chou?

(*Chuang Tzu,* Book II)
Translated from the Chinese by Chi-Chen Wang

Shen Chi-chi

ca. 750-800

Shen Chi-chi was a native of the district of Wu in modern Kiangsu. He served as a compiler in the Institute of Historiography and was admired for his Veritable Record of the Chien Chung Period. *His tale is essentially an elaboration of a short anecdote from the* Sou Shen Chi *or* Quest for the Gods *of Kan Pao, who lived between 290 and 320* A.D. *By comparing the following paraphrase of the earlier anecdote with the elaborations of Shen Chi-Chi and Li Kung-tso, the reader will be able to see the advance in the art of fiction made by the writers of the T'ang dynasty.*

"In a temple at Tsiao-hu there is a jade pillow with a crack on it. One day, when Yang Lin, a merchant of Shan-fu, visited the temple, the attendant asked him if he would like to have a good marriage. On Yang Lin's answering that he would, the attendant led him to the pillow and caused him to crawl into it. Inside he met a high

official named Chao, who lived in a palace of painted halls and gem-studded chambers, and who gave his daughter to him in marriage. Six sons were born to him and they all became members of the Imperial Secretariat. For thirty years he lived in the land of illusion and had no thoughts of returning. Then he suddenly awoke and found himself by the side of the pillow as before. He was greatly moved by the experience."

THE MAGIC PILLOW

In the seventh year of K'ai Yuan (719 A.D.) a Taoist priest by the name of Lü Weng, who had acquired the magic of the immortals, was traveling on the road to Hantan. He stopped at an inn and was sitting and resting with his back against his bag when he was joined in a very genial conversation by a young man named Lu Sheng, who wore a plain, short coat and rode a black colt and who had stopped at the inn on his way to the fields. After a while Lu Sheng suddenly sighed and said, looking at his shabby clothes, "It is because fate is against me that I have been such a failure in life!" "Why do you say that in the midst of such a pleasant conversation?" Lü Weng said, "For as far as I can see you suffer from nothing and appear to enjoy the best of health." "This is mere existence," Lu Sheng said. "I do not call this life." "What then do you call life?" asked the priest, whereupon the young man answered, "A man ought to achieve great things and make a name for himself; he should be a general at the head of an expedition or a great minister at court, preside over sumptuous banquets and order the orchestra to play what he likes, and cause his clan to prosper and his own family to wax rich—these things make what I call life. I have devoted myself to study and have enriched myself with travel; I used to think that rank and title were mine for the picking, but now at the prime of life I still have to labor in the fields. What do you call this if not failure?"

After he finished speaking he felt a sudden drowsiness. The innkeeper was steaming some millet at the time. Lü Weng reached into his bag and took out a pillow and gave it to Lu Sheng, saying, "Rest your head on this pillow; it will enable you to fulfill your wishes." The pillow was made of green porcelain and had an opening at each end. Lu Sheng bent his head toward it and as he did so the opening grew large and bright, so that he was able to crawl into it. He found himself back home. A few months later he married the daughter of the Tsui family of Chingho, who was very beautiful and made him exceedingly happy. His wealth increased and the number of luxuries with which he surrounded himself multiplied day by day. The following year he passed the examinations and thus "discarded his hempen coat" and joined the ranks at court. He was made a member of the Imperial Secretariat and had the honor of composing occasional poems at the emperor's command. After serving a term as inspector of Weinan, he was promoted to the Censorate, and made secretary in attendance. In the latter capacity he took part in the drafting of important decrees.

Then followed a succession of provincial posts, in one of which, as the governor of Shensi, he built a canal eighty *li* in length, which brought so many benefits to the people of the region that they commemorated his achievement upon stone. Next he was made governor of the metropolitan district. In the same year the Emperor's campaigns against the encroaching barbarians reached a critical stage, and when the Turfan and Chulung hordes invested Kuachou and Shachou and menaced the region of the Ho and the Huang, the Emperor, in his search for new talent, made Lu Sheng associate director of the Censorate and governor-general of the Hosi Circuit. Lu Sheng routed the barbarians, killing seven thousand men. He conquered nine hundred *li* of territory and built three cities to guard the frontier. The people of the frontier region built a monument on the Chuyen Mountain to commemorate his exploits, and when he returned to court he was received with triumphal honors and was made vice-president of the Board of Civil Service and then president of the Board of Revenue. No name carried so much prestige as his and he had the universal acclaim of popular sentiment, but these incurred the jealousy of the other ministers at court, and as a result of their slanderous attacks he was banished to a provincial post. Three years later, however, he was recalled to court and for more than ten years, with Hsiao Sung and P'ei Kuang-t'ing, he held the reins of government. Sometimes he received as many as three confidential messages from the Emperor in one day and was ever ready to assist His Majesty with his wise counsel.

Then again he fell victim to the jealousy of his colleagues. They charged him with conspiring with frontier generals to overthrow the dynasty and caused him to be thrown into prison. When the guards came to arrest him, he was stricken with terror and perplexity and said to his wife and sons: "Back in Shantung we have five hundred acres of good land, quite sufficient to keep us from cold and hunger. Why should I have sought rank and title, which in the end have only brought calamity? It is now too late to wish that I could again ride back and forth on the Hantan road as I once did, wearing my plain hempen coat!" Thereupon he drew his sword and attempted to kill himself, but was prevented from doing so by his wife. All those implicated in the plot were executed but Lu Sheng escaped death through the intercession of one of the eunuchs in the confidence of the Emperor. His sentence was commuted to exile to Huanchou. In a few years the Emperor, having ascertained his innocence, recalled him, made him president of the Imperial Council, and gave him the title of Duke of Yenkuo.

He had five sons, all of whom were gifted and were admitted into official ranks. They all married daughters of influential families of the time and presented him with more than ten grandchildren. And so he lived for over fifty years, during which he was twice banished to the frontier wilds only to be recalled to court, vindicated, and given greater honors than before. He was given to extravagance and was addicted to pleasures. His inner apartments were filled with dancers and beautiful women, and innumerable were the gifts of fertile lands, mansions, fleet horses, and such treasures that the Emperor bestowed upon him.

When advanced age made him wish to retire from court life, his petitions were repeatedly refused. When at last he fell ill, emissaries sent by the Emperor to inquire after his condition followed upon one another's heels and there was nothing left undone that eminent physicians could do. But all was in vain and one night he died, whereupon he woke up with a start and found himself lying as before in the roadside inn, with Lü Weng sitting by his side and the millet that his host was cooking still not yet done. Everything was as it had been before he dozed off. "Could it be that I have been dreaming all this while?" he said, rising to his feet. "Life as you would have it is but like that," said Lü Weng. For a long while the young man reflected in silence, then he said, "I now know at last the way of honor and disgrace and the meaning of poverty and fortune, the reciprocity of gain and loss and the mystery of life and death, and I owe all this knowledge to you. Since you have thus deigned to instruct me in the vanity of ambition, dare I refuse to profit thereby?" With this he bowed profoundly to Lü Weng and went away.

(Lu Hsun, *T'ang Sung Ch'uan-Ch'i Chi,* I)
Translated from the Chinese by Chi-Chen Wang

Li Kung-tso

ca. 770-850

The dates given above were suggested, tentatively, by Lu Hsun, author of the first history of Chinese fiction. His sources give very little information about the author aside from stating that he passed his chin-shih *examinations and served in various government posts. An interesting side light about him was provided by Po Hsing-chien (see* The Three Dreams *in this collection), who asserted, at the end of* The Story of Li Wa, *that it was at the suggestion of Li Kung-tso that he set down the tale. His only other extant writing appears to consist of a tale about a monkey demon and a single poem.*

GOVERNOR OF THE SOUTHERN BRANCH

Chunyu Fen, a native of Tungping and a well-known gallant of the Yangtse River region, was fond of drinking, hot-tempered and recklessly indifferent to conventions. He had amassed great wealth and acted as patron to many dashing young men. Because of his military prowess he had been made an adjutant of the Huainan Army, but in a fit of drunkenness he offended his general and was dismissed. Then in his disappointment he let himself go and spent his days drinking.

Chunyu's home was some three miles east of Yangchow. South of his house there was a huge old ash tree with great branches, thick with foliage, which shaded an acre of land; and under this tree Chunyu and his boon companions drank daily to their hearts' content. In the ninth month of the tenth year of the Chen Yuan period (794 A.D.), Chunyu got drunk, and two of his friends carried him back home and laid him in the eastern chamber. "You had better go to sleep," they said. "We shall give the horses some fodder and wash our feet. We shan't go until you feel better."

He took off his cap and rested his head on the pilow, lying there in an intoxicated state, half dreaming and half awoke. Presently he saw two messengers come in, dressed in purple, who knelt before him and said, "His Majesty the king of Ashendon has sent us, his humble subjects, to invite you to his kingdom."

Chunyu got up from his couch, dressed and followed the two messengers to the gate, where he saw a small green carriage drawn by four horses. Seven or eight attendants who were standing by helped him into the carriage. Driving out of the gate, they set forth in the direction of the ash tree and—to Chunyu's amazement—headed down the hollow under the tree. However, he dared ask no questions. The scenery along the road—the mountains and rivers, trees and plants—looked different from the world of men. The climate too had changed. After they had travelled about ten miles, city walls came into sight, and the road began to fill with carriages and people. The footmen on the carriage kept calling out to clear the road and the pedestrians moved hurriedly out of their way. They entered a great city through a turreted red gate over which was inscribed in letters of gold "The Great Kingdom of Ashendon." The gate-keepers bestirred themselves and bowed low to them.

Then a rider cantered up, calling, "As His Highness the prince consort has travelled so far, His Majesty orders him to be taken to the East Hostel to rest." And he led the way.

Chunyu saw a gate in front swing open. He got down from the

carriage and passed through the gate. There were brightly painted and finely carved balustrades and pilasters among terraces of blossoming trees and rare fruits, while tables and rugs, cushions and screens had been set ready in the hall and a rich feast laid out. Chunyu was enchanted. Presently it was announced that the prime minister had arrived, and Chunyu went to the foot of the hall steps to await him respectfully. Dressed in purple and holding an ivory sceptre, the minister approached, and they paid their respects to each other. This done, the minister said, "Though our land is far from yours, our king has asked you here because he hopes for an alliance with you by marriage."

"How can a humble person like myself aspire so high?" replied the young man.

The minister asked Chunyu to follow him to the palace. They walked a hundred yards and entered a red gate where spears, axes, and halberds were displayed, several hundred officers stood still by the side of the road to make way for Chunyu, among them an old drinking friend of his named Chou. Chunyu was secretly delighted, but dared not go forward to accost him.

Then the minister led Chunyu up to a court where guards were standing solemnly in formation, showing that they were in the royal presence. He saw a tall, imposing figure on the throne, wearing a white silk robe and a bright red cap. Overcome by awe, he did not look up, but bowed as the attendants told him. "At your father's wish," said the king, "we have asked you to our unworthy kingdom, to offer you our second daughter as your wife." When Chunyu kept his head bowed and dared not reply, the king told him, "You may go back to the guest house and prepare for the ceremony."

As the minister accompanied him back, Chunyu was thinking hard. Since his father was a frontier general who had been reported missing, it was possible that, having made peace with the border kingdoms, he was responsible for this invitation. Still, Chunyu was bewildered and at a loss to account for it.

That evening, amid pomp and splendour, betrothal gifts of lambs, swans and silk were displayed. There was music of stringed and bamboo instruments, feasting with lanterns and candles, and a concourse of carriages and horsemen. Some of the girls present were addressed as the nymphs of Huayang or Chinghsi, others as the fairies of the upper or lower region. Attended by a large retinue, they were dressed in green phoenix head-dresses and gold cloud-like garments and decked with golden trinkets and precious stones that dazzled the eye. These girls frolicked about and played pranks on Chunyu, with such bewitching charm and clever repartee that he found it hard to reply.

"On the last Spring Purification Festival," one girl said, "I went with Lady Lingchih to Chanchih Monastery to watch Yuyen perform the Brahmana dance in the Indian Quadrangle. I was sitting with the girls on the stone bench on the north side when you and your young gallants arrived, and got off your horses to watch. You accosted us and teased us and made jokes—don't you remember how Chiungying and I tied a scarlet scarf on the bamboo? Then, on the sixteenth of the seventh month, I went with Shang Chen-tse to Hsiaokan Monastery to listen to Monk Chihsuan discoursing on the Avalokiteshvara sutra. I donated two gold phoenix-shaped hairpins and my friend one rhinoceros horn case. You were there too, and you asked the monk to let you look at the things. After admiring them and praising the workmanship for a long time, you turned to us and said, 'These pretty things and their owners surely can't belong to the world of men!' Then you asked my name and wanted to know where I lived, but I wouldn't tell you. You kept staring at me as if you were quite lovelorn—don't you remember?"

Chunyu replied by quoting the song:

Deep in my heart it is hidden,
How can I ever forget?

And the girls said, "Who could imagine that you would become our relative?"

Just then three magnificently dressed men came up. Bowing to Chunyu, they announced, "By His Majesty's order we have come to be your groomsmen." One of them looked like an old friend.

"Aren't you Tien Tse-hua of Fengyi?" Chunyu asked him. When the other said that he was, Chunyu went forward to grasp his hand, and they talked about the past.

Asked how he came to be there, Tien replied, "On my travels I met Lord Tuan, the prime minister, and he became my patron." When Chunyu asked him if he knew that Chou was also there, he replied, "Chou has done very well. He is now the city commandant and has great influence. On several occasions he has done me a favour."

They talked cheerfully until it was announced that the prince consort should go to the wedding. As the three groomsmen handed him his sword, pendants, robes and head-dress, and helped him to put them on, Tien said, "I never thought I should be at such a grand ceremony for you today. You mustn't forget your old friends."

Several dozen fairy maids began to play rare music, piercingly tender and infinitely sad, the like of which Chunyu had never heard before. Dozens of other attendants held candles all the way down a mile-long path lined on both sides with gold and emerald-green screens vividly painted and intricately carved. Chunyu sat up straight in the carriage, feeling rather nervous, while Tien joked to put him at his ease. The girls he had seen were arriving too in phoenix-winged carriages. When he came to the gate of Hsiu Yi Palace, the girls were there too, and Chunyu was asked to alight. They went through a ceremony just like that in the world of men, at the end of which screens and fans were removed, enabling him to see his bride, the Princess of the Golden Bough. She was about fifteen, lovely as a goddess and well trained in the marriage ceremony.

After the wedding Chunyu and the princess came to love each other dearly, and his power and prestige increased daily. His equipage and entertainments were second only to the king's. One day the king took him and some other officials as his guards to hunt at the Divine Tortoise Mountain in the west, where there were high peaks, wide marshlands and luxuriant forests stocked with all kinds of birds and beasts. The hunters came back with a big bag of game that evening.

One day Chunyu said to the king, "On my wedding day Your Majesty said you had sent for me in compliance with my father's wishes. My father served formerly as a general at the frontier. After a defeat he was reported missing, and I have had no news of him for eighteen years. Since Your Majesty knows where he is now, I would like to call on him."

"Your father is still serving at the northern frontier," replied the king quickly. "We are in constant touch. You had better just write to him. There is no need for you to go there." The king ordered the princess to prepare gifts to send to Chunyu's father, and after a few days a reply came in his father's handwriting. He expressed his longing for his son, and wrote just as in former letters, asking whether certain relatives were still alive and what news there was of their home-town. Since the distance between them was so great, he said, it was difficult to send news. His letter was sad and full of grief. He told Chunyu not to come, but promised that they would meet in three years' time. With this letter in his hands, Chunyu wept bitterly, unable to restrain himself.

One day the princess asked him, "Don't you ever want to take up an official post?"

"I am used to a carefree life," answered Chunyu. "I don't understand official work."

"Just take a post," his wife said, "and I will help you." Then she spoke to the king.

A few days later the king said, "All is not well in my southern tributary state, and the governor has been dismissed. I would like to use your talents to set their affairs in order. You might go there with my daughter." When Chunyu consented, the king ordered those in charge to get his baggage ready. Gold, jade and silk, cases and servants, carriages and horsemen formed a long baggage train when he and the princess were ready to leave. And since Chunyu had mixed with gallants as a young man and never dreamed of becoming an official, he was very pleased.

He sent a memorandum to the king, saying, "As the son of a military family, I have never studied the art of government. Now that I have been given this important post, I fear I shall not only disgrace myself but ruin the prestige of the court. I would therefore like to seek far and wide for wise and talented men to help me. I have noticed that City Commandant Chou of Yingchuan is a loyal, honest officer, who firmly upholds the law and would make a good minister. Then there is Tien Tse-hua, a gentleman of Fengyi, who is prudent and full of stratagems and has probed deeply into the principles of government. I have known both these men for ten years. I understand their talents and consider them trustworthy, and therefore I ask to have Chou appointed the chief councillor and Tien the minister of finance of my state. For then the government will be well administered and the laws well kept." The two men were then appointed to these posts by the king.

The evening of Chunyu's departure, the king and queen gave a farewell feast for him south of the capital.

"The southern state is a great province," said the king. "The land is rich and the people prosperous, and you must adopt a benevolent policy there. With Chou and Tien assisting you, I hope you will do well and come up to our expectations."

Meantime the queen told the princess, "Your husband is impetuous and fond of drinking, and he is still young. A wife should be gentle and obedient. I trust you to look after him well. Though you will not be too far from us, you will no longer be able to greet us every morning and evening, and I find it hard not to shed tears now that you are going away." Then Chunyu and the princess bowed, got into their carriage and started south. They talked cheerfully on the way, and several days later reached their destination.

The officials of the province, the monks and priests, elders, musicians, attendants and guards had all come out in welcome. The streets were thronged, and drums and bells were being sounded for miles around. Chunyu saw a goodly array of turrets and pavilions as he entered the great city gate, above which was inscribed in letters of gold "The Southern Tributary State." In front there were red windows and a big gate with a fine view into the distance. After his arrival he studied the local conditions and helped all who were sick or distressed, entrusting his government to Chou and Tien, who administered the province well. He remained governor there for twenty years, and the people benefiting from his good rule sang his praises and set up tablets extolling his virtue or built temples to him. As a result, the king honoured him even more: he was given fiefs and titles and exalted to the position of a grand councillor of state, while both Chou and Tien also became well-known as good officials, and were promoted several times. Chunyu had five sons and two daughters. His sons were given official posts reserved for the nobility, while his daughters were married into the royal family. Thus his fame and renown were unrivalled.

One year the kingdom of Sandalvine attacked this province, and the king ordered Chunyu to raise an army to defend it. Chunyu made Chou commander of thirty thousand troops to resist the invaders at Jade Tower City, but Chou proved proud and reckless, underestimating the enemy. His troops were routed and, abandoning his armour, he fled back alone to the provincial capital at night. Meanwhile the invaders, after capturing their baggage train and arms, had withdrawn. Chunyu had Chou arrested and asked to be punished, but the king pardoned them both.

That same month Chou developed a boil on his back and died. Ten days later the princess died of illness too, and Chunyu's request to leave the province and accompany the hearse to the capital was granted. Tien, the minister of finance, was appointed deputy in his place. Bowed down with grief, Chunyu followed the hearse. On the way many people wept, officers and common citizens paid their last homage, while great crowds blocked the way and clung to the carriage. When he reached Ashendon, the king and queen were waiting outside the capital, wearing mourning and weeping. The princess was posthumously entitled Shun Yi (Obedient and Graceful). Guards, canopies and musicians were provided, and she was buried at Coiling Dragon Mount some three miles east of the city. During the same month, Chou's son Yung-hsin also arrived with his father's hearse.

Now though Chunyu had been ruling over a tributary state outside the kingdom for many years, he had managed to keep on good terms with all the nobles and influential officers at court. After his return to the capital he behaved unconventionally and gathered around himself many associates and followers, his power growing so rapidly that the king began to suspect him. Then some citizens reported to the king that a mysterious portent had appeared and the state was doomed to suffer a great catastrophe: the capital would be removed and the ancestral temples destroyed. This would be caused by someone of foreign birth who was close to the royal family. After deliberation the ministers decided that there was danger in Chunyu's luxury and presumption; accordingly the king deprived him of his attendants and forbade him to have any further dealings with his associates, ordering him to live in retirement.

Conscious that he had not governed badly all these years in his province, but was now slandered, Chunyu was in low spirits. The king, sensing this, said to him, "You have been my son-in-law for more than twenty years. Unhappily my daughter died young and could not live with you till old age. This is a great misfortune." Then the queen took charge of his children herself, and the king said, "You have left your home for a long time. You had better go back now for a while to see your relatives. Leave your children here and do not worry about them. In three years we shall fetch you back."

"Isn't this my home?" asked Chunyu. "What other home have I to go back to?"

"You came from the world of men," replied the king with a laugh. "This is not your home." At first Chunyu felt as if he were dreaming, but then he remembered how he had come there and, shedding tears, asked for permission to return. The king ordered his attendants to see him off, and with a bow Chunyu took his leave.

The same two messengers dressed in purple accompanied him out of the gate. But there he was shocked to see a shabby carriage with no attendants or envoys to accompany him. He got into the carriage, however, and after driving some miles they left the city behind. They travelled the same way that he had first come by. The mountains, rivers and plains were unchanged, but the two messengers with Chunyu looked so seedy that he felt let down. When he asked them when they would reach Yangchow, they went on singing without paying any attention. Only when he insisted did they answer, "Soon."

Presently they emerged from the hollow and Chunyu saw his own village unchanged. Sadness seized him, and he could not help shedding tears. The two messengers helped him down from the carriage, through the door of his house and up the steps. Then he saw himself lying in the eastern chamber, and was so frightened that he dared not approach. At that the two messengers called his name aloud several times, and he woke up.

He saw his servants sweeping the courtyard. His two guests were still washing their feet by the couch, the slanting sun had not yet set behind the west wall and his unfinished wine was still by the east window—but he had lived through a whole generation in his dream! Deeply moved, he could not help sighing. And when he called his two friends and told them, they were equally amazed. They went out to look for the hollow under the ash tree, and Chunyu, pointing to it, said, "This is where I went in the dream."

His friends believed this must be the work of some fox fairy or tree spirit, so servants were ordered to fetch an axe and cut through the tree trunk and branches to find where the hollow ended. It was some ten feet long, terminating in a cavity lit by the sun and large enough to hold a couch. In this were mounds of earth which resembled city walls, pavilions and courts, and swarms of ants were gathered there. In the ant-hill was a small, reddish tower occupied by two huge ants, three inches long, with white wings and red heads. They were surrounded by a few dozen big ants, and other ants dared not approach them. These huge ants were the king and queen, and this was the capital of Ashendon.

Then the men followed up another hole which lay under the southern branch of the tree and was at least forty feet long. In this tunnel there was another ant-hill with small towers, which swarmed with ants. This was the southern tributary state which Chunyu had governed. Another large, rambling tunnel of a fantastic shape ran westwards for twenty feet, and in this they found a rotten tortoise shell as big as a peck measure, soaked by rain and covered by luxuriant grass. This was the Divine Tortoise Mountain where Chunyu had hunted. They followed up yet another tunnel more than ten feet long in the east, where the gnarled roots of the tree had twisted into the shape of a dragon. Here there was a small earthen mound about a foot high, and this was the grave of the princess, Chunyu's wife.

As he thought back, Chunyu was very shaken, for all that they had discovered coincided with his dream. He would not let his friends destroy these ant-hills, and ordered that the tunnels be covered up as before. That night, however, there was a sudden storm, and in the morning when he examined the holes the ants had gone. Thus the prophecy that Ashendon would suffer a great catastrophe and that the capital would be removed was realized. Then he thought of the invasion by the kingdom of Sandalvine, and asked his two friends to trace it. They found that some six hundred yards east of his house was a river-bed long since dry, and next to it grew a big sandal tree so thickly covered with vines that the sun could not shine through it. A small hole beside it, where a swarm of ants had gathered, must be the kingdom of Sandalvine.

If even the mysteries of ants are so unfathomable, what then of the changes caused by big beasts in the hills and woods?

At that time Chunyu's friends Chou and Tien were both in Liuho County, and he had not seen them for ten days. He sent a servant posthaste to make enquiries, and found that Chou had died of a sudden illness, while Tien was lying ill in bed. Then Chunyu realized how empty his dream had been, and that all was vanity too in the world of men. He therefore became a Taoist and abstained from wine and women. Three years later he died at home, in his forty-seventh year, just as predicted in the dream.

In the eighth month of the 11th year of the Chen Yuan period (795 A.D.), while on a journey from Soochow to Loyang I had stopped at Huaipu and met Chunyu by chance. I questioned him and looked at the ant-hills, going into his story very thoroughly. Believing it to be quite genuine, I have written this tale for those who may be interested. Although it deals with supernatural and unorthodox things, it may have a moral for the ambitious. Let future readers not think this story a mere series of coincidences, and let them beware of taking pride in worldly fame and position.

For, as Li Chao, former adjutant general of Huachow commented:

His reputation reaches to the skies,
His influence can make a kingdom fall,
And yet this pomp and power, after all,
Are but an ant-heap in the wise man's eyes.

(Lu Hsun, *T'ang Sung Ch'uan-Ch'i Chi,* III)

Po Hsing-chien

776-827

Po Hsing-chien was the younger brother of Po Chü-i, one of the most celebrated poets of China. He is chiefly remembered as the author of The Story of Li wa, *which formed the basis of many later plays, and the tale included here, notable as a first attempt to formulate the varieties of dreams it is possible to have.*

THE THREE DREAMS

People sometimes have dreams that are out of the ordinary. I know of a case in which the dreaming spirits are encountered by a waking person, another case in which the doings of waking persons are observed by a person in his dreams, and still another case in which two people meet in their dreams.

In the time of Empress Wu (684-704 A.D.), Liu Yu-ch'iu served as the assistant magistrate of Chao-yi. Once he was sent on a mission and had to return home at night. While still some ten *li* from his house, he passed by a Buddhist temple enclosed by a low wall. Hearing the sound of singing and laughter, he stopped, bent over the wall and looked inside, and saw some ten persons of both sexes seated around a well-spread table. Among the company was his wife, talking and laughing with the rest. Liu was very much puzzled and did not know what to make of it, for he could not imagine his wife in this scene. Unable to tear himself away, he observed the woman carefully and found that her voice and gestures were exactly those of his wife. He wanted to go in and confront her, but the gate was closed. He picked up a broken tile and threw it at the merry-makers. The tile landed on the table with a crash and broke some dishes, whereupon the people suddenly vanished. Liu then climbed over the wall with his servant and searched the temple grounds carefully, but there was no one to be found. The gate was bolted as before. Liu was more dumbfounded than ever. On hastening home, he found that his wife had already gone to bed. After asking him about his journey, she said, laughing, "I have just had a strange dream. I visited a temple with a group of strangers and had dinner with them in the courtyard. Then someone threw a broken tile at us, breaking some dishes, at which point I woke up." Liu also told her what he had seen. This, then, is a case of dreaming spirits being encountered by a waking person.

In the fourth year of Yuan-ho (809 A.D.), Yuan Wei-chih of Honan was sent on a mission while serving as a censor. Some ten days later my elder brother Lo-t'ien,[1] Li Chih-shao and myself went on an excursion to Lake Ch'ü-chiang, where we spent a considerable period of time on the grounds of the Tz'u-en Temple. As it was getting late in the day, we repaired to Li Chih-shao's house in the Hsiu-hsing Ward, where wine was served and we had a merry time. My elder brother grew thoughtful and said, "Wei-chih ought to have reached Liang-chou by this time." Then turning to me he sug-

1. Po Chü-i

gested that I compose a verse and inscribe it on the wall. This I did and here are the words:

Spring is here and I have no way of dissipating the sadness of
Spring,
Drunk, I break off twigs to serve as counters for the wine game.
Suddenly my thoughts turn to a friend who's gone to a far corner
of the sky,
Who, if my calculation is right, must have arrived at Liang-chou.

This happened on the twenty-first day. Some ten days later, a messenger arrived from Liang-chou with a letter from Wei-chih. At the end of the letter was a poem entitled, *A Dream,* which read:

I dreamed of seeing you, my friends, at Ch'ü-chiang Lake
And visited with you the ground of the Tz'u-en Temple.
When I was awakened by the post master ordering horses,
I found that I was still in the ancient city of Liang-chou.

The date agreed exactly with the date of our visit. This is a case of the doings of waking persons being observed by someone in his dream.

During the Cheng-yuan period, (785-804 A.D.) Tou Chih of Fu-feng and Wei Hsun of Ching-chao traveled together from Po to Ch'in and stopped at an inn at the T'ung-kuan Pass. Tou dreamed of visiting the temple of the God of Hua Mountains and of meeting a tall and dark priestess in blue skirt and white coat, who received him courteously and asked him to make a votive offering. Unable to resist her importunities, Tou consented. Tou asked her name and she gave it as Chao. When he woke up, Tou told Wei his dream. The next day on arriving at the temple, the two travelers were met by a priestess whose features, stature and costume were all as he had dreamed. Turning to Wei, Tou said, "My dream has come true." Then he ordered his servant to take two strings of cash and give it to her, whereupon the priestess clapped her hands and laughed to her colleagues, saying, "This is as I have dreamed." Startled, Wei asked her what she meant, and she answered, "Last night I dreamed of two men arriving from the east. One of them, who was short and had a beard, made an offering and gave me two strings of cash. The next morning I told my colleagues about it; now the dream has come true." Tou asked her name and it turned out to be Chao. Everything from beginning to end tallied with the dream. This is then a case of people meeting in their dreams.

Hsing-chien remarks: In the *Spring and Autumn Annals* and the books of historians and philosophers we find many accounts of dreams, but there are none that are like these three. People dream many varieties of dreams, but there are none that are like these three. Is it mere coincidence or has it been preordained that these dreams should happen to these particular persons? I do not know. I now record these events for posterity.

(Lu Hsun, *T'ang Sung Ch'uan-Ch'i Chi,* III)
Translated from the Chinese by Chi-Chen Wang

Shen Ya-chih

ca. 800-850

The known facts about Shen Ya-chih are very meager: He was a native of Wu-hsing, his courtesy name was Hsia-hsien, he passed his chin-shih *examinations in 815 and served in various minor government offices. Though his collected works have survived, he is remembered today chiefly for three short tales, of which the present selection is one.*

A STRANGE DREAM

In the tenth year of Yuan Ho (815 A.D.) I, Ya-chih, was appointed secretary to the Lord of Lung-hsi and accompanied him to Ching-chou, where he gathered many of the worthy scholars of Chang-an under his patronage. On the eighteenth of the fifth month, the Lord of Lung-hsi entertained his guests in a pavilion overlooking the East Pond and said to them, after his guests had taken their seats, "In my younger days I used to go around with Hsing Feng and came to know one of his strange experiences. I should like to tell you about it." "We should like to hear it," the guests said, whereupon the Lord of Lung-hsi went on: "Feng was the son of a general without any particular accomplishment of his own. He lived in the southern part of the P'ing-k'ang Ward in Chang-an, where for a million *cash* he bought from an impoverished family a large house with many compounds and innumerable chambers. Once, while he was taking a daytime nap, he dreamed of seeing a beautiful woman emerging from the western veranda. She was strolling leisurely and reading softly from a book which she held in her hand. She was dressed in the ancient style. Her hair was done up in a knot high on the head, and her eyebrows were elongated. She wore a dress with square collars, and long sashes hung low from her waist. Over her shoulders was draped a broad cape with wide sleeves. Feng was delighted at her appearance and asked her, 'Where have you come from, O Beautiful One?' The beautiful one answered, laughing, 'This is my house, so how can you, who have only recently moved in here, ask me where I have come from?' 'Would you let me look at your book?' Feng asked. The beautiful one said, 'I am fond of poetry and am never without this.' 'Please tarry a while so that I can peruse it,' Feng said. The beautiful one gave him the book of verse and sat down on the couch to the west. Feng opened the book and found a poem of only four lines at the beginning, entitled *A Song of Spring,* followed by others of much greater length. 'If you wish to copy something from the book,' the beautiful one said, 'you may do so, but you must limit yourself to only one.' Feng rose and, taking a sheet of decorated paper, copied the first poem, which read:

"The young maidens of Chang-an are out 'treading the green' under
 the spring sun,
But the sun brings me no joy, does not make my heart sing.
I have long forgotten how to dance the dance of the bent bow,
For autumn frost has nine times touched my gauze robe light as a
 cicada's wing.

" 'What is the dance of the bent bow?' Feng asked after reading the poem. 'My parents made me learn it,' she answered, and then rose and, straightening her dress and spreading out her sleeves, she danced a few turns of the bent bow for the benefit of Feng. Her eyes were covered with tears as she finished, and she got up to take leave. Feng urged her to stay a while longer. This she did but not for long. Then she went as she had come. Feng woke up without any recollection of the dream. However, when he changed his clothes later, he found the sheet of paper on which he had written down the poem and this brought back to him the dream in all its vividness. This occurred in the Cheng Yuan period (785-805 A.D.) and Feng told me about it some time later."

All those present on this occasion—which included a number of subordinates attached to the local offices in addition to guests of the Lord of Lunghsi such as Tu-ku Hsuan of Lung-hsi, Lu Chien-tz'u of Fang-yang, Chang Yu-hsin of Chang-shan, and Su T'iao of Wu-kung—were greatly moved by the story and said that it should be written down. I have, therefore, done so accordingly.

(Lu Hsun, *T'ang Sung Ch'uan-Ch'i Chi*, IV)
Translated from the Chinese by Chi-Chen Wang

Su Shih 1036-1101

Su Shih or Su Tung-p'o, as he is better known, is one of the most famous names in Chinese literature, both as a poet and as a prose writer. He is also remembered by students of Chinese history as one of the most outspoken critics of the reform measures of Wang An-shih. There is a biography of him in English written by Lin Yütang, entitled The Gay Genius.

THE SECOND VISIT TO THE RED CLIFF

In the same year, when the tenth moon was full, I went again to the Red Wall. Two friends accompanied me; and as we crossed the hill, the landscape glittered white with frost, while the leafless trees cast our shadows upon the ground. The bright moon above inspired our hearts, and many a catch we sang as we strolled along. Then I sighed and said, "Here are the guests gathered together, but where are the cakes and ale? Here in the silver moonlight, here in the clear breeze,—what waste of a night like this!"

Then up spoke a friend and said, "This very eve I netted one of those *gobemouche* small-scaled fishes, for all the world like the famous perch of the Sung. But how about liquor?" However, we went back with our friend to consult his wife, and she at once cried out, "I have a stoup of wine, stored now some time in case of an accident like this." And so with wine and fish we retraced our steps towards the Red Wall.

The river was rushing noisily by, but with narrowed stream; and over the heightened hill-tops the moon was still scarcely visible, while through the shallowing tide naked boulders stood prominently forth. It was but three months since, yet I hardly knew the place again.

I picked up my skirts and began to ascend the steep cliff. I struggled through bramble-brake. I sat me down upon the Tiger rock. I climbed a gnarled tree, up to the dizzy hawk's nest, whence I looked down upon the River God's temple below, and whither my two friends were unable to follow.

Suddenly there arose a rushing mighty sound. Trees and shrubs began to wave, hills to resound, valleys to re-echo, while wind lashed water into waves. Fear and regret entered into my soul; for it was not possible to remain. I hurried back and got on board. We poled the boat into mid-channel, and letting it take its own course, our excursion came to an end.

The hour was midnight, and all around was still; when from the east, across the river, flew a solitary crane, flapping its huge wings of dusky silk, as, with a long shrill scream, it whizzed past our boat towards the west. By-and-by, my friends left me, and I slept and dreamed that a lame Taoist priest in a feathery robe passed by on the bank, and, bowing to me, said, "Have you had a pleasant trip, sir, to the Red Wall?" I enquired his name, but he merely bowed again and made no reply. "Ah!" exclaimed I, "I know who you are. Are you not that bird which flew past me last night and screamed?" Just then I awakened with a start. I opened the door of my boat and looked out, but no one was to be seen.

(Su Shih's *Collected Works*)

Translated from the Chinese by H. A. Giles

P'u Sung-ling 1640-1715

P'u Sung-ling passed his hsiu-ts'ai *examination in 1658, but failed to gain the next higher degree, although he tried for it regularly almost until his death. His collection of anecdotes and tales known as the* Liao-chai chih-i *has become, since its publication in 1766, the most widely read book of its kind in China. It is also one of the few works of Chinese literature generally known in the West, through the translation of H. A. Giles, published under the title* Strange Stories from a Chinese Studio. *Not so well known is the fact that he was also the author of the great novel* Hsing-shih yin-yuan (Marriage as Retribution) *and of numerous works in the* chante-fable *form.*

THE PAINTED WALL

A Kiang-si gentleman, named Mêng Lung-t'an, was lodging at the capital with a Mr. Chu, M.A., when one day chance led them to a certain monastery, within which they found no spacious halls or meditation chambers, but only an old priest in *déshabillé.* On observing the visitors, he arranged his dress and went forward to meet them, leading them round and showing whatever there was to be seen. In the chapel they saw an image of Chih Kung, and the walls on either side were beautifully painted with life-like representations of men and animals. On the east side were pictured a number of fairies, among whom was a young girl whose maiden tresses were not yet confined by the matron's knot. She was picking flowers and gently smiling, while her cherry lips seemed about to move, and the moisture of her eyes to overflow. Mr. Chu gazed at her for a long time without taking his eyes off, until at last he became unconscious of anything but the thoughts that were engrossing him. Then, suddenly he felt himself floating in the air, as if riding on a cloud, and found himself passing through the wall,[1] where halls and pavilions stretched away one after another, unlike the abodes of mortals. Here an old priest was preaching the Law of Buddha, surrounded by a large crowd of listeners. Mr. Chu mingled with the throng, and after a few moments perceived a gentle tug at his sleeve. Turning round, he saw the young girl above-mentioned, who walked laughing away. Mr. Chu at once followed her, and passing a winding balustrade arrived at a small apartment beyond which he dared not venture farther. But the young lady, looking back, waved the flowers she had in her hand as though beckoning him to come on. He accordingly entered and found nobody else within. Then they fell on their knees and worshipped heaven and earth together,[2] and rose up as man and wife, after which the bride went away, bidding Mr. Chu keep quiet until she came back. This went on for a couple of days, when the young lady's companions began to smell a rat and discovered Mr. Chu's hiding-place. Thereupon they all laughed and said, "My dear, you are now a married woman, and should leave off that maidenly *coiffure.*" So they gave her the proper hair-pins and head ornaments, and bade her go bind her hair, at which she blushed very much but said nothing. Then one of them cried out, "My sisters, let us be off. Two's company, more's none." At this they all giggled again and went away.

1. Which will doubtless remind the reader of "Alice through the Looking-glass, and what she saw there."

2. The all-important item of a Chinese marriage ceremony; amounting, in fact, to calling God to witness the contract.

Mr. Chu found his wife very much improved by the alteration in the style of her hair. The high top-knot and the coronet of pendants were very becoming to her. But suddenly they heard a sound like the tramping of heavy-soled boots, accompanied by the clanking of chains and the noise of angry discussion. The bride jumped up in a fright, and she and Mr. Chu peeped out. They saw a man clad in golden armour, with a face as black as jet, carrying in his hands chains and whips, and surrounded by all the girls. He asked, "Are you all here?" "All," they replied. "If," said he, "any mortal is here concealed amongst you, denounce him at once, and lay not up sorrow for yourselves." Here they all answered as before that there was no one. The man then made a movement as if he would search the place, upon which the bride was dreadfully alarmed, and her face turned the colour of ashes. In her terror she said to Mr. Chu, "Hide yourself under the bed," and opening a small lattice in the wall, disappeared herself. Mr. Chu in his concealment hardly dared to draw his breath; and in a little while he heard the boots tramp into the room and out again, the sound of the voices getting gradually fainter and fainter in the distance. This reassured him, but he still heard the voices of people going backwards and forwards outside; and having been a long time in a cramped position, his ears began to sing as if there was a locust in them, and his eyes to burn like fire. It was almost unbearable; however, he remained quiety awaiting the return of the young lady without giving a thought to the why and wherefore of his present position.

Meanwhile, Mêng Lung-t'an had noticed the sudden disappearance of his friend, and thinking something was wrong, asked the priest where he was. "He has gone to hear the preaching of the Law," replied the priest. "Where?" said Mr. Mêng. "Oh, not very far," was the answer. Then with his finger the old priest tapped the wall and called out, "Friend Chu! what makes you stay away so long?" At this, the likeness of Mr. Chu was figured upon the wall, with his ear inclined in the attitude of one listening. The priest added, "Your friend here has been waiting for you some time;" and immediately Mr. Chu descended from the wall, standing transfixed like a block of wood, with starting eye-balls and trembling legs. Mr. Mêng was much terrified, and asked him quietly what was the matter. Now the matter was that while concealed under the bed he had heard a noise resembling thunder and had rushed out to see what it was.

Here they all noticed that the young lady on the wall with the maiden's tresses had changed the style of her *coiffure* to that of a married woman. Mr. Chu was greatly astonished at this and asked the old priest the reason.

He replied, "Visions have their origin in those who see them: what explanation can I give?" This answer was very unsatisfactory to Mr. Chu; neither did his friend, who was rather frightened, know what to make of it all; so they descended the temple steps and went away.

Translated from the Chinese by H. A. Giles

A SCHOLAR OF FENG-YANG

Feng-yang, a scholar, shouldered his books and traveled afar to study. Before leaving, he said to his wife: "In six months I shall return." More than ten months passed but there was no news of him, and now the wife looked for his coming with keen anxiety.

One night, just when she had sought her pillow, the moon shining through the gauze curtain cast a shifting shadow; she tossed about unable to sleep, her heart filled with the sadness of separation. Presently a lovely girl in a purple cloak and with pearls in her hair raised the curtain and entered; smiling, she asked: "My elder sister, are you not longing to see your husband?" The wife quickly rose, and the girl invited her to go with her; she dreaded the long distance, but the girl begged her to have no fear and taking her by the hand, together they walked out in the moonlight. After they had gone about the distance of an arrow's flight, the girl walked so swiftly that the wife had difficulty in keeping up with her, so she called to her to wait until she returned and put on other shoes. The girl then had her sit down by the roadside, took off her own shoes, and gave them to her. The wife gladly put them on and fortunately they fitted, so she rose and went on, feeling now as though she had wings.

Before long they beheld the scholar on a white mule riding toward them. When he saw his wife he was greatly surprised, dismounted at once, and asked whither she was going. "I was going to seek you," she replied. The husband looked at the lovely girl and asked who she was. Before the wife had time to reply, the girl put her hand to her mouth and said laughing: "Do not question her yet, your wife is tired; it was not easy for her to come here. And you yourself have been riding half the night; both of you, and the beast also, must be weary. My home is quite near, so please come and rest there; starting off early in the morning, you will not be greatly delayed." And some steps further ahead they saw a village, so together they went on.

Now they entered a courtyard, and the girl hurriedly aroused a sleeping maidservant to attend to her guests. Then she said: "The moonlight is so bright tonight, we need not light candles; and here is a small table, so let us sit on these stone benches." The scholar, after tying up the mule to the eaves of the house, seated himself. Meanwhile the girl said to the wife: "My shoes, I well know, must be too large for you; did you not suffer on the way? And now since you will not return on foot, will you please let me have them back?" The wife handed the shoes to her and thanked her.

In no time a feast was prepared. The girl poured out wine and said: "Now that husband and wife are united again after a long separation, may I offer a goblet of this inadequate wine with my congratulations!" The scholar also poured wine and responded. They both laughed and talked and grew very merry. The scholar fixed his gaze on the lovely girl, and they flirted with each other; but husband and wife had met without the exchange of a tender word. The girl's lovely eyes softened and she spoke in words of hidden meaning; the wife, sitting apart, feigned not to understand. The two gradually grew tipsy and their conversation became more and more intimate. Then she pressed on him a large horn cup of wine which he refused, saying that he had already drunk too much. When she insisted, the scholar laughingly said: "If you will sing me a song, my love, then I will drink!" The girl needed no urging; with an ivory plectrum she struck the strings of the lute and sang:

The coolness of the west wind comes through the gauze curtain of my window;
I hear the murmur of palm leaves and shower on shower of fine rain.
Where is my beloved? Idly talking to others?
Gazing in expectation my eyes grow dim,
I do not see him return.
My tears stream like strands of hemp;
My thoughts are of him,
And because of him are my regrets.
I hold in my hands my red-embroidered shoe,
To divine from the spirits whether he will return.

At the end of the song she smiled and said: "This is only a popular song and not worth listening to, but the people like it and I have tried to imitate them." Her way of singing was wanton and her manner and bearing seductive. The scholar was thrilled and could scarcely contain himself. Presently the girl pretended to be sleepy and left her seat; the scholar rose and followed her. They were away a long while, so the tired maidservant lay down under the veranda and fell asleep.

The wife sat alone, her heart bursting with anger and resentment—it was intolerable! She thought of escaping for home; but night had darkened, and besides she could not remember the way. Turning it over and over in her mind, she knew not what to do. Then she rose and went to peep at them; just near the window she could vaguely hear the intimate talk of lovers. Listening, she heard her husband repeat the selfsame things he used to say to her of old—all these he poured out to the girl. At this point the wife's hands trembled and her heart throbbed; she was beside herself and thought rather than stay here, better would she die in a ditch!

In a rage she went out, and at that instant she saw her brother San-lang approaching on horseback. He dismounted and asked what had happened; she told him all, and San-lang was furious. At once he went back with his sister into the house. The door of the room was locked, but there still could be heard a murmuring on the pillow. San-lang lifted up a huge stone and hurled it through the window, shattering several panes. A voice screamed from within: "Oh, his head is smashed! What shall I do?" When the wife heard this she was terrified and loudly wailed to her brother: "I didn't mean you to kill my husband! Now what will become of me?" San-lang opened his eyes wide: "You cried for my help! And now when I rid you of this iniquity, you stand by your husband against your brother. I am not wont to follow the whims of a woman like you!" Instantly he turned around to depart, but she caught hold of his robe and cried: "If you don't take me with you, what is to become of me?" San-lang thrust her to the ground and took himself off.

The wife suddenly woke in terror—then she knew it was only a dream.

Next day the scholar actually did return, and he came riding on a white mule. The wife wondered at this, but said nothing. Later the scholar told his wife of a dream he had the previous night; and what he had seen and what had happened in the dream exactly tallied with the wife's dream. At this they both were startled.

And now when San-lang heard that his brother-in-law had returned, he came to see him. They talked a while, and then San-lang said to the scholar: "Last night I dreamed you had returned—and now here you really are! That is very strange." "Luckily you did not kill me with that huge stone!" laughingly said the scholar. San-lang in alarm asked why he said that; whereupon the scholar related to him his dream. And San-lang was astounded, for that night he also had dreamed that he met his sister weeping and that on her appeal he in anger threw the stone. The three dreams agreed in every detail. But who was the lovely girl? No one knew.

Translated from the Chinese by Rose Quong

WU CH'IU-YUEH

Wang Ting, courtesy name Hsien-hu, was a native of Kao-yu. He was a man of noble character and great physical strength, and had a wide circle of friends. He was married at eighteen but after the loss of his wife he took to traveling and was often gone for a year at a time. His brother Nai, well known for his scholarly attainments north of the Yangtze, urged him to give up his travels and had plans to arrange a suitable marriage for him. He would not listen, however. Hiring a boat, he went to Chinkiang to visit some friends. As his friend happened to be away, he found lodgings in a second-story chamber at an inn. From his window he was able to see the limpid waters of the great river and temple roofs on the Golden Mountain Island. He was so delighted with the view that when his friend came the next day to invite him to live at his house, he refused. One night, about half a month later, he dreamed that a girl came to visit him. She was only fourteen or fifteen and had beautiful and regular features. She climbed into his bed and held intercourse with him. On waking, he found that he had had an emission. He was struck by the experience but attributed it to mere coincidence. However, when he had the same dream the following night, and again for three or four nights in succession, he became alarmed and went to bed without extinguishing the candle light, maintaining a state of vigilance. But he dozed off at last and almost immediately the girl came to him. He suddenly awoke in the midst of disporting himself with her and, opening his eyes, he found the girl, beautiful as a fairy maiden, actually in his arms. She was embarrassed, but the young man was pleased to find her thus, though he realized that she was not an ordinary human, and proceeded to overwhelm her with his passion. "How violent you are," the girl protested. "It is a good thing that I took the precaution of coming to you in your dreams."

Whereupon the young man asked her about herself, and she replied, "My family name is Wu and my own name is Ch'iu-yueh (Autumn Moon). My father was a Confucian scholar well versed in the art of divination according to the *Book of Changes.* He loved me dearly, but he would not have me betrothed because he knew that I would die young. Later I indeed died at the age of fifteen. He had me buried just east of here, with neither mound nor tombstone above ground, but only a slab along with the coffin, on which he inscribed:

Here lies the body of Autumn Moon
Daughter I hold most dear.
She'll be married thirty years hence,
When Wang Ting arrives here.

When you came exactly thirty years later as prophesied, my heart was filled with happiness and I was eager to come to you, but being shy, I have chosen to appear before you indirectly through your dreams." Wang was pleased to hear this and proposed to consummate their union. "I need only a little touch of the Male Principle to come back to life," she said. "Really I cannot endure the kind of wind-and-rain you are wont to indulge in. Besides, we have many many years before us in which we can live in unbounded happiness; why must it be tonight?" Thereupon she rose and disappeared.

She came again the following day. They chatted and laughed as if they had always known each other. Later when they extinguished the light and went to bed, the young man found her no different from ordinary living humans. There was always a wet spot on the bedclothes afterwards.

One evening when the moon was bright, they strolled in the courtyard, and Wang asked her if in the other world there were cities also. "It is the same as in this world," the girl answered. "However, their cities do not occupy the same sites as yours, the nearest being three or four *li* from here, and they take your night as their day." Asked if a living person could visit one of these cities, the young lady answered yes, and consented to take him there. So they set off in the moonlight. The girl was as swift as the wind, with Wang following close behind as best he could. Soon the girl stopped, saying, "There it is!" Wang looked but saw nothing. The girl moistened her fingers with saliva and rubbed his eyes, whereupon the young man's vision became more acute and he was able to see, as well as in broad daylight, the battlements of the city wall in the distance and the stream of people on the road.

Presently, two officers guarding a group of three or four prisoners in chains passed by. One of the latter looked remarkably like Wang's elder brother and on closer inspection he found that it was indeed he. "How do you happen to be here?" Wang asked in astonishment. "I do not know myself why I have been arrested," his brother answered, weeping. "My brother is a gentleman who observes the proprieties," Wang said angrily. "He should not be put in chains like this." He asked the two officers to take the chains off, but they refused and were none too polite about it. Humiliated, Wang was about to argue more with the two men, but his brother intervened, saying, "They have their orders and must carry them out. But I am short of funds and I am being hard pressed to pay the customary fees. You must arrange to provide for me after your return." Wang held onto his brother's arm and cried. The officers became impatient and jerked violently on the chain, causing his elder brother to fall. This inflamed the young man; he drew his sword and with one blow cut off the head of the offending guard. He did likewise to the other man when he cried for help.

"You have killed two officers of the law," the girl said, greatly frightened. "It is an unpardonable offence. You must get yourself a boat and flee from here without delay. When you reach home, do not take off the funeral banners, but lock the gate and let no one come in or go out for seven days. After that you will be safe."

Wang fled the scene with his brother and hired a boat that same night for the homeward journey. Arriving home, Wang found mourning guests at their ancestral house and realized that his elder brother had indeed died. As soon as he ushered the guests out, he closed and bolted the gate. In the meantime his brother had vanished from his side. The dead man had come back to life in the chamber where he was laid, crying: "I am starved! Bring me some broth and bread." Now the brother had been dead for two days and great was the astonishment of the family when the young man told them his story. Seven days later, the gate was opened and the funeral banners removed. When friends and relatives learned that the brother had returned from the dead and asked about the circumstances, they were not told the real facts.

The young man could not forget Ch'iu-yueh and longed to see her. So once more he journeyed south, went to the old chamber and waited for her under the candlelight, but in vain. Then just as he was about to fall asleep, a woman came to him and said, "The young lady Ch'iu-yueh sends her greetings. She was arrested after the killing of the officers and has been in prison ever since. She is being cruelly treated by the jailers and has been hoping that you, sir, would come and deliver her from her suffering." Grieved and indignant, Wang followed the woman to a city and entered its western suburb, where, pointing to a gate, the woman said, "She is being detained in there." There were a great many buildings inside the first compound but Ch'iu-yueh was nowhere to be found. Wang passed through a small gate into another courtyard and saw a small chamber with a light inside. He went to the window and on peeping inside saw Ch'iu-yueh seated on a couch weeping, covering her face with her hands. Two jailers sat on either side of her and amused themselves by pinching her cheeks and squeezing her feet. This made the girl cry more piteously, whereupon one jailer said to her, "You are a prisoner now, how can you expect to keep yourself chaste?" Enraged, Wang rushed into the room and dispatched the two jailers with one blow each, seized the girl and carried her off before he was discovered. On arriving at the inn he suddenly woke up, wondering at the vividness of the nightmare. He was even more startled to find Ch'iu-yueh standing before him, her eyes still wet with tears. He made her sit down by him and told her of his dream.

"It actually happened," the girl said. "It is no dream." "What are we going to do?" the young man said, seized with fear. "This must be what has been preordained," the girl said, sighing. "I did not expect to come back to life till the end of the month, but under the circumstances we cannot wait. You must disinter me without delay and take me back home with you. You must keep on calling me by name for three days, when I shall come back to life. I am afraid that I won't be able to be of much use until I regain my strength when the month is up." She started to go out after saying this, but turned around again and said, "Oh, I almost forgot that we must take care of the pursuers. When I was still alive my father taught me a charm which he said would save me and my mate." So saying, she asked for a brush and wrote two charms, saying, "One you must wear yourself, the other you must paste on my back."

The young man followed Ch'iu-yueh out and noted the spot where she disappeared. Before he had reached the depth of a foot, the coffin came into sight. It had almost rotted away, but alongside it was a slab with the inscription she had mentioned. Removing the lid, he found the girl's body perfectly preserved as if she had never died. Her clothing, however, disintegrated at his touch. He carried her back to his chamber and, wrapping her securely in a quilt, carried her that same night to the river bank, where he hailed a boat, telling the boatman that his sister was critically ill and must be taken home at once. Fortunately a brisk south wind was blowing and it enabled the young man to reach his village just as dawn was breaking. He carried the girl's body into the house and put it in bed before he told his brother and sister-in-law what he had done. They looked at each other in disbelief, though they said nothing. Then, unwrapping the girl, he began to call her by name at regular intervals. At night he lay beside her. After a day had passed, her body grew warm and three days later she slowly came back to life. On the seventh day she was able to get up and walk, and be introduced to Wang's sister-in-law. Only she remained delicate and needed assistance when she had to walk more than ten steps; otherwise she would sway unsteadily as if the least stir of air would topple her over. But so beautiful was she and so fairylike that those who saw her all agreed that her weakness only made her more attractive.

She often exhorted Wang thus: "You have committed great sins and must perform good deeds and read the sutras to atone for them; otherwise you cannot expect to live long." Wang had never believed in Buddha, but after this he became a devout follower. He lived out his life without mishap.

The historian of unusual events says: "I have often wanted to propose that he who kills officers of the law should have his punishment remitted by three degrees, for there is not one of them that does not deserve death, and hence he who does away with them serves the cause of justice and should be dealt with leniently, even though he may have acted rashly. Moreover, the laws of the other world are not spelled out in detail; it is not considered too harsh to have the wicked hacked or sawed slowly into pieces or boiled in cauldrons of oil. Whatever acts satisfy our sense of justice must perforce win the approval of the King of the Nether World. Otherwise, how could Wang Ting have escaped punishment?"

(Liao Chai Chih I)

Translated from the Chinese by Chi-Chen Wang

Ts'ao Hsueh-ch'in

1720?-1764

For the general reader there is only one Hung Lou a Meng *or* Dream of the Red Chamber, *as the English version of China's greatest novel is known, and only one author for it. The book is a version with one hundred and twenty chapters first published in 1791 and the author is Ts'ao Hsueh-ch'in. In recent years, however, students of the novel have come to look upon the last forty chapters with suspicion and to feel that Kao O must have authored these chapters instead of merely editing them, as he asserted in his preface. There is no definite answer to this question and it need not concern us here, since the passage given below occurs in the fifty-sixth chapter. Our hero Pao-yü, whose family name was Chia (homophone for Unreal), had just been told about another Pao-yü, whose family name was Chen (Real), who not only looked exactly like him but behaved very much like him also.*

He did not believe what he heard until he actually met this counterpart of his some time later. In the meantime, he had the dream described below.

So before he knew what had happened Pao-Yü's head nodded, and he fell asleep. It seemed to him presently that he was in a great flower-garden which was extraordinarily like his own garden at home. "Is it possible," he said to himself in his dream, "that there is really another garden so exactly like mine?" While he was thus wondering to himself, there suddenly appeared in front of him a number of girls who seemed all to be waiting-maids in some great house. And Pao-Yü, more than ever surprised, said to himself again —"Can it really be that someone else has waiting-maids so exactly like Hsi-Jen, Ping-erh, and all my own maids at home?" Presently one of the girls called out: "Look, there's Pao-Yü! How ever did he get out here?" Pao-Yü naturally supposed that she knew it was he, and coming forward, he said: "I was just going for a walk, and got here quite by accident. I suppose this garden belongs to some family that my people visit. But in any case, dear Sisters, let me join you in your walk." No sooner had he finished speaking than the girls burst into peals of laughter. "What a silly mistake!" they said: "We thought you were our younger master Pao-Yü. But of course you are not half so good-looking and do not talk nearly so nicely." So they were servants of another Pao-Yü! "Dear Sisters," he said to them, "tell me who then *is* your master?" "He is Pao-yü," they said. "It was his grandmother and mother who wished him to use these two characters Pao (precious) and Yü (jade), hoping that such a name would make him have a long and happy life; and though we are only servants, it pleases him very much that we too should call him by this name. But where do you come from, we should like to know, and whose seedy little drudge are you, that you should use the same characters in your name? You dare try that on again, and we'll beat your nasty little body into jelly!" Another of them said, laughing: "Come on! Let's get away as quick as we can. What would our Pao-Yü think if he saw us talking to such a ragamuffin?" Another said: "If we stay near him much longer we shall all smell nasty!" And at one streak they were gone.

Pao-Yü was very much downcast. "No one," he thought, "has ever before treated me so rudely. Why should these particular girls have taken such a dislike to me? And is there really another Pao-Yü? I must somehow discover." While these thoughts were passing through his mind he had been walking on without noticing where he was going, and he now found himself in a courtyard that seemed strangely familiar. "Can there then," he asked himself, "be another courtyard exactly like ours at home?" He went up some steps and walked straight into a room. Here the first thing he saw was a young man lying on a bed, round which sat a number of girls laughing and playing while they did their needlework. The boy on the bed kept on sighing heavily, till at last one of the girls said to him—"Pao-Yü, why do you keep on sighing? Can't you get to sleep? No doubt you are worried over your cousin's illness. But it is silly to make such a fuss." When the real Pao-Yü heard this he was more than ever astonished. . . . "I have been having such an odd dream," said the young man on the bed. "I thought I was in a great flower-garden, where I met some girls who called me nasty names and would not play with me. But I followed them back to the house, and there what should I find but another Pao-Yü, lying senseless on his bed, for all the world like an empty bag. His thoughts and feelings seemed all to have flown somewhere far, far away." When the real Pao-Yü heard this dream, he could not contain himself and cried out to the boy on the bed: "I came to look for a Pao-Yü; and now it seems that you are the one!" The boy on the bed rose and coming quickly toward him, embraced him, saying: "So you are Pao-Yü, and it was not a dream!" "A dream!" cried Pao-Yü. "No, indeed. It was more true than truth itself." But hardly had he finished speaking when someone came to the door, crying: "Mr. Pao-Yü is to go to his father's room at once." At the sound of these words both Pao-Yüs trembled from head to foot. The dream Pao-Yü rushed away, and as he left the room the real Pao-Yü called after him: "Come back soon, Pao-Yü! Come back." His maid Hsi-Jen was by the bed, and hearing him calling out his own name in his dream she woke him, and said, laughing: "Where is this Pao-Yü that you are calling to?" Though he was no longer asleep, his mind was dazed and confused. "There he is," he said, pointing sleepily at the door. "He has just gone out." "Why, you are still dreaming!" said Hsi-Jen, much amused. "Do you know what it is you are staring at, screwing up your eyes and making such a funny face? It is your own reflection in the mirror!"

Translated from the Chinese by Arthur Waley

The Dream in Literature

Apuleius 125-180

Latin writer and philosopher, born in Madaura in Africa. He practiced law in Rome, wrote a novel in eleven volumes for which he is chiefly known, Metamorphoses *or* The Golden Ass. *The episode of Cupid and Psyche is to be found in this work. Accused of having employed magic arts to win the affection of his wife, he defended himself in his highly entertaining* Apology. *He is also the author of various treatises of Platonic philosophy. The* Tale of Aristomenes *is taken from the first book of* The Golden Ass.

I will swear to you by that sun, the all-seeing god, that what I relate I know by experience to be true. Nor will you any longer doubt that such is the fact, when once you come to the next city of Thessaly, for there the story is in everybody's mouth, as it relates to matters that publicly took place there. But, that you may first know who I am, and of what country, and by what pursuits I live, listen to my narrative.

I am a native of Ægina, and I travel to and fro through Thessaly, Ætolia, and Bœotia, for the purpose of purchasing honey of Hypata, as also cheese, and other articles of traffic used in cookery. Having understood that at Hypata, which is the principal city of all Thessaly, new cheese of exquisite flavour was to be sold at a very reasonable price, I made the best of my way to that place, with the intention of buying up the whole of it. But, as generally is the case, starting unluckily with the left foot foremost, all my hopes of gain were utterly disappointed. For a person named Lupus, a merchant in a large way of business, had bought the whole of it the day before.

Weary with my rapid journey, undertaken to so little purpose, I proceeded, early in the evening, to the public baths, when, to my surprise, I espied an old companion of mine, named Socrates. He was sitting on the ground, half covered with a sorry, tattered cloak, and looked almost another person, he was so miserably wan and thin; just like those outcasts of Fortune, who beg alms in the streets. Consequently, although he had been my friend and particular acquaintance, I yet accosted him with feelings of hesitation.

"How now, friend Socrates," said I, "what is the meaning of this? Why this appearance? What crime have you been guilty of? Why, you have been lamented at home, and for some time given up for dead. Guardians have been assigned to your children, by decree of the provincial magistrate. Your wife, having fulfilled what was due to the dead, all disfigured by grief and long-continued sorrow, and having almost cried herself blind with excessive weeping, is being worried by her parents to repair the misfortune of the family by the joys of a new marriage. But here you come before our eyes like some special apparition, to our extreme confusion."

"O Aristomenes!" said he, "it is clear that you are ignorant of the slippery turns, the unstable freaks, and the ever-changing vicissitudes of Fortune."

As he said this, he hid his face, which was crimsoned with shame, in his cobbled covering of tatters, so that he left the rest of his body naked, from the navel downward, as far as the groin. At last, unable to endure the sight of such a miserable spectacle of woe, I took hold of him, and endeavoured to raise him from the ground. But, with his head covered up as it was, he exclaimed, "Let me alone, let me alone; let Fortune still enjoy the trophy she has erected."

However, I prevailed upon him to accompany me: and at the same time pulling off one of my own two garments, I speedily—clothed, or covered him, shall I say? immediately after which, I took him to a bath, and, myself, applied to him the requisite anointing and scrubbing processes, and laboriously rubbed off the coat of filth with which he was defiled. Having paid every attention to him, though tired myself, I supported his enfeebled steps, and with great difficulty brought him to my inn; where I made him rest on a couch, gave him plenty of food, cheered him with wine, and entertained him with the news of the day. And now our conversation took quite a merry turn, we cracked jokes, and grew noisy in our prattle; when, heaving a bitter sigh from the bottom of his breast, and violently striking his forehead with his right hand:

"Miserable man that I am!" said he; "to have fallen into these misfortunes while intent on gratifying myself with a famous gladiatorial spectacle. For, as you are very well aware, I went to Macedonia on an affair of business; and after being detained there for the space of ten months, I was on my return homewards, having gained a very pretty sum of money. I had nearly reached Larissa, which I had included in my route for the purpose of seeing the spectacle I mentioned, when I was attacked by some desperate robbers, in a lonely and rugged valley, and only effected my escape, after being plundered by them of all I possessed. Being thus reduced to extreme distress, I betook myself to a certain woman named Meroë, who kept a tavern, and who, though old, was remarkably engaging; and to her I related the circumstances of my lengthened absence, of my earnest desire to reach home, and of my being plundered of my property on that day. After I, unfortunate wretch, had related such particulars as I remembered, she treated me with the greatest kindness, supplied me with a good supper, all for nothing, and afterwards, instigated by lust, admitted me to her bed. But from the very moment that I, unhappy man, first lay with her, my mind contracted a lasting malady; and I even made her a present of those garments which the robbers, in their humanity, had left me to cover my nakedness. I likewise presented her with the little ear-rings I made by working as a cloakmaker while I was yet in good condition of body; until at length this worthy partner, and ill fortune together, reduced me to that state in which you just now saw me."

"By Pollux, then," said I, "you deserve to suffer extreme misfortunes, if there is anything still more extreme than that which is most extreme, for having preferred the pleasures of dalliance and a wrinkled harlot, to your home and children."

"Hush! hush!" said he, raising his forefinger to his mouth, and looking round with a terror-stricken countenance to see if he might speak with safety; "Forbear to revile a woman skilled in celestial matters, lest you do yourself an injury through an intemperate tongue."

"Say you so?" said I. "What kind of woman is this tavernkeeper, so powerful and queenly?"

"She is a sorceress," he replied, "and endowed with powers divine; she is able to draw down the heavens, to uplift the earth, to harden the running water, to dissolve mountains, to raise the shades of the dead, to dethrone the Gods, to extinguish the stars, and to illumine the depths of Tartarus itself."

"Come, come," said I, "do draw asunder this tragic curtain, and fold up the theatric drop-scene, and let's hear your story in ordinary parlance."

"Should you like," said he, "to hear of one or two, ay, or a great many of her performances? Why, as for making not only her fellow-countrymen love her to distraction, but the Indians even, or the inhabitants of both the Æthiopias, and even the Antichthones themselves; these are only the leaves, as it were, of her art, and mere trifles. Listen, then, and hear what she has performed in the presence of many witnesses. By a single word only, she changed a lover of hers into a beaver, because he had by force debauched another woman; since that beast, when in fear of being taken, escapes from its pursuers by the abscission of its genitals; and she desired that the same might likewise befall him, as a punishment for having been connected with another woman. She likewise changed an innkeeper, who was her neighbour, and of whom she was envious on that account, into a frog; and now the old fellow, swimming about in a cask of his own wine, or buried in the dregs, croaks hoarsely to his old customers, quite in the way of business. She likewise transformed another person, an advocate of the Forum, into a ram, because he had conducted a cause against her; and to this very day that ram is always at loggerheads. Then there was the wife of a lover of hers, whom she condemned to perpetual pregnancy, when on the point of increasing her family, by closing her womb against the egress of the infant, because she had chattered scandal against the witch; and, for these eight years, according to the general computation, this poor creature has been swelling with her burden, as if she were about to be brought to bed of an elephant.

"After this woman, however, and many other persons, had been injured by her arts, the public indignation became aroused against her; and it was determined that on the following day a most dire vengeance should be wreaked upon her, by stoning her to death. But, by the power of her enchantments, she frustrated this design: and as Medea, having obtained by entreaty from Creon the truce of a single day, prior to her departure, burned his whole palace, his daughter, together with the old man himself, with flames issuing from a garland, so, likewise, did this sorceress, having performed certain deadly incantations in a ditch, (as she herself lately told me in a fit of drunkenness), confine all the inhabitants of the town, each in his own house, through a secret spell of the dæmons; so that, for two whole days together, neither could the bars be wrenched off, nor the doors be taken off the hinges, nor, in fine, could a breach be made in the walls; until, by mutual consent, the people unanimously cried out, and swore in the most sacred manner, that they would not lift a hand against her, and would, in case any one should think of so doing, afford her timely assistance. Being after this manner appeased, she liberated the whole city.

"In the middle of the night, however, she conveyed the author of this conspiracy, together with all his house, that is to say, with the walls, the very ground, and all the foundations, closed shut as it was, into another city, situate at the hundredth milestone hence, and on the summit of a craggy mountain, in consequence of which it is deprived of water. And, as the dwellings of the inhabitants were built so close together, that they did not afford room to this new comer, she threw down the house before the gate of the city, and took her departure."

"You narrate," said I, "marvellous things, my good Socrates, and no less terrible than marvellous. In fine, you have excited in me too, no small anxiety, indeed, I may say, fear, not inoculating me with a mere grain of apprehension, but piercing me with dread as with a spear, lest this old hag, employing in a similar manner the assistance of some dæmon, should come to know this conversation of ours. Let us, therefore, with all speed, betake ourselves to rest, and when we have relieved our weariness by a night's sleep, let us fly hence as far as we possibly can, before daylight."

While I was yet advising him thus, the worthy Socrates, overcome by more wine than he had been accustomed to, and by the fatigue of the day, had fallen asleep, and was now snoring aloud. Shutting the door, therefore, securing the bolts, and placing my bed close against the hinges, I tossed it up well, and lay down upon it. At first, indeed, I lay awake some time through fear, but closed my eyes at last a little about the third watch.

I had just fallen asleep, when suddenly the door was burst open with too great violence for one to believe that it was robbers; nay, the hinges being entirely broken and wrenched off, it was thrown to the ground. The bedstead, too, which was but small, wanting one foot, and rotten, was thrown down with the violence of the shock, and falling upon me, who had been rolled out and pitched upon the ground, completely covered and concealed me. Then was I sensible that certain emotions of the mind are naturally excited by contrary causes. For as tears very often proceed from joy, so, amid my extreme fear, I could not refrain from laughing, to see myself turned, from Aristomenes, into a tortoise. And so, while prostrate on the floor, peeping askance to see what was the matter, and completely covered by the bed, I espied two women, of advanced age, one of whom carried a lighted lamp, and the other a sponge and a drawn sword. Thus equipped, they planted themselves on either side of Socrates, who was fast asleep.

She who carried the sword then addressed the other, "This, sister Panthia, is my dear Endymion, my Ganymede, who by day and by night, hath laughed my youthful age to scorn. This is he who, despising my passion, not only defames me with abusive language, but is preparing also for flight—and I, forsooth, deserted through the craft of this Ulysses, just like another Calypso, am to be left to lament in eternal loneliness."

Then extending her right hand, and pointing me out to her friend Panthia; "And there," said she, "is his worthy counsellor Aristomenes, who was the proposer of this flight, and who now, half dead, is lying flat on the ground beneath the bedstead, and is looking at all that is going on, while he fancies that he is to relate disgraceful stories of me with impunity. I'll take care, however, that some day, ay, and before long too, this very instant in fact, he shall repent of his recent loquacity, and his present inquisitiveness."

On hearing this, wretch that I was, I felt myself streaming with cold perspiration, and my vitals began to throb with agitation; so much so, that even the bedstead, shaken by the violence of my palpitations, moved up and down upon my back.

"Well, sister," said the worthy Panthia, "shall we hack him to pieces at once, after the fashion of the Bacchanals, or, shall we bind his limbs and deprive him of virility?"

To this, Meroë replied—for I perceived from the circumstances, as well as from the narrative of Socrates, how well that name fitted her—"Rather let him live, if only that he may cover with a little earth the body of this wretched creature." Then, moving the head of Socrates to one side, she plunged the whole sword into him up to the hilt, through the left side of his throat, carefully receiving the flowing blood into a small leathern bottle, placed under it, so that not a drop of it was anywhere to be seen. All this did I witness with my own eyes; and, what is more, the worthy Meroë, that she might not, I suppose, omit any due observance in the sacrifice of the victim, thrusting her right hand through the wound, into the very entrails, and groping among them, drew forth the heart of my unhappy companion; while, his windpipe being severed by the thrust of the weapon, he emitted through the wound a voice, or rather I should say, an indistinct gurgling noise, and poured forth his spirit with his bubbling blood. Panthia then stopped the gaping wound with the sponge, exclaiming, "Beware, O sea-born sponge, how thou dost pass through a river."

When she had thus said, they lifted my bed from the ground, and squatting astride over my face, discharged their bladders, until they had entirely drenched me with their most filthy contents.

Hardly had they passed over the threshold, when the door resumed its former state; the hinges resettled on the panels, the posts returned to the bars, and the bolts flew back once more to their sockets. But I, left in such a plight, prostrate on the ground, scared, naked, cold, and drenched in chamber-lye, just like some babe that has recently emerged from the womb of its mother, indeed, I may say, half dead, but still surviving myself, and pursuing, as it were, a posthumous train of reflections, or, to say the least, like a candidate for the cross, to which I was surely destined: "What," said I, "will become of me, when this man is found in the morning with his throat cut? Though I tell the truth, who will think my story probable? You ought at least, they will say, to have called for assistance, if you, such a stout man as you are, could not resist a woman. Is a man's throat to be cut before your eyes, and are you to be silent? How was it you were not likewise assassinated? Why did the barbarous wretch spare you, a witness of the murder, and not kill you, if only to put an end to all evidence of the crime? Inasmuch, then, as you have escaped death, now return to it."

These remarks I repeated to myself, over and over again, while the night was fast verging towards day.

"It appeared to me, therefore, most advisable to escape by stealth before daylight, and to pursue my journey, though with trembling steps. I took up my bundle, and putting the key in the door, drew back the bolts. But this good and faithful door, which during the night had opened of its own accord, was now to be opened but with the greatest difficulty, after putting in the key a multitude of times.

"Hallo! porter," said I, "where are you? Open the gates of the inn; I want to be off before break of day."

The porter, who was lying on the ground behind the door of the inn, still half asleep, replied, "Who are you, who would begin your journey at this time of night? Don't you know that the roads are infested by robbers? Ay, ay, though you may have a mind to meet your death, stung by your conscience, belike for some crime you have committed, still, I haven't a head like a pumpkin, that I should die for your sake."

"It isn't very far from day-break," said I; "and besides, what can robbers take from a traveller in the greatest poverty? Are you ignorant, you simpleton, that he who is naked cannot be stripped by ten athletes even?"

The drowsy porter, turning himself on his other side, made answer, "And how am I to know that you have not murdered that fellow-traveller of yours, with whom you came hither last night, and are now consulting your safety in flight? And now I recollect that just at that hour I saw the depths of Tartarus through the yawning earth and in them the dog Cerberus, looking ready to devour me."

Then truly I came to the conclusion that the worthy Meroë had not spared my throat through any compassion, but that she had cruelly reserved me for the cross. Accordingly, on returning to my chamber, I thought about some speedy mode of putting an end to myself: but as Fortune had provided me with no weapon with which to commit self-destruction, except the bedstead alone—"Now, bedstead," said I, "most dear to my soul, who hast been partner with me in enduring so many sorrows, who art fully conscious, and a spectator of this night's events, and whom alone, when accused, I can adduce as a witness of my innocence, do thou supply me, who would fain hasten to the shades below, with a welcome instrument of death."

Thus saying, I began to undo the rope with which the bed was corded, and throwing one end of it over a small beam which projected above the window, and there fastening it, and making a strong slip-knot at the other end, I mounted upon the bed, and thus elevated for my own destruction, I put my head into the noose. But while with one foot I was kicking away the support on which I rested, so that the noose, being tightened about my throat by the strain of my weight, might stop the functions of my breath; the rope, which was old and rotten, broke asunder, and falling from aloft, I tumbled with great force upon Socrates (for he was lying close by), and rolled with him on to the floor.

Lo and behold! at the very same instant the porter burst into the room, bawling out, "Where are you, you who were in such monstrous haste to be off at midnight, and now lie snoring, rolled up in the bed-clothes?

At these words, whether awakened by my fall, or by the discordant notes of the porter, I know not, Socrates was the first to start up, and exclaim, "Assuredly, it is not without good reason that all travellers detest these hostlers. For this troublesome fellow, intruding so impertinently, with the intention, no doubt, of stealing something, has roused me out of a sound sleep, by his outrageous bellowing."

On hearing him speak, I jumped up briskly, in an ecstasy of unhoped-for joy: "Faithfullest of porters," I exclaimed, "my friend, my own father, and my brother, behold him whom you, in your drunken fit, falsely accused me of having murdered." So saying, I embraced Socrates, and was for loading him with kisses; but he, being assailed by the stench of the most filthy liquor with which those hags had drenched me, repulsed me with considerable violence. "Get out with you," he cried, "for you stink like the bottom of a sewer," and then began jocularly to enquire the cause of this nasty smell. Sorely confused, I trumped up some absurd story on the spur of the moment, to give another turn to the conversation, and, taking him by the right hand, "Why not be off," said I, "and enjoy the freshness of the morning on our journey?" So I took my bundle, and, having paid the innkeeper for our night's lodging, we started on our road.

We had proceeded some little distance, and now everything being illumined by the beams of the rising sun, I keenly and attentively examined that part of my companion's neck, into which I had seen the sword plunged. "Foolish man," said I to myself, "buried in your cups, you certainly have had a most absurd dream. Why look, here's Socrates safe, sound, and hearty. Where is the wound? where is the sponge? where, in fine, is the scar of a wound, so deep, and so recent?"

Addressing myself to him, "Decidedly," said I, "skilful doctors have good reason to be of opinion that it is those who are stuffed out with food and fermented liquors who are troubled with portentous and horrible dreams. My own case is an instance of this: for having in my evening cups exceeded the bounds of temperance, a wretched night has been presenting to me shocking and dreadful visions, so that I still fancy myself besprinkled and defiled with human gore."

" 'Tis not gore," he replied with a smile, "you are sprinkled with, but chamber-lye; and yet I too thought in my sleep that my throat was cut: some pain, too, I felt in my neck, and I fancied that my very heart was being plucked out: and even now I am quite faint, my knees tremble, I stagger as I go, and feel in want of some food to refresh my spirits."

"Look," cried I, "here's breakfast all ready for you;" and so saying, I lifted my wallet from off my shoulders, and at once handed him some cheese and bread, saying, "Let us sit down near that plane-tree."

We did so, and I also helped myself to some refreshment. While looking at him somewhat more intently, as he was eating with a voracious appetite, I saw that he was faint, and of a hue like boxwood; his natural colour in fact had so forsaken him, that as I recalled those nocturnal furies to my frightened imagination, the very first piece of bread I put into my mouth, though a very tiny bit, stuck in the middle of my throat, so that it could neither pass downward, nor yet return upward. And then besides, the number of people passing along increased my apprehensions; for who would believe that one of two companions could meet with his death without any harm done by the other?

Meanwhile, after having devoured a sufficient quantity of food, he began to be impatient for some drink; for he had voraciously eaten a good part of a most excellent cheese; and not very far from the roots of the plane tree, a gentle stream flowed slowly along, just like a placid lake, rivalling silver of glass in its lustre. "Look," said I, "drink your fill of the water of this stream, bright as the Milky Way."

He arose, and, wrapping himself in his cloak, with his knees doubled under him, knelt down upon the shelving bank, and bent greedily towards the water. Scarcely had he touched the dewy surface of the water with the edge of his lips, when the wound in his throat burst wide open, the sponge suddenly rolled out, a few drops of blood accompanying it; and then, his body, bereft of life, would have fallen into the river, had I not laid hold of one of his feet, and dragged it with the utmost difficulty and labour to the top of the bank; where, having, as well as the time permitted, lamented my unfortunate companion, I buried him in the sandy soil that eternally begirt the stream. For my own part, trembling and terror-stricken, I fled through various and unfrequented places; and, as though conscious of the guilt of homicide, abandoning my country and my home, and embracing a voluntary exile, I now dwell in Ætolia, where I have married another wife.

Marco Polo ca. 1254-1324

Venetian traveler who crossed Persia and then later the Gobi Desert, meeting Kublai Khan at Shangtu in 1275. He later made trips for the Mongol ruler to the furthest reaches of the empire. He returned to Venice in 1295, fought against Genoa, and was captured. There a fellow prisoner took down from dictation Polo's remarkable accounts. This excerpt is taken from The Book of Ser Marco Polo the Venetian, *translated and edited by Col. Henry Yule, C. B., Chapters XXIII-XXIV.*

Mulehet is a country in which the Old Man of the Mountain dwelt in former days; and the name means *"Place of the Aram."* I will tell you his whole history as related by Messer Marco Polo, who heard it from several natives of that region.

The Old Man was called in their language *Aloadin.* He had caused a certain valley between two mountains to be enclosed, and had turned it into a garden, the largest and most beautiful that ever was seen, filled with every variety of fruit. In it were erected pavilions and palaces the most elegant that can be imagined, all covered with gilding and exquisite painting. And there were runnels too, flowing freely with wine and milk and honey and water; and numbers of ladies, and of the most beautiful damsels in the world, who could play on all manner of instruments, and sung most sweetly, and danced in a manner that it was charming to behold. For the Old Man desired to make his people believe that this was actually Paradise. So he had fashioned it after the description that Mahommet gave of his Paradise, to wit, that it should be a beautiful garden running with conduits of wine and milk and honey and water, and full of lovely women for the delectation of all its inmates. And sure enough the Saracens of those parts believed that it *was* Paradise!

Now no man was allowed to enter the Garden save those whom he intended to be his *Ashishin.* There was a Fortress at the entrance to the Garden, strong enough to resist all the world, and there was no other way to get in. He kept at his Court a number of the youths of the country, from 12 to 20 years of age, such as had a taste for soldiering, and to these he used to tell tales about Paradise, just as Mahommet had been wont to do, and they believed in him just as the Saracens believe in Mahommet. Then he would introduce them into his garden, some four, or six, or ten at a time, having first made them drink a certain potion which cast them into a deep sleep, and then causing them to be lifted and carried in. So when they awoke, they found themselves in the Garden, in a place so charming, they deemed that it was Paradise in very truth. And the ladies and damsels dallied with them to their heart's content, so that they had what young men would have; and with their own good will they never would have quitted the place.

Now this Prince whom we call the Old One kept his Court in grand and noble style, and made those simple hill-folks about him believe firmly that he was a great Prophet. And when he wanted one of his *Ashishin* to send on any mission, he would cause that potion whereof I spoke to be given to one of the youths in the garden, and then had him carried into his Palace. So when the young man awoke, he found himself in the Castle, and no longer in that Paradise; whereat he was not over well pleased. He was then conducted to the Old Man's presence, and bowed before him with great veneration as believing himself to be in the presence of a true Prophet. The Prince would then ask whence he came, and he would reply that he came from Paradise! and that it was exactly such as Mahommet had described it in the Law. This of course gave the others who stood by, and who had not been admitted, the greatest desire to enter therein.

So when the Old Man would have any Prince slain, he would say to such a youth: "Go thou and slay So and So; and when thou returnest my Angels shall bear thee into Paradise. And shouldst thou die, natheless even so will I send my Angels to carry thee back into Paradise." So he caused them to believe; and thus there was no order of his that they would not affront any peril to execute, for the great desire they had to get back into that Paradise of his. And in this manner the Old One got his people to murder any one whom he desired to get rid of. Thus, too, the great dread that he inspired all Princes withal, made them become his tributaries in order that he might abide at peace and amity with them.

Translated from the French by Henry Yule

Prosper Mérimée

1803-1870

French writer, born in Paris. His principal works are Chronique du règne de Charles IX, Le Théâtre de Clara Gazul, *and* Carmen. *The selection below was published in 1829 and was part of a collection entitled* Mosaïque.

THE VISION OF CHARLES XI

"There are more things in heav'n and earth, Horatio,
Than are dreamt of in your philosophy."
SHAKESPEARE: *Hamlet.*

Though people laugh at visions and supernatural apparitions, several have been too well authenticated to be discredited, for, should one be consistent, it would be necessary to ignore the whole witness of historic evidence.

A correctly drawn-up report, signed by four reliable witnesses, is the guarantee of the truth of the incident about to be related. I should add that the prediction set forth in this report was so set forth and cited a very long time before the events occurred in our days which seemed to fulfil it.

Charles XI, father of the famous Charles XII, was a most despotic king, but at the same time the wisest of the monarchs who have reigned over Sweden. He restricted the overbearing privileges of the nobility, abolished the power of the Senate, and created laws by his own authority; in fact, he changed the constitution of the country, which before was an oligarchy, and compelled the states to vest the absolute control in him. He was, besides, an enlightened man, steadfastly attached to the Lutheran religion, brave, of an inflexible, self-contained, decided character, and entirely devoid of imagination.

He had just lost his wife, Ulrique Eléonore. Although it is said that his severity had hastened her end, he held her in esteem, and appeared more affected by her death than would have been expected of a man so hard of heart. After that event he grew still more taciturn and gloomy than before, and gave himself up to work with an application that showed an urgent desire to dispel sad thoughts.

At the close of one autumn evening he was sitting in his private apartment in the Stockholm Palace, in his dressing-gown and slippers, before a great fire. With him was his chamberlain, Count Brahé, who was one of his most favoured courtiers, and his physician, Baumgarten, who, it may be remarked in passing, set up for a skeptic, and who would have liked people to disbelieve in everything but in medicine. This night he had been summoned to advise on some slight ailment.

The evening lengthened, but contrary to his habit the King made no sign of dismissal to his companions. He sat in deep silence, his head lowered, and his eyes fixed upon the burning logs, wearied of their company, but afraid, without knowing why, of being left alone. Count Brahé had shrewdly observed that his presence was distasteful to the King, and had several times hinted that he feared His Majesty was in need of repose; but the King had signified by a gesture that he wished him to remain. The physician, in his turn, spoke of the ill-effects to health of keeping late hours. Charles only muttered, "Stay where you are; I have no desire to sleep yet."

At this stage the courtiers tried several different topics of conversation, but all fell flat at the end of the second or third sentence. It was evident that His Majesty was in one of his black moods, and in such circumstances the position of a courtier is decidedly delicate. Count Brahé, suspecting that the King was brooding over the loss of his wife, gazed for some time at the portrait of the Queen which hung on the wall of the room, and remarked with a deep sigh—

"What an excellent likeness! Just the expression she wore, so majestic and yet so gentle."

"Bah!" the King broke in rudely. "That portrait is too flattering. The Queen was ugly."

He was always suspicious of there being underlying reproaches whenever any one mentioned her name in his presence. Then, vexed at his harshness, he rose and paced the room to hide a blush of shame. He stopped in front of the window which looked on to the courtyard.

It was a dark night and the moon was in its first quarter. The palace in which the Kings of Sweden now reside was not then finished, so that Charles XI, who had begun it, lived then in the old palace on the promontory of Ritterholm overlooking the Lake Moëler. It was a vast building in the form of a horse-shoe. The King's cabinet was at one of the extremities, and nearly opposite it was the large audience hall where Parliament assembled to receive communications from the Crown.

The windows of this chamber appeared to be illuminated with a bright light. This struck the King as strange, but at first he thought the light might be produced by the torch of some valet. Still, what could anybody be doing there at such an hour, and in a room which had not been opened for some time? Besides, the light was too bright to proceed from a single torch. It might be the work of an incendiary, but there was no smoke, and the windows were not broken.

Charles watched the windows some time in silence. No sound could be heard; everything betokened simply an illumination. Meanwhile Count Brahé extended his hand toward the bell-rope to summon a page in order to send him to find out the cause of this singular light, but the King stopped him. "I will go to the hall myself," he said.

Whilst he spoke they saw his face grow pale with superstitious fear; but he went out with a firm tread, followed by the chamberlain and physician, each holding a lighted candle.

Baumgarten went to rouse the sleeping porter who had charge of the keys, with an order from the King to open immediately the doors of the assembly hall. The man was greatly surprized at this unexpected order. He dressed himself quickly, and joined the King with his bunch of keys. At first he opened the door of a gallery which was used as an antechamber or private entrance to the assembly hall. The King entered. Imagine his surprize at finding the walls completely draped in black!

"Who gave the order for hanging this room thus?" he demanded angrily.

"No one, Sire, to my knowledge," replied the uneasy porter. "The last time I swept out the gallery it was paneled, as it always has been. . . . I am certain this hanging never came out of Your Majesty's depository."

The King, walking at a rapid pace, had already traversed more than two-thirds of the gallery. The Count and porter followed closely; the physician Baumgarten was a little behind, divided between his fears of being left alone and of being exposed to the consequences of what promised to be such a strange adventure.

"Go no further, Sire," exclaimed the porter. "Upon my soul, there is sorcery behind this. At such an hour . . . and since the death of the Queen, your gracious wife . . . they say she walks in this gallery. . . . May God protect us!"

"Stop, Sire," entreated the Count in turn. "Do you not hear the noise that comes from the assembly hall? Who knows to what dangers Your Majesty may be exposed?"

"Sire," broke in Baumgarten, whose candle had just been blown out by a gust of wind, "at least allow me to go and fetch a score of your halberdiers."

"Let us go in," said the King sternly, stopping before the door of the great apartment. "Porter, open the door immediately."

He kicked it with his feet, and the noise, echoing from the roof, resounded along the gallery like the report of a cannon.

The porter trembled so much that he could not find the keyhole.

"An old soldier trembling!" said Charles, shrugging his shoulders. "Come, Count, you open the door."

"Sire," replied the Count, recoiling a step, "if Your Majesty commanded me to walk up to the mouth of a German or a Danish cannon I would obey unhesitatingly, but you wish me to defy the powers of hell."

The King snatched the key from the hands of the porter.

"I quite see," he observed contemptuously, "that I must attend to this matter myself," and before his suite could stay him he had opened the heavy oaken door and entered the great hall, pronouncing the words "By the power of God!" His three acolytes, urged by a curiosity stronger than their fear—and perhaps ashamed to desert their King—went in after him. The great hall was lighted up by innumerable torches, and the old figured tapestry had been replaced by black hangings. Along the walls hung, as usual, the German, Danish, and Russian flags—trophies taken by the soldiers of Gustavus Adolphus. In their midst were the Swedish banners, covered with crape as for a funeral.

An immense assembly filled the seats. The four orders of the State (the nobility, clergy, citizens and peasants) were arranged in their proper order. All were clothed in black, and this array of human faces, lit up against a dark background, so dazzled the eyes of the four witnesses of this extraordinary scene that not one figure was recognizable in the crowd. Thus an actor who stands before a large audience is not able to distinguish a single individual; he sees but a confused mass of faces.

Seated on the raised throne from which the King usually addressed his Parliament, they saw a bleeding corpse clothed in the royal insignia. At his right stood a child with a crown on his head and a sceptre in his hand; at his left an old man, or rather another spectre, leaned against the throne. He wore the State cloak as used by the former administrators of Sweden before Vasa had made it a kingdom. In front of the throne, seated before a table covered with large books and rolls of documents, were several grave and austere-looking personages, clothed in long black robes, who looked like judges. Between the throne and the seats of the assembly a block was raised covered with black crape; against it lay an axe.

No one in that supernatural assembly seemed to notice the presence of Charles and the three people with him. At their entry they could only hear at first a confused murmur of inarticulate words; then the oldest of the black-robed judges arose—the one who seemed to be the president—and struck the book which lay open in front of him three times with his hand. Deep silence immediately followed. Then there came into the hall by a door opposite to that by which Charles had entered several young men of noble bearing and richly clad. Their hands were tied behind their backs, but they walked with heads erect and confident looks. Behind them a stalwart man in a jerkin of brown leather held the ends of the cords which bound their hands. The most important of the prisoners—he who walked first—stopped in the middle of the hall before the block and looked at it with supreme disdain. While this was going on the corpse seemed to shake convulsively, and a fresh stream of crimson blood flowed out of its wounds. The youth kneeled down and laid his head on the block, the axe flashed in the air and the sound of its descent followed immediately. A stream of blood gushed over the dais and mingled with that from the corpse; the head bounded several times on the crimsoned pavement, and then rolled at the feet of Charles. It dyed him with its blood.

Up to this moment surprize had held the King dumb, but this frightful spectacle unloosed his tongue. He stepped forward toward the dais, and, addressing himself to the figure who was clothed in the administrator's robes, he pronounced boldly the well-known form of words—

"If thou are of God, speak; if thou art from the Other, leave us in peace."

The phantom spoke to him slowly in solemn tones—

"King Charles! this blood will not be shed during your reign . . ." (here the voice grew less distinct) "but five reigns later. Woe, woe, woe to the House of Vasa!"

Then the spectres of the countless personages who formed this extraordinary assembly gradually became fainter, until they soon looked like coloured shadows, and then they completely disappeared. All the fantastic lights were extinguished, and those of Charles and his suite revealed only the old tapestries, slightly waving in the draught. They heard for some time afterward a melodious sound, which one of the witnesses described as like the sighing of wind amongst leaves, and another to the rasping sound given by the strings of a harp that is being tuned. All agreed as to the duration of the apparition, which they judged to have lasted about ten minutes.

The black draperies, the dissevered head, the drops of blood which had stained the dais—all had vanished with the phantoms; only upon Charles's slipper was there a bloodstain. This was the sole witness left by which to recall the scene of that night, had it not been sufficiently engraved upon his memory.

When the King returned to his chamber he had an account written of what he had seen, signed it himself, and caused it to be signed by his fellow-witnesses. In spite of the precautions taken to keep the contents of this document secret it was soon known, even during the lifetime of Charles XI. It still exists, and up to the present time no one has thought fit to throw doubts upon its authenticity. In it the King concludes with these remarkable words:—

"And if that which I herein relate is not the simple truth, I renounce all my hope in the life to come, the which I may have merited for some good deeds done, and, above all, for my zeal in working for the welfare of my people, and in preserving the faith of my forefathers."

Now, when the reader recollects the death of Gustavus III, and the doom of Ankarstroem, his assassin, they will find more than a mere coincidence between that event and the circumstances of this extraordinary prophecy.

The young man beheaded before the State Assembly should be called Ankarstroem.

The crowned corpse should be Gustavus III.

The child, his son and successor, Gustavus Adolphus IV.

Finally, the old man was the Duke of Sudermania, uncle of Gustavus IV, regent of the Crown, and, in the end, King, after the deposition of his nephew.

Translated from the French by Emily Mary Waller and Mary Helena Day

Edgar Allan Poe

1809-1849

American writer, born of itinerant actors in Boston, one of the world's great masters of the fantastic tale. He is best known for such stories as The Pit and the Pendulum, The Murders in the Rue Morgue. The Cask of Amontillado, *and such poems as* The Raven *and* Annabel Lee.

A TALE OF THE RAGGED MOUNTAINS

During the fall of the year 1827, while residing near Charlottesville, Virginia, I casually made the acquaintance of Mr. Augustus Bedloe. This young gentleman was remarkable in every respect, and excited in me a profound interest and curiosity. I found it impossible to comprehend him either in his moral or his physical relations. Of his family I could obtain no satisfactory account. Whence he came, I never ascertained. Even about his age—although I call him a young gentleman—there was something which perplexed me in no little degree. He certainly *seemed* young—and he made a point of speaking about his youth—yet there were moments when I should have had little trouble in imagining him a hundred years of age. But in no regard was he more peculiar than in his personal appearance. He was singularly tall and thin. He stooped much. His limbs were exceedingly long and emaciated. His forehead was broad and low. His complexion was absolutely bloodless. His mouth was large and flexible, and his teeth were more wildly uneven, although sound, than I had ever before seen teeth in a human head. The expression of his smile, however, was by no means unpleasing, as might be supposed; but it had no variation whatever. It was one of profound melancholy—of a phaseless and unceasing gloom. His eyes were abnormally large, and round like those of a cat. The pupils, too, upon any accession or diminution of light, underwent contraction or dilation, just such as is observed in the feline tribe. In moments of excitement the orbs grew bright to a degree almost inconceivable; seeming to emit luminous rays, not of a reflected but of an intrinsic lustre, as does a candle or the sun; yet their ordinary condition was so totally vapid, filmy, and dull, as to convey the idea of the eyes of a long-interred corpse.

These peculiarities of person appeared to cause him much annoyance, and he was continually alluding to them in a sort of half explanatory, half apologetic strain, which, when I first heard it, impressed me very painfully. I soon, however, grew accustomed to it, and my uneasiness wore off. It seemed to be his design rather to insinuate than directly to assert that, physically, he had not always been what he was—that a long series of neuralgic attacks had reduced him from a condition of more than usual personal beauty, to that which I saw. For many years past he had been attended by a physician, named Templeton—an old gentleman, perhaps seventy years of age—whom he had first encountered at Saratoga, and from whose attention, while there, he either received, or fancied that he received, great benefit. The result was that Bedloe, who was wealthy, had made an arrangement with Dr. Templeton, by which the latter, in consideration of a liberal annual allowance, had consented to devote his time and medical experience exclusively to the care of the invalid.

Doctor Templeton had been a traveller in his younger days, and at Paris had become a convert, in great measure, to the doctrine of Mesmer. It was altogether by means of magnetic remedies that he had succeeded in alleviating the acute pains of his patient; and this success had very naturally inspired the latter with a certain degree of confidence in the opinions from which the remedies had been educed. The Doctor, however, like all enthusiasts, had struggled hard to make a thorough convert of his pupil, and finally so far gained his point as to induce the sufferer to submit to numerous experiments. By a frequent repetition of these, a result had arisen, which of late days has become so common as to attract little or no attention, but which, at the period of which I write, had very rarely been known in America. I mean to say, that between Doctor Templeton and Bedloe there had grown up, little by little, a very distinct and strongly marked *rapport,* or magnetic relation. I am not prepared to assert, however, that this *rapport* extended beyond the limits of the simple sleep-producing power; but this power itself had attained great intensity. At the first attempt to induce the magnetic somnolency, the mesmerist entirely failed. In the fifth or sixth he succeeded very partially, and after long-continued effort. Only at the twelfth was the triumph complete. After this the will of the patient succumbed rapidly to that of the physician, so that, when I first became acquainted with the two, sleep was brought about almost instantaneously by the mere volition of the operator, even when the invalid was unaware of his presence. It is only now, in the year 1845, when similar miracles are witnessed daily by thousands, that I dare venture to record this apparent impossibility as a matter of serious fact.

The temperature of Bedloe was, in the highest degree sensitive, excitable, enthusiastic. His imagination was singularly vigorous and creative; and no doubt it derived additional force from the habitual use of morphine, which he swallowed in great quantity, and without which he would have found it impossible to exist. It was his practice to take a very large dose of it immediately after breakfast each morning,—or, rather, immediately after a cup of strong coffee, for he ate nothing in the forenoon,—and then set forth alone, or attended only by a dog, upon a long ramble among the chain of wild and dreary hills that lie westward and southward of Charlottesville, and are there dignified by the title of the Ragged Mountains.

Upon a dim, warm, misty day, toward the close of November, and during the strange *interregnum* of the seasons which in America is termed the Indian summer, Mr. Bedloe departed as usual for the hills. The day passed, and still he did not return.

About eight o'clock at night, having become seriously alarmed at his protracted absence, we were about setting out in search of him, when he unexpectedly made his appearance, in health no worse than usual, and in rather more than ordinary spirits. The account which he gave of his expedition, and of the events which had detained him, was a singular one indeed.

"You will remember," said he "that it was about nine in the morning when I left Charlottesville. I bent my steps immediately to the mountains, and, about ten, entered a gorge which was entirely new to me. I followed the windings of this pass with much interest. The scenery which presented itself on all sides, although scarcely entitled to be called grand, had about it an indescribable and to me a delicious aspect of dreary desolation. The solitude seemed absolutely virgin. I could not help believing that the green sods and the gray rocks upon which I trod had been trodden never before by the foot of a human being. So entirely secluded, and in fact inaccessible, except through a series of accidents, is the entrance of the ravine, that it is by no means impossible that I was indeed the first adventurer—the very first and sole adventurer who had ever penetrated its recesses.

"The thick and peculiar mist, or smoke, which distinguishes the Indian summer, and which now hung heavily over all objects, served, no doubt, to deepen the vague impressions which these objects created. So dense was this pleasant fog that I could at no time see more than a dozen yards of the path before me. This path was excessively sinuous, and as the sun could not be seen, I soon lost all idea of the direction in which I journeyed. In the meantime the morphine had its customary effect—that of enduing all the external world with an intensity of interest. In the quivering of a leaf—in the hue of a blade of grass—in the shape of a trefoil—in the humming of a bee—in the gleaming of a dew-drop—in the breathing of the wind—in the faint odors that came from the forest—there came a whole universe of suggestion—a gay and motley train of rhapsodical and immethodical thought.

"Busied in this, I walked on for several hours, during which the mist deepened around me to so great an extent that at length I was reduced to an absolute groping of the way. And now an indescribable uneasiness possessed me—a species of nervous hesitation and tremor. I feared to tread, lest I should be precipitated into some abyss. I remembered, too, strange stories told about these Ragged Hills, and of the uncouth and fierce races of men who tenanted their groves and caverns. A thousand vague fancies oppressed and disconcerted me—fancies the more distressing because vague. Very suddenly my attention was arrested by the loud beating of a drum.

"My amazement was, of course, extreme. A drum in these hills was a thing unknown. I could not have been more surprised at the sound of the trump of the Archangel. But a new and still more astounding source of interest and perplexity arose. There came a wild rattling or jingling sound, as if of a bunch of large keys, and upon the instant a dusky-visaged and half-naked man rushed past me with a shriek. He came so close to my person that I felt his hot breath upon my face. He bore in one hand an instrument composed of an assemblage of steel rings, and shook them vigorously as he ran. Scarcely had he disappeared in the mist, before, panting after him, with open mouth and glaring eyes, there darted a huge beast. I could not be mistaken in its character. It was a hyena.

"The sight of this monster rather relieved than heightened my terrors—for I now made sure that I dreamed, and endeavored to arouse myself to waking consciousness. I stepped boldly and briskly forward. I rubbed my eyes. I called aloud. I pinched my limbs. A small spring of water presented itself to my view, and here, stooping, I bathed my hands and my head and neck. This seemed to dissipate the equivocal sensations which had hitherto annoyed me. I arose, as I thought, a new man, and proceeded steadily and complacently on my unknown way.

"At length, quite overcome by exertion, and by a certain oppressive closeness of the atmosphere, I seated myself beneath a tree. Presently there came a feeble gleam of sunshine, and the shadow of the leaves of the tree fell faintly but definitely upon the grass. At this shadow I gazed wonderingly for many minutes. Its character stupefied me with astonishment. I looked upward. The tree was a palm.

"I now arose hurriedly, and in a state of fearful agitation—for the fancy that I dreamed would serve me no longer. I saw—I felt that I had perfect command of my senses—and these senses now brought to my soul a world of novel and singular sensation. The heat became all at once intolerable. A strange odor loaded the breeze. A low, continuous murmur, like that arising from a full, but gently flowing river, came to my ears, intermingled with the peculiar hum of multitudinous human voices.

"While I listened in an extremity of astonishment which I need not attempt to describe, a strong and brief gust of wind bore off the incumbent fog as if by the wand of an enchanter.

"I found myself at the foot of a high mountain, and looking down into a vast plain, through which wound a majestic river. On the margin of this river stood an Eastern-looking city, such as we read of in the Arabian Tales, but of a character even more singular than any there described. From my position, which was far above the level of the town, I could perceive its every nook and corner, as if delineated on a map. The streets seemed innumerable, and crossed each other irregularly in all directions, but were rather long winding alleys than streets, and absolutely swarmed with inhabitants. The houses were wildly picturesque. On every hand was a wilderness of balconies, of verandas, of minarets, of shrines, and fantastically carved oriels. Bazaars abounded; and there were displayed rich wares in infinite variety and profusion—silks, muslins, the most dazzling cutlery, the most magnificent jewels and gems. Besides these things, were seen, on all sides, banners and palanquins, litters with stately dames close-veiled, elephants gorgeously caparisoned, idols grotesquely hewn, drums, banners, and gongs, spears, silver and gilded maces. And amid the crowd, and the clamor, and the general intricacy and confusion—amid the million of black and yellow men, turbaned and robed, and of flowing beard, there roamed a countless multitude of holy filleted bulls, while vast legions of the filthy but sacred ape clambered, chattering and shrieking, about the cornices of the mosques, or clung to the minarets and oriels. From the swarming streets to the banks of the river, there descended innumerable flights of steps leading to bathing places, while the river itself seemed to force a passage with difficulty through the vast fleets of deeply burdened ships that far and wide encountered its surface. Beyond the limits of the city arose, in frequent majestic groups, the palm and the cocoa, with other gigantic and weird trees of vast age; and here and there might be seen a field of rice, the thatched hut of a peasant, a tank, a stray temple, a gypsy camp, or a solitary graceful maiden taking her way, with a pitcher upon her head, to the banks of the magnificent river.

"You will say now, of course, that I dreamed; but not so. What I saw—what I heard—what I felt—what I thought—had about it nothing of the unmistakable idiosyncrasy of the dream. All was rigorously self-consistent. At first, doubting that I was really awake, I entered into a series of tests, which soon convinced me that I really was. Now, when one dreams, and, in the dream, suspects that he dreams, the suspicion *never fails to confirm itself,* and the sleeper is almost immediately aroused. Thus Novalis errs not in saying that 'we are near waking when we dream that we dream.' Had the vision occurred to me as I describe it, without my suspecting it as a dream, then a dream it might absolutely have been, but, occurring as it did, and suspected and tested as it was, I am forced to class it among other phenomena."

"In this I am not sure that you are wrong," observed Dr. Templeton, "but proceed. You arose and descended into the city."

"I arose," continued Bedloe, regarding the Doctor with an air of profound astonishment, "I arose, as you say, and descended into the city. On my way I fell in with an immense populace, crowding through every avenue, all in the same direction, and exhibiting in every action the wildest excitement. Very suddenly, and by some inconceivable impulse, I became intensely imbued with personal interest in what was going on. I seemed to feel that I had an important part to play, without exactly understanding what it was. Against the crowd which environed me, however, I experienced a deep sentiment of animosity. I shrank from amid them, and, swiftly, by a circuitous path, reached and entered the city. Here all was the wildest tumult and contention. A small party of men, clad in garments half Indian, half European, and officered by gentlemen in a uniform partly British, were engaged, at great odds, with the swarming rabble of the alleys. I joined the weaker party, arming myself with the weapons of a fallen officer, and fighting I knew not whom with the nervous ferocity of despair. We were soon overpowered by numbers, and driven to seek refuge in a species of kiosk. Here we barricaded ourselves, and, for the present, were secure. From a loop-hole near the summit of the kiosk, I perceived a vast crowd, in furious agitation, surrounding and assaulting a gay palace that overhung the river. Presently, from an upper window of this palace, there descended an effeminate-looking person, by means of a string made of the turbans of his attendants. A boat was at hand, in which he escaped to the opposite bank of the river.

"And now a new object took possession of my soul. I spoke a few hurried but energetic words to my companions, and, having succeeded in gaining over a few of them to my purpose, made a frantic sally from the kiosk. We rushed amid the crowd that surrounded it. They retreated, at first, before us. They rallied, fought madly, and retreated again. In the meantime we were borne far from the kiosk, and became bewildered and entangled among the narrow streets of tall, overhanging houses, into the recesses of which the sun had never been able to shine. The rabble pressed impetuously upon us, harassing us with their spears, and overwhelming us with flights of arrows. These latter were very remarkable, and resembled in some respects the writhing creese of the Malay. They were made to imitate the body of a creeping serpent, and were long and black, with a poisoned barb. One of them struck me upon the right temple. I reeled and fell. An instantaneous and dreadful sickness seized me. I struggled—I gasped—I died."

"You will hardly persist *now,*" said I, smiling, "that the whole of your adventure was not a dream. You are not prepared to maintain that you are dead?"

When I said these words, I of course expected some lively sally from Bedloe in reply; but, to my astonishment, he hesitated, trembled, became fearfully pallid, and remained silent. I looked toward Templeton. He sat erect and rigid in his chair—his teeth chattered, and his eyes were starting from their sockets. "Proceed!" he at length said hoarsely to Bedloe.

"For many minutes," continued the latter, "my sole sentiment—my sole feeling—was that of darkness and nonentity, with the consciousness of death. At length there seemed to pass a violent and sudden shock through my soul, as if of electricity. With it came the sense of elasticity and of light. This latter I felt—not saw. In an instant I seemed to rise from the ground. But I had no bodily, no visible, audible, or palpable presence. The crowd had departed. The tumult had ceased. The city was in comparative repose. Beneath me lay my corpse, with the arrow in my temple, the whole head greatly swollen and disfigured. But all these things I felt—not saw. I took interest in nothing. Even the corpse seemed a matter in which I had no concern. Volition I had none, but appeared to be impelled into motion, and flitted buoyantly out of the city, retracing the circuitous path by which I had entered it. When I had attained that point of the ravine in the mountains at which I had encountered the hyena, I again experienced a shock as of a galvanic battery; the sense of weight, of volition, of substance, returned. I became my original self, and bent my steps eagerly homeward—but the past had not lost the vividness of the real—and not now, even for an instant, can I compel my understanding to regard it as a dream."

"Nor was it," said Templeton, with an air of deep solemnity, "yet it would be difficult to say how otherwise it should be termed. Let us suppose only, that the soul of the man of to-day is upon the verge of some stupendous psychal discoveries. Let us content ourselves with this supposition. For the rest I have some explanation to make. Here is a water-color drawing, which I should have shown you before, but which an unaccountable sentiment of horror has hitherto prevented me from showing."

We looked at the picture which he presented. I saw nothing in it of an extraordinary character; but its effect upon Bedloe was prodigious. He nearly fainted as he gazed. And yet it was but a miniature portrait—a miraculously accurate one, to be sure—of his own very remarkable features. At least this was my thought as I regarded it.

"You will perceive," said Templeton, "the date of this picture—it is here, scarcely visible, in this corner—1780. In this year was the portrait taken. It is the likeness of a dead friend—a Mr. Oldeb—to whom I became much attached at Calcutta, during the administration of Warren Hastings. I was then only twenty years old. When I first saw you, Mr. Bedloe, at Saratoga, it was the miraculous similarity which existed between yourself and the painting which induced me to accost you, to seek your friendship, and to bring about those arrangements which resulted in my becoming your constant companion. In accomplishing this point, I was urged partly, and perhaps principally, by a regretful memory of the deceased, but also, in part by an uneasy, and not altogether horrorless curiosity respecting yourself.

"In your detail of the vision which presented itself to you amid the hills, you have described, with the minutest accuracy, the Indian city of Benares, upon the Holy River. The riots, the combat, the massacre, were the actual events of the insurrection of Cheyte Sing, which took place in 1780, when Hastings was put in imminent peril of his life. The man escaping by the string of turbans was Cheyte Sing himself. The party in the kiosk were sepoys and British officers, headed by Hastings. Of this party I was one, and did all I could to prevent the rash and fatal sally of the officer who fell, in the crowded alleys, by the poisoned arrow of a Bengalee. That officer was my dearest friend. It was Oldeb. You will perceive by these manuscripts," (here the speaker produced a note-book in which several pages appeared to have been freshly written) "that at the very period in which you fancied these things amid the hills, I was engaged in detailing them upon paper here at home."

In about a week after this conversation, the following paragraphs appeared in a Charlottesville paper:

"We have the painful duty of announcing the death of MR. AUGUSTUS BEDLO, a gentleman whose amiable manners and many virtues have long endeared him to the citizens of Charlottesville.

"Mr. B., for some years past, has been subject to neuralgia, which has often threatened to terminate fatally; but this can be regarded only as the mediate cause of his decease. The proximate cause was one of especial singularity. In an excursion to the Ragged Mountains, a few days since, a slight cold and fever were contracted, attended with great determination of blood to the head. To relieve this, Dr. Templeton resorted to topical bleeding. Leeches were applied to the temples. In a fearfully brief period the patient died, when it appeared that, in the jar containing the leeches, had been introduced, by accident, one of the venomous vermicular sangsues which are now and then found in the neighboring ponds. This creature fastened itself upon a small artery in the right temple. Its close resemblance to the medicinal leech caused the mistake to be overlooked until too late.

"N.B.—The poisonous sangsue of Charlottesville may always be distinguished from the medicinal leech by its blackness, and especially by its writhing or vermicular motions, which very nearly resemble those of a snake."

I was speaking with the editor of the paper in question, upon the topic of this remarkable accident, when it occurred to me to ask how it happened that the name of the deceased had been given as Bedlo.

"I presume," said I, "you have authority for this spelling, but I have always supposed the name to be written with an *e* at the end."

"Authority?—no," he replied. "It is a mere typographical error. The name is Bedlo with an *e*, all the world over, and I never knew it to be spelt otherwise in my life."

"Then," said I mutteringly, as I turned upon my heel, "then indeed has it come to pass that one truth is stranger than any fiction—for Bedlo, without the *e*, what is it but Oldeb conversed! And this man tells me it is a typographical error."

Théophile Gautier

1811-1872

French poet, novelist, and journalist, born at Tarbes (Gascony), lived principally in Paris. He first studied painting, before deciding definitely in 1830 on a career in literature. His best-known poetry is Emaux et Camées, *and his best-known works* Mademoiselle de Maupin, *a novel, and various shorter works of which* The Dead Leman *and* Arria Marcella *are chiefly remembered.*

THE DEAD LEMAN

You ask me, brother, if I have ever loved; yes. It is a strange and terrible story, and although I am sixty-six years old, I hardly dare to stir the ashes of that memory. I am unwilling to refuse you anything, but I would not tell such a tale to a mind less experienced than yours. The incidents are so extraordinary that I cannot believe that they ever happened to me. For more than three years I was the sport of a strange and devilish delusion. I, a poor country priest, led the life of one damned, the life of a worldling, of a Sardanapalus, every night in dreams (God grant they were dreams!). One single look too freely cast upon a woman nearly caused the ruin of my soul; but at last, with the aid of God and of my blessed patron saint, I succeeded in expelling the wicked spirit which had taken possession of me. My life was intermingled with a nocturnal life entirely different. By day I was a priest of the Lord, chaste, intent upon prayer and sacred things; at night, as soon as I had closed my eyes, I became a young nobleman, a fine connoisseur in women, dogs, and horses, throwing dice, drinking, and blaspheming; and when I woke at sunrise, it seemed to me that, on the other hand, I had fallen asleep, and that I was dreaming that I was a priest. My mind has retained memories, objects, and words of that somnambulistic life, from which I cannot escape, and although I have never gone without the bounds of my presbytery, one would say, to hear me, that I was a man who, having become satiated with everything and having turned his back upon the world, had betaken himself to religion, and proposed to end his too agitated life in the bosom of God, rather than a humble seminarist, who had grown old in this obscure curacy, in the depths of the woods, and aloof from all connection with the affairs of his time.

Yes, I loved as no one in the world has ever loved, with an insensate and furious passion, so violent that I am surprised that it did not cause my heart to burst. Ah! what nights! what nights!

From my earliest childhood, I had felt a calling to the priesthood; so that all my studies tended in that direction, and my life, up to the age of twenty-four, was simply a prolonged novitiate. My theological studies completed, I passed through all the minor orders in succession, and my superiors deemed me worthy, despite my extreme youth, to take the last and formidable step. The day of my ordination was fixed for Easter week.

I had never been into society; for me the world was the enclosure of the college and the seminary. I had a vague knowledge that there was a something called woman, but I never dwelt upon the subject; I was absolutely innocent. I saw my infirm old mother only twice a year; that was the extent of my connection with the outside world.

I had no regrets, I felt not the slightest hesitation in the face of that irrevocable engagement; I was overflowing with joy and impatience. Never did a young fiancé count the hours with more feverish ardour; I did not sleep, I dreamed that I was saying mass; I could imagine nothing nobler in the world than to be a priest; I would have declined to be a king or a poet. My ambition could conceive of no loftier aim.

I say this to show you that the things that happened to me should not have happened, and how inexplicable was the fascination to which I fell a victim.

When the great day came, I walked to the church with a step so light that it seemed to me that I was sustained in air, or that I had wings on my shoulders. I fancied myself an angel, and I was amazed at the gloomy and preoccupied faces of my companions; for there were several of us. I had passed the night in prayer, and I was in a condition almost bordering on ecstasy. The bishop, a venerable old man, seemed to me to be God the Father leaning over His eternity, and I beheld Heaven through the arched ceiling of the temple.

You know the details of the ceremony: the benediction, the communion under both forms, the anointing of the palms of the hands with the novice's oil, and lastly the holy sacrifice, administered by the priest in conjunction with the bishop. I will not dwell upon it. Oh! how truly did Job say that he is imprudent who does not conclude a covenant with his eyes! I chanced to raise my head, which I had thus far kept lowered, and I saw before me, so near that it seemed I could have touched her, although in reality she was at a considerable distance and on the other side of the rail, a young woman of rare beauty, attired with royal magnificence. It was as if scales fell from my eyes. I experienced the sensation of a blind man suddenly recovering his sight. The bishop, but now so radiant, suddenly faded away, the candles turned pale in their golden sconces, like stars at dawn, and the whole church was enveloped in complete darkness. The charming creature stood out against the dark background like an angelic revelation; she seemed illuminated by herself, and to shed light rather than to receive it.

I lowered my eyes, fully determined not to raise them again, in order to escape the influence of exterior objects; for distraction took more and more complete possession of me, and I hardly knew what I was doing.

A moment later I opened my eyes again, for through my lashes I could see her glistening with all the colours of the rainbow, and in a purplish penumbra as when one looks at the sun.

Oh! how lovely she was! The greatest painters, when, turning to Heaven for ideal beauty, they have brought to earth the divine portrait of the Madonna, do not even approach that wondrous reality. Neither the verses of the poet nor the painter's palette can convey an idea of it. She was rather tall, with the form and bearing of a goddess; her hair, of a soft, light shade, was parted on top of her head, and fell over her temples like two golden waves; she was like a queen with her diadem; her forehead, of a bluish and transparent whiteness, rose broad and serene over arched eyebrows, almost black; a peculiarity which intensified the effect of sea-green pupils of an unsustainable vivacity and brilliancy. What eyes! With one flash they decided a man's destiny; they had a limpidity, a life, an ardour, a glistening humidity which I have never seen in other human eyes; they shot forth rays like arrows, which I distinctly saw flying towards my heart. I do not know whether the flame which illuminated them came from heaven or hell, but it surely came from one or the other. That woman was an angel or a demon, perhaps both; she certainly did not issue from the loins of Eve, our common mother. Teeth of the purest pearl sparkled in her ruddy smile, and little dimples appeared with each motion of her mouth, in the satiny rose of her adorable cheeks. As for her nostrils, they were regal in their graceful and dignified shape, and indicated the noblest origin. A lustre as of agate played upon the smooth, glossy skin of her half-bare shoulders, and strings of great blonde pearls, of a shade almost like her neck, hung down upon her bosom. From time to time she elevated her head with the undulating grace of a snake, or of a startled peacock, and imparted a slight quiver to the high embroidered openwork ruff which surrounded her neck like a silver trelliswork.

She wore a dress of flame-coloured velvet, and from the broad sleeves lined with ermine peeped forth patrician hands of infinite delicacy, with long, plump fingers, and so transparent that they allowed the light to shine through, like Aurora's.

All these details are still vivid as if they were of yesterday, and although I was extremely perturbed, nothing escaped me: the faintest touch of shading, the little dark spot at the point of the chin, the imperceptible down at the parting of the lips, the velvety softness of the forehead, the quivering shadow of the eyelashes on the cheeks, I grasped them all with amazing lucidity.

As I gazed at her, I felt doors open within me which had hitherto been closed; the rubbish was cleared away from choked-up openings on every side, and gave me a glimpse of prospects theretofore undreamed of; life appeared to me in a totally different aspect; I was born to a new order of ideas. A frightful anguish gnawed at my heart; every moment that passed seemed to me but a second and yet a century. The ceremony progressed, however, and I was carried very far from the world, the entrance to which my rising passions fiercely besieged. I said yes, however, when I longed to say no;

when everything within me rose in revolt and protest against the violence my tongue exerted on my mind; a hidden force tore the words from my throat against my will. It is the same feeling, perhaps, that makes so many maidens go to the altar with the firm resolution of refusing publicly the husband who is forced upon them, although not a single one fulfils her intention. It is that, without doubt, which makes so many unhappy novices take the veil, although they are firmly resolved to tear it in shreds when the times comes to pronounce their vows. One dares not cause such a scandal before the world, or disappoint the expectation of so many people; all their wishes, all their glances seem to weigh upon you like a cloak of lead; and then, measures are so carefully taken, everything is so fully arranged beforehand, in so clearly irrevocable a fashion, that the will yields to the weight of the thing and collapses utterly.

The expression of the fair unknown changed as the ceremony progressed. Tender and caressing at first, it became disdainful and dissatisfied, as if because it had not been understood.

I made an effort that might have moved a mountain, to cry out that I would not be a priest; but I could not accomplish it; my tongue was glued to my palate, and it was impossible for me to give effect to my desire by the least syllable of negation. Fully awake as I was, I was in a plight similar to that stage of a nightmare where you try to utter a word upon which your life depends, but cannot succeed.

She seemed to appreciate the martyrdom I was suffering, and, as if to encourage me, she flashed at me a glance replete with divine promise. Her eyes were a poem of which each glance formed a stanza.

She seemed to say to me:

"If thou wilt be mine, I will make thee happier than God Himself in His Paradise; the very angels will be jealous of thee. Tear away that funereal shroud in which thou art about to wrap thyself; I am Beauty, I am Youth, I am Life; come to me and together we shall be Love. What can Jehovah offer you in exchange? Our lives will flow on like a dream, and will be but an everlasting kiss. Pour the wine from that chalice, and thou art free. I will bear thee away to unknown isles; thou shalt sleep between my breasts, in a bed of massy gold, beneath a canopy of silver; for I love thee and I long to take thee away from this God of thine, before whom so many noble hearts pour out floods of love which never reach Him."

It seemed to me that I could hear these words, uttered in a rhythm of infinite sweetness; for her glance was actually sonorous, and the sentences that her eyes sent forth to me echoed in the depths of my heart as if an invisible mouth had breathed them into my very being. I felt that I was ready to renounce God, and yet my heart mechanically went through with the formalities of the ceremony. The beautiful creature cast at me a second glance, so beseeching, so despairing, that keen blades pierced my heart, and I felt more sword-points in my breast than Our Lady of Sorrows herself.

All was consummated; I had become a priest.

Never did human features express such poignant suffering; the maiden who sees her betrothed suddenly fall dead at her side, the mother by her child's empty cradle, Eve seated at the threshold of the gate of Paradise, the miser who finds a stone in place of his hoard, the poet who has allowed the only copy of the manuscript of his finest work to fall into the fire, seem no more crushed and inconsolable. The blood entirely left her charming face, and she became as white as marble; her beautiful arms fell beside her body, as if the muscles had lost their power; and she leaned against a pillar, for her limbs trembled and gave way beneath her. As for myself, with livid cheeks and brow bathed in sweat more bloody than that of Calvary, I walked with tottering steps towards the door of the church; I was suffocating; the arches seemed to rest on my shoulders, and I fancied that my head alone bore the whole weight of the dome.

As I was about to cross the threshold, a hand suddenly seized mine, a woman's hand! I had never touched one before. It was as cold as the skin of a serpent, and yet the impression burned like the brand of a red-hot iron. It was she. "Unhappy man! unhappy man! what hast thou done?" she said in a low voice; then she disappeared in the crowd.

The aged bishop passed; he looked at me with a stern expression. I cut the most extraordinary figure imaginable; I turned pale, I flushed, I was giddy. One of my comrades had pity on me, and led me away; I was incapable of finding the road to the seminary alone. At the corner of the street, while the young priest's head was turned in another direction, a negro page, singularly attired, approached me and placed in my hand, without stopping, a small wallet with corners of carved gold, motioning to me to hide it; I slipped it up my sleeve and kept it there until I was alone in my cell. Then I broke the lock; there was nothing inside save two sheets of paper with the words: "Clarimonde, at the Concini Palace." I was then so little acquainted with the affairs of life that I knew nothing of Clarimonde despite her celebrity, and I was absolutely ignorant as to the location of the Concini Palace. I made a thousand conjectures, each more extravagant than the last; but in truth, provided that I might see her again, I cared very little what she might be, whether a great lady or a courtesan.

That passion, born in an instant, had taken imperishable root;

I did not even think of trying to tear it up, I realised so fully that it was impossible. That woman had taken complete possession of me; a single glance had sufficed to change me; she had breathed her will into me; I no longer lived in myself, but in her and through her. I did a thousand foolish things; I kissed the spot on my hand that she had touched, and I repeated her name hours at a time. I had only to close my eyes to see her as distinctly as if she were really present, and I said to myself again and again the words that she had said to me beneath the church porch: "Unhappy man! unhappy man! what hast thou done?" I realised all the horror of my situation, and the terrible and fatal aspects of the profession I had embraced were clearly revealed to me. To be a priest! That is to say, to be chaste, not to love, to distinguish neither sex nor age, to turn aside from all beauty, to put out one's eyes, to crawl beneath the icy shadow of a cloister or a church, to see none but the dying, to keep vigil by unknown corpses, and to wear mourning for yourself over your black soutane, so that your garment may be used to make your winding-sheet!

And I felt life rising within me like a subterranean lake expanding and overflowing; my blood beat violently in my veins; my youth, so long held in restraint, suddenly burst forth like the aloe which takes a hundred years to flower and then blossoms with a clap of thunder.

How was I to arrange to see Clarimonde again? I had no pretext for leaving the seminary, as I knew no one in the city; indeed, I was not to remain there, and I was waiting only until I should be told what curacy I was to occupy. I tried to loosen the bars at the window; but it was terribly high, and as I had no ladder, I could not think of escaping that way. Besides, I could descend only at night; and how could I find my way through the inextricable labyrinth of streets? All these obstacles, which would have been nothing at all to others, were enormous to me, a poor seminarist, in love since yesterday, without experience, without money, and without attire.

"Ah! if I had not been a priest, I might have seen her every day; I might have been her lover, her husband," I said to myself in my blindness; "instead of being wrapped in my dismal winding-sheet, I should have garments of silk and velvet, gold chains, a sword, and plumes, like the gallant young cavaliers. My hair, instead of being dishonoured by a broad tonsure, would play about my neck in waving curls; I should have a fine waxed mustache, I should be a hero." But an hour passed in front of an altar, a few words barely spoken, had cut me off forever from the ranks of the living, and I myself had sealed the door of my tomb; I had shot with my own hand the bolt of my prison!

I stood at the window. The sky was beautifully blue, the trees had donned their spring robes; Nature bedecked herself with ironical joy. The square was full of people, going and coming; young beaux and youthful beauties, two by two, walked towards the garden and the arbours. Merry companions passed, singing drinking-songs; there was a bustle, an animation, a merriment, which made my black garments and my solitude stand out in painful relief. A young mother, on her doorstep, was playing with her child; she kissed its little red lips, still empearled with drops of milk, and indulged in a thousand of those divine puerilities which mothers alone can invent. The father, standing at a little distance, smiled pleasantly at the charming group, and his folded arms pressed his joy to his heart. I could not endure that spectacle; I closed my window and threw myself on my bed with a horrible hatred and jealousy in my heart, gnawing my fingers and my bedclothes like a tiger who has fasted three days.

I do not know how long I remained in this condition; but as I turned over in a spasm of frenzy, I saw the Abbé Sérapion standing in the middle of the room and watching me closely. I was ashamed of myself, and dropping my head upon my breast, covered my eyes with my hand.

"Romuald, my friend, something extraordinary is taking place in you," said Sérapion after a few moments of silence; "your conduct is really inexplicable! You, who were so pious, so quiet, and so gentle, rave in your cell like a wild beast. Beware, my brother, and do not listen to the suggestions of the devil; the evil spirit, irritated because you have consecrated yourself forever to the Lord, is prowling about you like a savage wolf, making a last effort to lure you to him. Instead of allowing yourself to be vanquished, my dear Romuald, make a shield for yourself with prayers, a buckler with mortifications, and fight valiantly against the foe; you will overcome him. Trial is necessary to virtue, and gold comes forth refined from the crucible. Do not be dismayed or discouraged; the most watchful and steadfast souls have had such moments. Pray, fast, meditate, and the evil spirit will depart."

The Abbé Sérapion's words caused me to reflect, and I became a little calmer.

"I came to inform you of your appointment to the curacy of C——. The priest who held it has died, and monseigneur the bishop has instructed me to go with you and install you; be ready to-morrow."

I answered with a nod that I would be, and the abbé withdrew. I opened my missal and began to read prayers; but the lines soon became blurred beneath my eyes; the thread of the ideas became entangled in my brain, and the book slipped from my hands unheeded.

To go away on the morrow without seeing her again! To add still another impossibility to those which already lay between us! To lose forever the hope of meeting her, unless by a miracle! Write to her?—by whom could I send my letter? With the sacred character which I bore, to whom could I open my heart, in whom could I confide? I was terribly perplexed. And then, what Abbé Sérapion had said to me of the wiles of the devil returned to my mind; the oddity of the adventure, the supernatural beauty of Clarimonde, the phosphorescent gleam of her eyes, the burning touch of her hand, the confusion into which she had thrown me, the sudden change which had taken place in me, my piety vanished in an instant—all these clearly demonstrated the presence of the devil, and perhaps that satiny hand was only the glove with which he had covered his claw. These ideas caused me the greatest alarm; I picked up the missal which had fallen from my knees to the floor, and began anew to pray.

The next day Sérapion called for me; two mules awaited us at the door, laden with our thin valises; he mounted one and I the other as well as we might. As we rode through the streets of the city, I looked at all the windows and all the balconies to see if I could not espy Clarimonde; but it was too early, the city had not yet opened its eyes. My glance tried to pierce behind the blinds and through the curtains of all the palaces we passed. Sérapion doubtless attributed my curiosity to the beauty of the architecture, for he slackened the pace of his steed to give me time to look. At last we reached the city gates and began to climb the hill. When I was at the top, I turned to glance once more at the place where Clarimonde lived. The shadow of a cloud covered the city entirely; its blue and red roofs were blended in the prevailing half-light, above which rose here and there, like patches of white foam, the morning smoke. By a curious optical effect, a single edifice surpassing in height the neighbouring buildings, which were completely drowned in vapour, stood out, golden-hued, in a single beam of light; although it was more than a league away, it seemed very near. I could distinguish the slightest details, the turrets, the platforms, the windows, and even the weather-vanes in the shape of a swallow's tail.

"What is the palace that I see yonder, all lighted up by the sun?" I asked Sérapion. He put his hand over his eyes, and, having looked, he answered:

"It is the ancient palace which Prince Concini has given to the courtesan Clarimonde; shocking scenes take place there."

At that moment—and I do not know even now whether it was a reality or an illusion—I fancied that I saw a slender white form glide along the terrace, gleam for an instant, and vanish. It was Clarimonde!

Oh! did she know that at that moment, from the height of the rugged road which separated me from her, and which I was never to descend again, I was gazing, ardent and restless, at the palace in which she dwelt, and which a mocking trick of the light seemed to bring nearer to me, as if to invite me to enter as its lord? Doubtless she knew it, and her soul was too closely bound to mine not to feel its slightest emotions; and it was that sympathy which had impelled her, still clad in her night-robe, to go out upon the terrace amid the icy dews of the morning.

The shadow gained the palace, and there was nothing but a motionless ocean of roofs and gables, in which one could distinguish naught save one mountainous undulation. Sérapion urged forward his mule, whose gait mine immediately imitated, and a turn in the road concealed from me forever the city of S———; for I was destined never to go thither again. After travelling three days through an unattractive country, we saw the weather-vane of the steeple of the church in which I was to officiate appear through the trees; and after riding through a number of winding streets, lined with hovels and garden-plots, we found ourselves in front of the edifice, which was not very magnificent. A porch ornamented with a moulding or two, and two or three pillars of rough-hewn sandstone, a tile roof, and buttresses of the same material as the pillars—that was all. At the left was the cemetery, full of high weeds, with a tall iron cross in the centre; at the right, and in the shadow of the church, the presbytery. It was a house of extreme simplicity, clean, but bare. We entered; a few hens were pecking at grains of oats scattered on the ground; accustomed apparently to the black garments of ecclesiastics, they did not take fright at our presence and hardly moved aside to let us pass. We heard a hoarse, wheezy bark, and an old dog ran towards us. It was my predecessor's dog. He had the dull eye, the gray hair, and all the other symptoms of the extremest old age which a dog may attain. I patted him gently with my hand and he at once walked beside me with an air of inexpressible gratification. A woman advanced in years, who had been the former curé's housekeeper, also came to meet us, and after showing me into a room on the ground floor, asked me if I intended to keep her. I told her that I would retain her and the dog, the hens, too, and all the furniture which her master had left her at his death; this caused her a transport of joy, and the Abbé Sérapion at once gave her the price that she asked.

My installation completed, the Abbé Sérapion returned to the seminary. So I was left alone, with nobody to lean upon but myself. Thoughts of Clarimonde began to haunt me once more, and strive as I would to banish them, I could not always succeed. One evening, as I walked along the box-bordered paths of my little garden, it seemed to me that I saw through the hedge a female form following my every movement, and sea-green eyes gleaming among the leaves; but it was only an illusion, and, having gone to the other side of the hedge, I found nothing there but a footprint on the gravel, so small that one would have said that it was made by a child's foot. The garden was enclosed by very high walls; I searched every nook and corner, and there was no one there. I have never been able to explain that circumstance, which, however, was as nothing compared with the strange things which were to happen to me.

I had been living thus a year, performing with scrupulous exactitude all the duties of my profession, praying, fasting, exhorting, and assisting the sick, and giving alms to such an extent that I went without the most indispensable necessities of life. But I was conscious of a great aridness within me, and the sources of grace were closed to me. I enjoyed none of that happiness which the accomplishment of a sacred mission affords; my thoughts were elsewhere, and Clarimonde's words often came to my lips like a sort of involuntary refrain. O brother, consider this well! Because I raised my eyes a single time to a woman's face, for a fault apparently so venial, I experienced for many years the most wretched perturbation of spirit, and the happiness of my life was forever destroyed.

I will dwell no longer upon these defeats and these inward victories always followed by heavier falls, but I will pass at once to a decisive incident. One night some one rang violently at my door. The aged housekeeper answered the bell, and a copper-coloured man, richly clad, but in outlandish fashion, and wearing a long dagger, appeared in the rays of Barbara's lantern. Her first impulse was one of terror; but the man reassured her and told her that he must see me at once about a matter concerning my ministry. Barbara showed him upstairs, where I was on the point of retiring. The man told me that his mistress, a very great lady, was at death's door and desired to see a priest. I replied that I was ready to accompany him; I took with me what I needed for administering extreme unction, and I went downstairs in all haste. At the door two horses black as night were pawing the ground impatiently and blowing from their nostrils long streams of vapour against their breasts. He held the stirrup for me and assisted me to mount one of them; then he leaped upon the other, simply placing one hand upon the pommel of the saddle. He pressed his knees against the horse's flanks and dropped the reins; the beast started off like an arrow. Mine, whose bridle he held, also fell into a gallop and kept pace with him. We devoured the road; the ground glided away beneath our feet, gray and streaked; and the black silhouettes of the trees fled like an army in full retreat. We passed through a forest so intensely dark and so icy chill that I felt a shudder of superstitious terror run through my body. The sparks that our horses' shoes struck upon the stones left a trail of fire as it were behind us as we passed; and if any one had seen my guide and myself, at that hour of the night, he would have taken us for two spectres riding upon night-mares. Will-o'-the-wisp crossed the road from time to time and the jackdaws shrieked fearsomely in the dense woods, where at intervals we saw the gleam of the phosphorescent eyes of wildcats. The manes of the horses tossed more and more wildly, the sweat poured down their sides, and their breath came through the nostrils hard and fast. But when he saw them losing heart, the guide, to encourage them, uttered a guttural cry in which there was nothing human, and they resumed their frenzied course. At last the whirlwind paused; a black mass, with points of light here and there, suddenly reared itself before us; the hoofs of our beasts rang out more loudly upon a strong wooden drawbridge, and we rode beneath an arch which darkly yawned between two enormous towers.

Intense excitement reigned in the palace; servants were crossing the courtyard in all directions, with torches in their hands, and lights ascended and descended from landing to landing. I caught a confused glimpse of huge masses of masonry, of columns, arcades, staircases and balustrades—a riotous luxury of construction, altogether regal and fabulous. A negro page, the same who had handed me Clarimonde's tablets and whom I instantly recognised, assisted me to dismount, and the majordomo, dressed in black velvet, with a gold chain about his neck and an ivory cane in his hand, came forward to meet me. Great tears streamed from his eyes and rolled down his cheeks to his white beard. "Too late!" he cried, shaking his head; "too late, sir priest! But although you have not been able to save the soul, come and keep vigil over the poor body."

He took my arm and led me to the hall of death; I wept as bitterly as he, for I understood that the dead woman was no other than that Clarimonde whom I had loved so fondly and so madly. A *prie-dieu* was placed beside the bed; a bluish flame, flickering in a bronze patera, cast a wan and deceptive light about the room, and here and there caused some protruding decoration of a piece of furniture or a cornice to twinkle in the darkness. On the table, in a carved vase, was a faded white rose, whose leaves, with the exception of a single one which still clung to the stalk, had all fallen at the foot of the vase, like odorous tears; a broken black masque, a fan, and disguises of all sorts, were lying about on the chairs, and showed that death had appeared in that sumptuous abode unexpectedly and unannounced. I knelt, not daring to turn my eyes towards the bed, and I began to recite the Psalms with great fervour, thanking God that he had placed the grave between the thought of that woman and myself, so that I might add to my prayers her name, thenceforth sanctified. But gradually that burst of enthusiasm subsided and I fell into a revery. That room had nothing of the aspect of a chamber of death. Instead of the fetid and cadaverous air which I was accustomed to breathe in such death-vigils, a languorous vapour of Oriental essences, an indefinable amorous odour of woman, floated softly in the warm air. That pale gleam had rather the aspect of a subdued light purposely arranged for purposes of pleasure, than of the yellow night-light which flickers beside corpses. I mused upon the strange chance which had led me to Clarimonde at the very moment that I lost her forever, and a sigh of regret escaped from my breast. It seemed to me that there was an answering sigh behind me, and I involuntarily turned. It was the echo. In that movement my eyes fell upon the bed of death, which they had thus far avoided. The curtains of red damask with large flowers, looped back by golden tassels, revealed the dead woman lying at full length, her hands clasped upon her breast. She was covered with a linen veil of dazzling whiteness, of which the dark purple of the hangings heightened the effect, and of such fineness that it did not at all conceal the charming outlines of her body, and enabled me to follow those lovely lines, as undulating as the neck of a swan, which death itself had not been able to stiffen. She was like an alabaster statue made by some clever sculptor to place upon the tomb of a queen, or like a slumbering maiden upon whom snow had fallen.

I could endure it no longer; that voluptuous atmosphere intoxicated me, that feverish odour of half-withered roses went to my brain, and I paced restlessly back and forth, pausing at every turn beside the platform of the bed to gaze upon the lovely dead woman beneath her transparent winding-sheet. Strange thoughts passed through my mind; I imagined that she was not really dead, and that it was only a feint to which she had resorted to lure me to her palace, and to tell me of her love. For an instant, I even thought that I saw her foot move under the white veil, and disarrange the smooth folds of the shroud.

And then I said to myself: "Is this really Clarimonde? What proof have I of it? May not that black page have entered the service of another woman? I am very foolish to despair thus and to become so excited." But my heart replied with a throb: "It is really she; it is really she." I drew near the bed and gazed with redoubled attention upon the object of my uncertainty. Shall I confess it to you? That perfection of form, although purified and sanctified by the shadow of death, aroused my senses more than it should have done; and that repose was so like sleep that any one might have been deceived.

I forgot that I had come there to perform a solemn duty, and I fancied that I was a young bridegroom, entering the bedroom of his betrothed, who conceals her face, from modesty, and refuses to allow him to see her features. Heartbroken with grief, beside myself with joy, quivering with dread and with pleasure, I leaned over her and seized the upper corner of the sheet; I raised it slowly, holding my breath for fear of waking her. My pulses throbbed with such force that I felt the blood hissing through my temples, and my forehead dripped with perspiration, as if I had lifted a marble flagstone. It was in very truth Clarimonde, as I had seen her in the church at the time of my ordination; she was as fascinating as then, and, in her, death seemed but an additional coquetry. The pallor of her cheeks, the less vivid red of her lips, her long lashes, downcast and standing out with their dark fringe against that white flesh, imparted to her face an expression of chaste melancholy and of pensive suffering, whose power of seduction was immeasurable; her long flowing hair, with which were mingled still a few small blue flowers, made a pillow for her head and sheltered with its curls her bare shoulders; her beautiful hands, purer and more transparent than the consecrated wafer, were clasped in an attitude of pious rest and silent prayer, which neutralised what there might have been too alluring, even in death, in the exquisite roundness and ivory polish of her arms, from which the pearl bracelets had not been removed. I stood for a long while absorbed in mute contemplation, and the more I gazed at her, the less I could believe that life had abandoned that lovely body forever. I know not whether it was an illusion or a reflection of the lamp, but one would have said that the blood began to circulate anew beneath that lifeless pallor; however, she continued absolutely motionless. I touched her arm lightly; it was cold, but no colder than her hand on the day that it had touched mine beneath the church porch. I resumed my position, bending my face over hers, and letting the warm dew of my tears rain upon her cheeks. Ah! what a bitter sensation of despair and helplessness! What a period of agony was that vigil! I would have been glad to be able to collect my life in a pile, in order to give it to her, and to breathe upon her chill remains the flame that consumed me. The night was passing, and realising that the moment of eternal separation was drawing nigh, I could not deny myself the melancholy and supreme pleasure of imprinting a kiss upon the dead lips of her who had had all my love. Oh, miracle! a faint breath mingled with mine, and Clairmonde's lips responded to the pressure of mine; her eyes opened and took on a little life, she heaved a sigh, and unclasping her hands, she put her arms about my neck with an expression of ineffable rapture.

"Ah! is it thou, Romuald?" she said in a voice as languishing and sweet as the dying vibrations of a harp; "what art thou doing, pray? I waited for thee so long that I am dead; but now we are betrothed, and I shall be able to see thee and to come to thee. Adieu, Romuald, adieu! I love thee; that is all that I wished to say to thee, and I give thee back the life to which thou hast recalled me for an instant by thy kiss; we shall soon meet again."

Her head fell back, but she kept her arms about me as if to detain me. A fierce gust of wind blew the window in and entered the room; the last leaf of the white rose fluttered a little longer, like a wing, on the end of the stalk, then became detached and flew away through the open window, carrying with it Clarimonde's soul. The lamp went out, and I fell unconscious on the dead woman's bosom.

When I returned to myself, I was lying in my bed, in my little room at the presbytery, and the former curé's old dog was licking my hand, which lay upon the coverlet. Barbara was bustling about the room with a senile trembling, opening and closing drawers, or stirring powders in glasses. When she saw me open my eyes, the old woman uttered a joyful cry, the dog yelped and wagged his tail; but I was still so weak that I could not utter a single word, nor make a single movement. Afterwards I learned that I had been three days in that condition, giving no other sign of life than an almost imperceptible breathing. Those three days do not count in my life, and I know not where my mind had journeyed during all that time; I have no recollection whatever of it. Barbara told me that the same man with the copper-coloured complexion, who had come to fetch me during the night, had brought me back in the morning in a closed litter and had gone away immediately. As soon as I could collect my thoughts, I reviewed all the incidents of that fatal night. At first I thought that I had been the plaything of some trick of magic; but real and palpable circumstances soon dispelled that theory. I could not believe that I had dreamed, for Barbara had seen as well as I the man with the black horses, whose costume and appearance she described exactly. But no one knew of any castle in the neighobourhood answering to the description of that where I had seen Clarimonde.

One morning I saw the Abbé Sérapion enter my room. Barbara had written him that I was ill, and he had hastened to me at once. Although that zeal denoted interest and affection for my person, his visit did not cause me the pleasure which it should have done. There was in the Abbé Sérapion's glance a penetrating and searching expression which embarrassed me. I felt ill at ease and guilty in his presence. He had been the first to discover my inward distress, and I was angry with him for his clairvoyance.

While he asked me about my health in a hypocritically sweet tone, he fixed his yellow lion-eyes upon me, and plunged his glance into my very soul, like a sounding-lead. Then he asked me some questions as to the way in which I performed my duties, whether I enjoyed them, how I passed the time which my ministry left at my disposal, whether I had made any acquaintances among the people of the parish, what my favourite books were, and a thousand other similar details. I answered as briefly as possible, and he himself, without waiting for me to finish my answer, passed to another subject. This conversation evidently had no connection with what he desired to say. At last, without any prelude, and as if it were a piece of news which he recalled at the moment and which he was afraid of forgetting, he said to me in a clear and vibrating voice, which rang in my ear like the trumpets of the Last Judgment:

"The famous courtesan Clarimonde died recently, as the result of an orgy which lasted eight days and eight nights. It was something infernally magnificent. They revived the abominations of the feasts of Belshazzar and Cleopatra. Great God! what an age this is in which we live! The guests were served by swarthy slaves speaking an unknown tongue, who to my mind had every appearance of veritable demons; the livery of the meanest among them might have served as a gala-costume for an emperor. There have always been current some very strange stories concerning this Clarimonde, and all her lovers have come to a miserable or a violent end. It has been said that she was a ghoul, a female vampire; but I believe that she was Beelzebub in person."

He ceased to speak and watched me more closely than ever, to see what effect his words had produced upon me. I was unable to refrain from a movement when he mentioned Clarimonde's name, and the news of her death, in addition to the pain that it caused me by reason of its extraordinary coincidence with the nocturnal scene which I had witnessed, produced within me a confusion and a terror which appeared upon my face, strive as I would to control it. Sérapion cast an anxious and stern glance at me; then he said:

"My son, I must warn you that you are standing on the brink of an abyss; beware lest you fall into it. Satan's claws are long, and the grave is not always trustworthy. Clarimonde's tomb should be sealed with a triple seal; for this is not the first time that she has died, so it is said. May God watch over you, Romuald!"

Having said this, Sérapion walked slowly to the door, and I saw him no more; for he returned to S——— almost immediately.

I was entirely restored to health and I had resumed my usual duties. The memory of Clarimonde and the old abbé's words were always present in my mind; but nothing extraordinary had happened to confirm the lugubrious presentiments of Sérapion, and I was beginning to believe that his fears and my own terrors were exaggerated; but one night I had a dream. I had hardly imbibed the first mouthfuls of slumber when I heard the curtains of my bed open and the rings slide upon the rod with a loud noise; I instantly raised myself on my elbow, and I saw a female figure standing before me. I recognised Clarimonde on the instant. She held in her hand a small lamp of the shape of those which are placed in tombs, and its light imparted to her taper fingers a pink transparence which extended by insensible degrees to the opaque and milky whiteness of her bare arm. Her only clothing was the linen winding-sheet which had covered her upon the bed of death, the folds of which she held about her breast as if ashamed of being so scantily clad; but her little hand did not suffice; she was so white that the colour of the drapery blended with that of the flesh in the pale light of the lamp. Enveloped in that subtle tissue, which revealed the whole contour of her body, she resembled a marble statue of a woman bathing, rather than a real woman endowed with life. Dead or alive, statue or woman, ghost or body, her beauty was still the same: but the green splendour of her eyes was slightly dimmed, and her mouth, formerly so ruddy, was tinted with a faint tender rosiness, almost like that of her cheeks. The little blue flowers which I had noticed in her hair were entirely withered and had lost almost all their petals; all of which did not prevent her from being charming, so charming that, despite the extraordinary character of the adventure, and the inexplicable manner in which she had entered my room, I was not terrified for an instant.

She placed the lamp on the table and seated herself at the foot of my bed; then, leaning towards me, said to me in that voice, at once silvery and soft as velvet, which I have never heard from other lips:

"I have kept thee long in waiting, dear Romuald, and thou mayst well have thought that I had forgotten thee. But I have come from a long distance and from a place from which no one has ever before returned; there is neither moon nor sun in the country from which I come; there is naught but space and shadow; neither road nor path; no ground for the foot, no air for the wing; and yet here I am, for love is stronger than death, and it will end by vanquishing it. Ah! what gloomy faces and what terrible things I have seen in my journeying! What a world of trouble my soul, returned to this earth by the power of my will, has had in finding its body and reinstating itself therein! What mighty efforts I had to put forth before I could raise the stone with which they had covered me! See! the palms of my poor hands are all blistered from it. Kiss them to make them well, dear love!"

She laid the cold palms of her hands on my mouth one after the other; I kissed them again and again, and she watched me with a smile of ineffable pleasure.

To my shame I confess that I had totally forgotten the Abbé Sérapion's warnings and my own priestly character. I fell without resistance and at the first assault. I did not even try to spurn the tempter; the coolness of Clarimonde's flesh penetrated mine, and I felt a voluptuous tremor pass over my whole body.

Poor child! Despite all I have seen, I still have difficulty in believing that she was a demon; at all events she had not the aspect of one, and Satan never concealed his claws and his horns more deftly. She had drawn her feet up beneath her, and sat thus on the edge of my couch, in an attitude full of negligent coquetry. From time to time she passed her little hand through my hair and twisted it about her fingers, as if to try the effect of new methods of arranging my locks about my face. I allowed her to do it with the most guilty pleasure, and she accompanied it all with the most fascinating prattle. It is a lamentable fact that I felt no astonishment at such an extraordinary occurrence, and, with the facility with which one in a dream looks upon the most unusual events as perfectly simple, I saw nothing in it all that was not quite natural.

"I loved thee a long while ere I saw thee, dear Romuald, and I sought thee everywhere. Thou wert my dream, and I spied thee in the church at the fatal moment. I said instantly: 'It is he!' I cast a glance at thee, in which I put all the love that I had felt, that I was then feeling, and that I was destined to feel for thee; a glance to lead a cardinal to perdition, to force a king to kneel at my feet before his whole court. Thou didst remain unmoved, and didst prefer thy God to me. Ah! how jealous I am of God, whom thou lovedst and whom thou dost still love better than me! Unhappy woman, unhappy woman that I am! I shall never have thy heart all to myself, I, whom thou didst bring back to life with thy kiss; dead Clarimonde, who for thy sake has forced the doors of the tomb, and who now consecrates to thee a life which she has resumed only to make thee happy!"

All these words were accompanied by maddening caresses which bewildered my senses and my reason to such a point that I did not shrink from uttering a horrible blasphemy to comfort her, and from telling her that I loved her as much as I loved God.

Her eyes recovered their fire and shone like chrysoprases.

"In truth! in very truth? as much as God?" she said, flinging her lovely arms about me. "Since it is so, thou wilt come with me, thou wilt follow me wherever I list. Thou wilt lay aside thy ugly black garments, thou shalt be my lover. To be the acknowledged lover of Clarimonde, who has refused a pope, is magnificent! Ah! what a happy life, what a lovely, golden life we will lead! When shall we start, my fair sir?"

"To-morrow! to-morrow!" I cried in my delirium.

"To-morrow, so be it," she replied. "I shall have time to change my dress, for this is a little scanty and is not suited for travelling. I must also go and notify my servants, who really believe me to be dead and who are as distressed as they can be. Money, clothes, carriages, everything will be ready, and I shall call for thee at this same hour. Adieu, dear heart!"

And she lightly touched my forehead with the ends of her lips. The lamp went out, the curtains closed again, and I saw nothing more; a leaden, dreamless sleep fell upon me, and held me unconscious until the morning. I woke later than usual, and the recollection of that strange vision troubled me all day; I ended by persuading myself that it was naught but the vapour of my overheated imagination. And yet the sensation had been so vivid that it was difficult to believe that it was not real; and not without some presentiment of what was about to happen did I retire, after praying God to put away from me evil thoughts and to protect the chastity of my slumber.

I was soon sleeping soundly, and my dream was continued. The curtains were drawn aside and I beheld Clarimonde, not as before, pale in her pale winding-sheet, and with the violet hue of death upon her cheeks, but merry, alert, and smartly dressed, in a magnificent travelling-dress of green velvet, trimmed with gold lace and caught up at the side to reveal a satin petticoat. Her fair hair escaped in huge curls from beneath a broad-brimmed hat of black felt decorated with white feathers capriciously arranged; she held in her hand a little riding-whip with a gold whistle in the handle. She tapped me lightly with it, and said:

"Well! my fine sleeper, is this the way you make your preparations? I expected to find you on your feet. Rise at once, we have no time to lose."

I leaped out of bed.

"Come, dress yourself and let us go," she said, pointing to a small bundle which she had brought; "the horses are impatient and are champing their bits at the door. We should be already ten leagues away."

I dressed myself hastily and she handed me the different parts of my costume, bursting into laughter at my awkwardness, and indicating their respective uses when I made a mistake. She gave a twist to my hair, and when it was done, she handed me a little pocket-mirror of Venetian crystal, with a rim of silver filigree, and said to me:

"How dost find thyself now? Wouldst care to take me into thy service as valet?"

I was no longer the same, and I did not know myself. I resembled myself no more than a finished statue resembles a block of stone.

My former face seemed to be only the rough sketch of that which the mirror reflected. I was handsome, and my vanity was sensibly tickled by the metamorphosis. That elegant apparel, that richly embroidered vest, made of me a totally different person, and I marvelled at the power of a few yards of cloth cut in a certain way. The spirit of my costume penetrated my very skin, and within ten minutes I was reasonably conceited.

I walked about the chamber several times to give myself ease of manner. Clarimonde watched me with an air of maternal pleasure, and appeared well satisfied with her work.

"We have had enough of child's play; let us be off, Romuald dear; we have a long way to go and we shall never arrive."

She took my hand and led me away. All the doors opened before her as soon as she touched them, and we passed by the dog without waking him.

At the gate we found Margheritone; he was the groom who had escorted me before; he was holding three horses, black like the first ones; one for me, one for Clarimonde, and one for himself. Those horses must have been Spanish jennets, born of mares mated with a zephyr; for they went as swiftly as the wind, and the moon, which had risen at our departure to give us light, rolled through the sky like a wheel detached from its carriage; we saw it at our right, jumping from tree to tree, and panting for breath as it ran after us. We soon reached a level tract where, in a clump of trees, a carriage drawn by four beautiful horses awaited us; we entered it, and the postillions urged them into a mad gallop. I had one arm about Clarimonde's waist and one of her hands clasped in mine; she rested her head on my shoulder, and I felt her bosom, half bare, pressing against my arm. I had never known such bliss. I forgot everything at that moment, and I no more remembered that I had once been a priest than I remembered what I had been doing in my mother's womb, so great was the fascination that the evil spirit exerted upon me. From that night my nature was in a certain sense halved, and there were within me two men, neither of whom knew the other. Sometimes I fancied myself a priest who dreamed every night he was a gentleman, at other times a gentleman who dreamed he was a priest. I could no longer distinguish between dreaming and waking, and I knew not where reality began and illusion ended. The conceited and dissipated young nobleman railed at the priest; the priest loathed the debauchery of the young nobleman. Two spirals entangled in each other and inextricably confounded without ever touching would represent very well the bicephalous life which I led. Despite the abnormality of my position, I do not think that I was mad, for a single instant. I always retained very clearly the consciousness of my two existences. But there was one absurd fact which I could not explain: that was that the consciousness of the same ego could exist in two men so entirely different. It was an anomaly which I did not understand, whether I fancied myself the curé of the little village of C———, or Il Signor Romualdo, the titled lover of Clarimonde.

However, I was, or at least I fancied that I was, at Venice; I have never been able to distinguish between illusion and reality in that extraordinary adventure. We occupied a large marble palace on the Canaleio, filled with frescoes and statues, with two Titians, of the artist's best period, in Clarimonde's bedroom. It was a palace worthy of a king. We had each our gondola and our boatmen in our livery, our music-hall, and our poet. Clarimonde had a magnificent idea of life, and she had a touch of Cleopatra in her nature. As for me, I cut the swath of a prince's son, and I raised such a dust as if I had belonged to the family of one of the twelve apostles or of the four evangelists of the Most Serene Republic; I would not have turned aside from my path to allow the Doge to pass, and I do not believe that since Satan fell from heaven, any creature was ever prouder or more insolent than I. I went to the Ridotto, and I gambled frantically. I consorted with the best society in the world, ruined sons of noble families, actresses, swindlers, parasites, and swashbucklers; however, despite the dissipated life I led, I remained faithful to Clarimonde. I loved her wildly. She would have excited satiety itself and chained inconstancy. To have Clarimonde was to have twenty mistresses, she was so mobile, so changing, and so unlike herself; a very chameleon! She would make you commit with her the infidelity you might have committed with others, by assuming the nature, the manners, and the style of beauty of the woman who seemed to please you. She returned my love a hundredfold; and in vain did young patricians, and even the Ancients of the Council of Ten, make her the most magnificent offers. A Foscari even went so far as to propose to marry her; but she refused everything. She had money enough; she wanted only love, a pure, youthful love, inspired by herself, which should be a first and last passion. I should have been perfectly happy but for an infernal nightmare which recurred every night, and in which I imagined myself a village curé, macerating himself and doing penance for my orgies during the day. Reassured by the habit of being with her, I hardly ever thought of the strange way in which I had made Clarimonde's acquaintance. However, what the Abbé Sérapion had said returned sometimes to my memory and never failed to cause me uneasiness.

For some time Clarimonde's health had become impaired; her bright colour faded from day to day. The doctors whom I summoned failed utterly to understand her disease, and they had no idea what to do. They prescribed some insignificant remedies and came no more. Meanwhile she turned visibly paler, and became colder and colder. She was almost as white and as dead as on that memorable night in the unknown castle. I was in despair to see her thus slowly fall away. She, touched by my grief, would smile at me sweetly and sadly, with the fateful smile of those who feel that they must die.

One morning I was seated by her bed, breakfasting at a small table, in order not to leave her for an instant. As I was cutting some fruit, I accidentally made a deep gash in my finger. The blood immediately gushed forth in a purple jet, and a few drops spurted upon Clarimonde. Her eyes flashed and her face assumed an expression of fierce and savage joy which I had never before seen upon it. She jumped out of bed with the agility of a monkey or a cat, and pounced upon my wound, which she began to suck with an expression of unutterable pleasure. She swallowed the blood in little mouthfuls, slowly and gloatingly, as a gourmand sips a wine of Xeres or of Syracuse; she half closed her green eyes, and the lids about them became oblong instead of round. From time to time she paused in order to kiss my hand, then pressed her lips once more to the lips of the wound, to coax forth a few more red drops. When she found that no more blood came, she stood erect with liquid and gleaming eyes, rosier than a May dawn; her face full and fresh, her hand warm and moist,—in fine, lovelier than ever and in the most perfect health.

"I shall not die! I shall not die!" she exclaimed, half mad with joy and clinging to my neck; "I shall be able to love thee for a long time to come. My life is in thine, and all that is of me comes from thee. A few drops of thy rich and noble blood, more precious and more potent than all the elixirs of the world, have restored me to life."

This scene engrossed my thoughts for a long while and aroused within me strange doubts concerning Clarimonde; and that same night, when sleep had taken me back to my presbytery, I saw the Abbé Sérapion, more grave and more anxious than ever. He gazed at me attentively and said:

"Not content with losing your soul, you propose to destroy your body. Wretched young man, into what a snare have you fallen!"

The tone in which he said these few words impressed me deeply; but despite his earnestness, that impression soon vanished and a thousand other preoccupations blotted it from my mind. But one evening I saw in my mirror, the treacherous position of which she had not reckoned upon, Clarimonde pour a powder into the cup of spiced wine which she was accustomed to prepare after our dinner. I took the cup, I pretended to put my lips to it, then placed it upon some piece of furniture, as if to finish it later at my leisure; and taking advantage of a moment when she had her back turned, I tossed the contents under the table; after which I withdrew to my apartment and went to bed, fully determined not to go to sleep and to see what it all meant. I did not wait long; Clarimonde entered in her night-robe, and, having cast it aside, knelt beside my bed. When she was fully assured that I was asleep, she bared my arm and drew a gold pin from her hair; then she murmured in a low voice:

"One drop, just one little red drop, one ruby at the end of my pin! Since thou dost still love me, I must not die. Ah! poor love! I will drink his noble blood, his brilliant purple blood. Sleep, my only treasure, sleep, my god, my child! I will not hurt thee, I will take of thy life only what is necessary to prevent mine from departing. If I did not love thee so dearly I might determine to have other lovers upon whose veins I might draw; but since I have known thee I have held all the world in horror. Ah! the lovely arm! how round it is! and how white! I shall never dare to prick that pretty blue vein."

And as she said this she wept, and I felt her tears raining upon my arm, as she clasped it in her hands. At last she made up her mind, made a little prick with her pin, and began to suck the blood that flowed from it. Although she had drunk but a few drops, the fear of exhausting me seized her, and she carefully wrapped around my arm a little bandage, afterward rubbing the wound with an unguent which cicatrised it instantly.

I could doubt no longer. The Abbé Sérapion was right. However, despite that certainty, I could not help loving Clarimonde, and I would gladly have given her all the blood that she needed to sustain her factitious life. Besides, I was not much afraid; the woman reassured me concerning the vampire, and what I had heard and seen set my mind at rest; in those days my veins were richly supplied, and could not be easily exhausted, and I would not haggle for my life drop by drop. I would have opened my arm myself and have said to her: "Drink! and let my love infuse itself into thy body with my blood!" I carefully avoided making the slightest allusion to the narcotic which she had poured out for me, or to the scene of the pin, and we lived in the most absolute harmony.

Yet my priestly scruples tormented me more than ever, and I did not know what new maceration to invent, to punish and mortify my flesh. Although all these visions were involuntary and I had no share in bringing them about, I dared not touch the Christ with hands so impure, and with a mind sullied by such debauchery, real or dreamed. To avoid the recurrence of these fatiguing hallucinations, I tried to keep from sleeping; I held my eyelids open with my fingers, and I stood against the wall, struggling against sleep with all my might; but the sand of drowsiness soon entered my eyes, and, seeing that it was useless to struggle, I would drop my arms in discouragement and weariness, and the current would sweep me away towards my perfidious dreams.

Sérapion exhorted me most vehemently, and reproached me severely for my listlessness and my lack of fervour. One day, when I had been more agitated than usual, he said to me:

"To rid you of this obsession, there is but one means, and, although it is an extreme means, we must resort to it; great evils demand heroic remedies. I know where Clarimonde is buried; we must disinter her, so that you may see in what a pitiful plight the object of your love is; you will be tempted no more to imperil your soul for a disgusting corpse, devoured by worms and ready to crumble to dust; that sight will assuredly cause you to reflect."

For my own part, I was so wearied of that double life that I assented, desiring to know once for all whether the priest or the nobleman was the dupe of a delusion; I was determined to kill, for the benefit of the other, one of the two men who lived in me, or to kill them both; for such a life could not last.

Abbé Sérapion provided himself with a mattock, a lever, and a lantern, and at midnight we betook ourselves to the cemetery of ———, of which he knew perfectly the location and the arrangement. After turning the light of the dark lantern upon the inscriptions of several tombs, we reached at last a stone, half hidden by tall grass, and devoured by mosses and parasitic plants, upon which we deciphered the opening lines of the epitaph:

"Here lies Clarimonde
Who was famed in her lifetime
As the fairest of women——"

"Here is the place," said Sérapion; and putting his lantern on the ground, he inserted the lever in the interstice between the stones and began to pry. The stone yielded, and he set to work with his mattock. For my part, I watched him, more gloomy and silent than the night itself; meanwhile he, bending over his ghastly task, was dripping with perspiration, and his hurried breath was like the rattle of a dying man. It was an extraordinary spectacle, and whoever had seen us from without would have taken us for profane robbers of graves rather than for priests of God. There was something stern and savage in Sérapion's ardour, which made him resemble a demon rather than an apostle or an angel; and his face, with its large, stern features sharply outlined by the light of the lantern, was in no wise reassuring. I felt an icy sweat upon my limbs, and my hair stood painfully erect upon my head; in the inmost depths of my heart, I looked upon the pitiless Sérapion's act as an outrageous sacrilege, and I would have been glad if a triangle of fire had come forth from the dark clouds that moved slowly over our heads and had reduced him to dust. The owls perched upon the cypresses, disturbed by the light of the lantern, beat heavily against the glass with their dusty wings, uttering plaintive cries; wild foxes yelped in the distance, and a thousand sinister noises detached themselves from the silence. At last Sérapion's mattock came in contact with the coffin, the boards of which resounded with a deep, sonorous sound, with that terrible sound nothing utters when stricken. He drew back the lid, and I saw Clarimonde, pale as a marble statue, with clasped hands; her white winding-sheet covered her in a single fold from head to feet. A tiny little drop showed like a rose in the corner of her leaden-hued lips. Sérapion, at that sight, flew into a rage.

"Ah! there you are, demon, shameless courtesan, drinker of blood and gold!" And he drenched with holy-water the body in the coffin, upon which he made the sign of the cross with his sprinkler. Poor Clarimonde was no sooner touched by the blessed spray than her beautiful body crumbled into dust; there was nothing left but a ghastly, shapeless mass of cinders and of half-calcined bones.

"Behold your mistress, my Lord Romuald!" cried the inexorable priest, pointing to the sad remains; "shall you be tempted again to promenade on the Lido or at Fusina with your beauty?"

I hung my head; a great catastrophe had taken place within me. I returned to my presbytery, and Lord Romuald, Clarimonde's lover, parted from the poor priest, with whom he had maintained such a strange companionship for so long. But the following night I saw Clarimonde; she said to me as she said the first time, in the church porch: "Unhappy man! Unhappy man! What hast thou done? Why didst thou listen to that foolish priest? Wert thou not happy? And what had I done to thee that thou shouldst violate my poor grave and lay bare the shame of my nothingness? All communication between our souls and our bodies is broken henceforth. Adieu! thou wilt yet regret me."

She vanished in the air like smoke, and I never saw her again.

Alas! she told the truth. I have regretted her more than once, and I regret her still. My soul's peace was purchased very dearly; the love of God was none too much to replace hers. Such, brother, is the story of my youth. Never look upon a woman, and walk abroad always with your eyes on the ground; for, however chaste and watchful you may be, the error of a single moment is enough to cause you to lose eternity.

Translated from the French by George Burnham Ives

Ambrose Bierce

1842-1913

American journalist and short-story writer, born in Ohio. He is the author of several short-story collections and The Devil's Dictionary, *works characterized by an unusual pessimism and extreme misanthropy. Little is known of his death; he disappeared in Mexico in 1913 in the confusion of an uprising by Pancho Villa.*

AN OCCURRENCE AT OWL CREEK BRIDGE

A man stood upon a railroad bridge in northern Alabama, looking down into the swift water twenty feet below. The man's hands were behind his back, the wrists bound with a cord. A rope closely encircled his neck. It was attached to a stout cross-timber above his head and the slack fell to the level of his knees. Some loose boards laid upon the sleepers supporting the metals of the railway supplied a footing for him and his executioners—two private soldiers of the Federal army, directed by a sergeant who in civil life may have been a deputy sheriff. At a short remove upon the same temporary platform was an officer in the uniform of his rank, armed. He was a captain. A sentinel at each end of the bridge stood with his rifle in the position known as "support," that is to say, vertical in front of the left shoulder, the hammer resting on the forearm thrown straight across the chest—a formal and unnatural position, enforcing an erect carriage of the body. It did not appear to be the duty of these two men to know what was occurring at the center of the bridge; they merely blockaded the two ends of the foot planking that traversed it.

Beyond one of the sentinels nobody was in sight; the railroad ran straight away into a forest for a hundred yards, then, curving, was lost to view. Doubtless there was an outpost farther along. The other bank of the stream was open ground—a gentle acclivity topped with a stockade of vertical tree trunks, loopholed for rifles, with a single embrasure through which protruded the muzzle of a brass cannon commanding the bridge. Midway of the slope between the bridge and fort were the spectators—a single company of infantry in line, at "parade rest," the butts of the rifles on the ground, the barrels inclining slightly backward against the right shoulder, the hands crossed upon the stock. A lieutenant stood at the right of the line, the point of his sword upon the ground, his left hand resting upon his right. Excepting the group of four at the center of the bridge, not a man moved. The company faced the bridge, staring stonily, motionless. The sentinels, facing the banks of the stream, might have been statues to adorn the bridge. The captain stood with folded arms, silent, observing the work of his subordinates, but making no sign. Death is a dignitary who when he comes announced is to be received with formal manifestations of respect, even by those most familiar with him. In the code of military etiquette silence and fixity are forms of deference.

The man who was engaged in being hanged was apparently about thirty-five years of age. He was a civilian, if one might judge from his habit, which was that of a planter. His features were good—a straight nose, firm mouth, broad forehead, from which his long, dark hair was combed straight back, falling behind his ears to the collar of his well-fitting frock coat. He wore a mustache and pointed beard, but no whiskers; his eyes were large and dark gray, and had a kindly expression which one would hardly have expected in one whose neck was in the hemp. Evidently this was no vulgar assassin. The liberal military code makes provision for hanging many kinds of persons, and gentlemen are not excluded.

The preparations being complete, the two private soldiers stepped aside and each drew away the plank upon which he had been standing. The sergeant turned to the captain, saluted and placed himself immediately behind that officer, who in turn moved apart one pace. These movements left the condemned man and the sergeant standing on the two ends of the same plank, which spanned three of the cross-ties of the bridge. The end upon which the civilian stood almost, but not quite, reached a fourth. This plank had been held in place by the weight of the captain; it was now held by that of the sergeant. At a signal from the former the latter would step aside, the plank would tilt and the condemned man go down between two ties. The arrangement commended itself to his judgment as simple and effective. His face had not been covered nor his eyes bandaged. He looked a moment at his "unsteadfast footing," then let his gaze wander to the swirling water of the stream racing madly beneath his feet. A piece of dancing driftwood caught his attention and his eyes followed it down the current. How slowly it appeared to move! What a sluggish stream!

He closed his eyes in order to fix his last thoughts upon his wife and children. The water, touched to gold by the early sun, the brooding mists under the banks at some distance down the stream, the fort, the soldiers, the piece of drift—all had distracted him. And now he became conscious of a new disturbance. Striking through the thought of his dear ones was a sound which he could neither ignore nor understand, a sharp, distinct, metallic percussion like the stroke of a blacksmith's hammer upon the anvil; it had the same ringing quality. He wondered what it was, and whether immeasurably distant or near by—it seemed both. Its recurrence was regular, but as slow as the tolling of a death knell. He awaited each stroke with impatience and—he knew not why—apprehension. The intervals of silence grew progressively longer; the delays became maddening. With their greater infrequency the sounds increased in strength and sharpness. They hurt his ear like the thrust of a knife; he feared he would shriek. What he heard was the ticking of his watch.

He unclosed his eyes and saw again the water below him. "If I could free my hands," he thought, "I might throw off the noose and spring into the stream. By diving I could evade the bullets and, swimming vigorously, reach the bank, take to the woods and get away home. My home, thank God, is as yet outside their lines; my wife and little ones are still beyond the invader's farthest advance."

As these thoughts, which have here to be set down in words, were flashed into the doomed man's brain, rather than evolved from it, the captain nodded to the sergeant. The sergeant stepped aside.

II

Peyton Farquhar was a well-to-do planter, of an old and highly respected Alabama family. Being a slave owner and like other slave owners a politician he was naturally an original secessionist and ardently devoted to the Southern cause. Circumstances of an imperious nature, which it is unnecessary to relate here, had prevented him from taking service with the gallant army that had fought the disastrous campaigns ending with the fall of Corinth, and he chafed under the inglorious restraint, longing for the release of his energies, the larger life of the soldier, the opportunity for distinction. That opportunity, he felt, would come, as it comes to all in war time. Meanwhile he did what he could. No service was too humble for him to perform in aid of the South, no adventure too perilous for him to undertake if consistent with the character of a civilian who was at heart a soldier, and who in good faith and without too much qualification assented to at least a part of the frankly villainous dictum that all is fair in love and war.

One evening while Farquhar and his wife were sitting on a rustic bench near the entrance to his grounds, a gray-clad soldier rode up to the gate and asked for a drink of water. Mrs. Farquhar was only too happy to serve him with her own white hands. While she was fetching the water her husband approached the dusty horseman and inquired eagerly for news from the front.

"The Yanks are repairing the railroads," said the man, "and are getting ready for another advance. They have reached the Owl Creek bridge, put it in order and built a stockade on the north bank. The commandant has issued an order, which is posted everywhere, declaring that any civilian caught interfering with the railroad, its bridges, tunnels or trains will be summarily hanged. I saw the order."

"How far is it to the Owl Creek bridge?" Farquhar asked.

"About thirty miles."

"Is there no force on this side the creek?"

"Only a picket post half a mile out, on the railroad, and a single sentinel at this end of the bridge."

"Suppose a man—a civilian and student of hanging—should elude the picket post and perhaps get the better of the sentinel," said Farquhar, smiling, "what could he accomplish?"

The soldier reflected. "I was there a month ago," he replied. "I observed that the flood of last winter had lodged a great quantity of driftwood against the wooden pier at this end of the bridge. It is now dry and would burn like tow."

The lady had now brought the water, which the soldier drank. He thanked her ceremoniously, bowed to her husband and rode away. An hour later, after nightfall, he repassed the plantation, going northward in the direction from which he had come. He was a Federal scout.

III

As Peyton Farquhar fell straight downward through the bridge he lost consciousness and was as one already dead. From this state he was awakened—ages later, it seemed to him—by the pain of a sharp pressure upon his throat, followed by a sense of suffocation. Keen, poignant agonies seemed to shoot from his neck downward through every fiber of his body and limbs. These pains appeared to flash along well-defined lines of ramification and to beat with an inconceivably rapid periodicity. They seemed like streams of pulsating fire heating him to an intolerable temperature. As to his head, he was conscious of nothing but a feeling of fulness—of congestion. These sensations were unaccompanied by thought. The intellectual part of his nature was already effaced; he had power only to feel, and feeling was torment. He was conscious of motion. Encompassed in a luminous cloud, of which he was now merely the fiery heart, without material substance, he swung through unthinkable arcs of oscillation, like a vast pendulum. Then all at once, with terrible suddenness, the light about him shot upward with the noise of a loud plash; a frightful roaring was in his ears, and all was cold and dark. The power of thought was restored; he knew that the rope had broken and he had fallen into the stream. There was no additional strangulation; the noose about his neck was already suffocating him and kept the water from his lungs. To die of hanging at the bottom of a river!—the idea seemed to him ludicrous. He opened his eyes in the darkness and saw above him a gleam of light, but how distant, how inaccessible! He was still sinking, for the light became fainter and fainter until it was a mere glimmer. Then it began to grow and brighten, and he knew that he was rising toward the surface—knew it with reluctance, for he was now very comfortable. "To be hanged and drowned," he thought, "that is not so bad; but I do not wish to be shot. No; I will not be shot; that is not fair."

He was not conscious of an effort, but a sharp pain in his wrist apprised him that he was trying to free his hands. He gave the struggle his attention, as an idler might observe the feat of a juggler, without interest in the outcome. What splendid effort!—what magnificent, what superhuman strength! Ah, that was a fine endeavor! Bravo! The cord fell away; his arms parted and floated upward, the hands dimly seen on each side in the growing light. He watched them with a new interest as first one and then the other pounced upon the noose at his neck. They tore it away and thrust it fiercely aside, its undulations resembling those of a water snake. "Put it back, put it back!" He thought he shouted these words to his hands, for the undoing of the noose had been succeeded by the direst pang that he had yet experienced. His neck ached horribly; his brain was on fire; his heart, which had been fluttering faintly, gave a great leap, trying to force itself out at his mouth. His whole body was racked and wrenched with an insupportable anguish! But his disobedient hands gave no heed to the command. They beat the water vigorously with quick, downward strokes, forcing him to the surface. He felt his head emerge; his eyes were blinded by the sunlight; his chest expanded convulsively, and with a supreme and crowning agony his lungs engulfed a great draught of air, which instantly he expelled in a shriek!

He was now in full possession of his physical senses. They were, indeed, preternaturally keen and alert. Something in the awful disturbance of his organic system had so exalted and refined them that they made record of things never before perceived. He felt the ripples upon his face and heard their separate sounds as they struck. He looked at the forest on the bank of the stream, saw the individual trees, the leaves and the veining of each leaf—saw the very insects upon them: the locusts, the brilliant-bodied flies, the gray spiders stretching their webs from twig to twig. He noted the prismatic colors in all the dewdrops upon a million blades of grass. The humming of the gnats that danced above the eddies of the stream, the beating of the dragon flies' wings, the strokes of the water-spiders' legs, like oars which had lifted their boat—all these made audible music. A fish slid along beneath his eyes and he heard the rush of its body parting the water.

He had come to the surface facing down the stream; in a moment the visible world seemed to wheel slowly round, himself the pivotal point, and he saw the bridge, the fort, the soldiers upon the bridge, the captain, the sergeant, the two privates, his executioners. They were in silhouette against the blue sky. They shouted and gesticulated, pointing at him. The captain had drawn his pistol, but did not fire; the others were unarmed. Their movements were grotesque and horrible, their forms gigantic.

Suddenly he heard a sharp report and something struck the water smartly within a few inches of his head, spattering his face with spray. He heard a second report, and saw one of the sentinels with his rifle at his shoulder, a light cloud of blue smoke rising from the muzzle. The man in the water saw the eye of the man on the bridge gazing into his own through the sights of the rifle. He observed that it was a gray eye and remembered having read that gray eyes were keenest, and that all famous marksmen had them. Nevertheless, this one had missed.

A counter-swirl had caught Farquhar and turned him half round; he was again looking into the forest on the bank opposite the fort. The sound of a clear, high voice in a monotonous singsong now rang out behind him and came across the water with a distinctness that pierced and subdued all other sounds, even the beating of the ripples in his ears. Although no soldier, he had frequented camps enough to know the dread significance of that deliberate, drawling, aspirated chant; the lieutenant on shore was taking a part in the morning's work. How coldly and pitilessly—with what an even, calm intonation, presaging, and enforcing tranquility in the men—with what accurately measured intervals fell those cruel words:

"Attention, company! . . . Shoulder arms! . . . Ready! . . . Aim! . . . Fire!"

Farquhar dived—dived as deeply as he could. The water roared in his ears like the voice of Niagara, yet he heard the dulled thunder of the volley and, rising again toward the surface, met shining bits of metal, singularly flattened, oscillating slowly downward. Some of them touched him on the face and hands, then fell away, continuing their descent. One lodged between his collar and neck; it was uncomfortably warm and he snatched it out.

As he rose to the surface, gasping for breath, he saw that he had been a long time under water; he was perceptibly father down stream—nearer to safety. The soldiers had almost finished reloading; the metal ramrods flashed all at once in the sunshine as they were drawn from the barrels, turned in the air, and thrust into their sockets. The two sentinels fired again, independently and ineffectually.

The hunted man saw all this over his shoulder; he was now swimming vigorously with the current. His brain was as energetic as his arms and legs; he thought with the rapidity of lightning.

"The officer," he reasoned, "will not make that martinet's error a second time. It is as easy to dodge a volley as a single shot. He has probably already given the command to fire at will. God help me, I cannot dodge them all!"

An appalling plash within two yards of him was followed by a loud, rushing sound, *diminuendo,* which seemed to travel back through the air to the fort and died in an explosion which stirred the very river to its deeps! A rising sheet of water curved over him, fell down upon him, blinded him, strangled him! The cannon had taken a hand in the game. As he shook his head free from the commotion of the smitten water he heard the deflected shot humming through the air ahead, and in an instant it was cracking and smashing the branches in the forest beyond.

"They will not do that again," he thought; "the next time they will use a charge of grape. I must keep my eye upon the gun; the smoke will apprise me—the report arrives too late; it lags behind the missile. That is a good gun."

Suddenly he felt himself whirled round and round—spinning like a top. The water, the banks, the forests, the now distant bridge, fort and men—all were commingled and blurred. Objects were represented by their colors only; circular horizontal streaks of color—that was all he saw. He had been caught in a vortex and was being whirled on with a velocity of advance and gyration that made him giddy and sick. In a few moments he was flung upon the gravel at the foot of the left bank of the stream—the southern bank—and behind a projecting point which concealed him from his enemies. The sudden arrest of his motion, the abrasion of one of his hands on the gravel, restored him, and he wept with delight. He dug his fingers into the sand, threw it over himself in handfuls and audibly blessed it. It looked like diamonds, rubies, emeralds; he could think of nothing beautiful which it did not resemble. The trees upon the bank were giant garden plants; he noted a definite order in their arrangement, inhaled the fragrance of their blooms. A strange, roseate light shone through the spaces among their trunks and the wind made in their branches the music of Æolian harps. He had no wish to perfect his escape—was content to remain in that enchanting spot until retaken.

A whiz and rattle of grapeshot among the branches high above his head roused him from his dream. The baffled cannoneer had fired him a random farewell. He sprang to his feet, rushed up the sloping bank, and plunged into the forest.

All that day he traveled, laying his course by the rounding sun. The forest seemed interminable; nowhere did he discover a break in it, not even a woodman's road. He had not known that he lived in so wild a region. There was something uncanny in the revelation.

By nightfall he was fatigued, footsore, famishing. The thought of his wife and children urged him on. At last he found a road which led him in what he knew to be the right direction. It was as wide and straight as a city street, yet it seemed untraveled. No fields bordered it, no dwelling anywhere. Not so much as the barking of a dog suggested human habitation. The black bodies of the trees formed a straight wall on both sides, terminating on the horizon in a point, like a diagram in a lesson in perspective. Overhead, as he looked up through this rift in the wood, shone great golden stars looking unfamiliar and grouped in strange constellations. He was sure they were arranged in some order which had a secret and malign significance. The wood on either side was full of singular noises, among which—once, twice, and again—he distinctly heard whispers in an unknown tongue.

His neck was in pain and lifting his hand to it found it horribly swollen. He knew that it had a circle of black where the rope had bruised it. His eyes felt congested; he could no longer close them. His tongue was swollen with thirst; he relieved its fever by thrusting it forward from between his teeth into the cold air. How softly the turf had carpeted the untraveled avenue—he could no longer feel the roadway beneath his feet!

Doubtless, despite his suffering, he had fallen asleep while walking, for now he sees another scene—perhaps he has merely recovered from a delirium. He stands at the gate of his own home. All is as he left it, and all bright and beautiful in the morning sunshine. He must have traveled the entire night. As he pushes open the gate and passes up the wide white walk, he sees a flutter of female garments; his wife, looking fresh and cool and sweet, steps down from the veranda to meet him. At the bottom of the steps she stands waiting, with a smile of ineffable joy, an attitude of matchless grace and dignity. Ah, how beautiful she is! He springs forward with extended arms. As he is about to clasp her he feels a stunning blow upon the back of the neck; a blinding white light blazes all about him with a sound like the shock of a cannon—then all is darkness and silence!

Peyton Farquhar was dead; his body, with a broken neck, swung gently from side to side beneath the timbers of the Owl Creek bridge.

Ksaver Sandor Gjalski

1845-1935

Pseudonym of Ljuba Babic-Gjalski, the most prolific and popular fiction writer of modern Croatia. He specialized in the depiction of the country people of his own land, and wrote in a realistic style. The selection below was first published in 1890.

THE DREAM OF DOCTOR MIŠIĆ

From time immemorial the Jabučevac manor house had been famous as the abode of ghosts, apparitions, and sundry other marvels. It was an old wooden structure, very much battered. Its first lords had died long ago and subsequent holders, for some reason or other, had never succeeded in keeping possession very long: ownership of the manor changed hands every five or six years. At last a Jew got hold of the estate: the land he leased to farmers, but the house he left empty and deserted. From year to year the wretched dwelling presented a more and more pitiful appearance, and every autumn the wind blew more and more shingles from its roof. This wobegone appearance increased the already evil repute of the house, so that not even the most drunken villager would pass it at night without crossing himself piously and devoutly.

But the time came when a tenant was found for the deserted place. A new doctor was appointed for the district. As it was impossible for him to find a house in the district seat or elsewhere in the neighborhood, he was forced to accept the manor for his new abode. The ill-fame of his chosen home did not bother him in the least. He was only afraid of the rats and mice and of the dilapidated roof. So that when the roof was patched up and the house cleaned, Dr. Mišić was thoroughly satisfied with his new home. And when he learned from his neighbor Batorić that he was distantly related to the first lords of the manor, the noble family of the Jabukoci, he felt as though he were in his ancestral home. To the gossip that was in circulation concerning the manor house and its horrors, he paid no attention, nor did it worry him for a moment. How could he, a man of science—real, experimental, positive science—imbued with the ideas of "the enlightened nineteenth century," believe in things upon which he could not put his finger, and which he could not prove experimentally! Especially in such nonsense as ghosts, prophetic dreams, and so on! His modern intellect, with its cold logic, was so far removed from all that, that "magnificus" Radičević, who tried to explain all these stories in terms of the fourth dimension, appeared to him mentally unbalanced; and the elderly ladies, still saturated with romanticism, who forced themselves into believing such tales, impressed him as immeasurably stupid. To their awed questions whether he had already seen any apparitions, he could only answer by laughing in their faces with gay, carefree, almost Homeric laughter. Indeed, the reputation of the manor was actually pleasing to him. It afforded him many pleasantries in society, and in his work it did him no harm.

Despite the fearful reputation of the manor, people would come to it, and the doctor's waiting room was always filled with patients. Of course, at night no one would come. "At least the night is my own!" the doctor would say contentedly to himself; and every night he went to bed feeling positive that he should not be disturbed by any emergency calls. "That's a bad enough business in the city, but here in the village, with these abominable roads, gullies and ditches!" he would mutter, despite all his devotion to his calling.

He was a very capable and serious man, who had passed his first youth. His age may have been thirty-four. He was not married, nor did he contemplate marrying in the near future. Devotion to his calling was uppermost in his mind. A physician's duty he likened to that of a soldier. Both physician and soldier must always be ready for any sacrifice. "There are in our calling thousands of situations which are very similar to those in battle, where bullets fly about your head. Much too frequently it is a very precarious kind of business. How then can a man assume the additional burden of a wife!" Moreover he was not overconfident of his health. His parents had died early; his mother had been afflicted with a serious nervous disease. "I am not conscious of any illness; but still you never can tell—'an apple never falls far from the tree.' It would not do to leave a widow behind me," he would usually reply to the solicitations and advice of relatives and friends.

But there was still another reason why he had never ventured on matrimony. He had never in his life been in love. This was not because his temperament was cold and phlegmatic. On the contrary, his was one of those fiery and passionate natures that because of their very fire and passion cannot confide their feelings and desires to one single beauty. He was carried away and inflamed by every beauty. It could be said that he loved the whole of the fair sex, with their fine and graceful forms, their soft flesh, their luxuriant hair and the grace of their sweet and delicate motions. He never spoke in his enthusiasm of any particular fair woman that might catch his artistic eye, inflame his blood, and inebriate his spirit. Instead of any single woman he would glorify the whole sex as such, its wondrous Juno-like forms as such, its charming and captivating Venus-like lines as such. And in the dark flashing glance of a lovely woman whom he embraced, he would always behold the glance of the whole sex and the glance of beauty personified. This enthusiasm kept him from sinking into the mire of ordinary animal passion. His desires left his soul pure because he always yearned for perfection; in it alone could he find means to quench the thirst of his soul and body. With this attitude toward the fair sex, there was nothing to prevent him from devoting himself with his whole heart to the medical profession, which carried him to the highest spiritual levels.

Such was Doctor Mišić. —His life in the Jabučevac manor house he made comfortable. In a short time he acquired the reputation of a capable and conscientious physician, so that his practice yielded him a goodly income, despite the proverbial slowness of the nobility in paying for doctors' visits. Little by little the old house lost a great deal of its rustiness and acquired a certain amount of respectability. But the manor retained its evil reputation. The doctor to be sure, remained of necessity as much of an unbeliever as ever, although he used the worst reputed chamber in the house as his bed room. But the servants! With them the poor doctor was always having difficulties. They were continually giving up their positions and deserting him. And despite the fact that he was kind to them and that he never supervised their manipulation of wine, coffee and sugar, but let them manage everything, no one would stay with him longer than a month. Every man and woman would leave him with tearful eyes, kissing his hands and assuring him that he or she was not leaving the household on his account—the master was so kind—but because he could not stand any longer the frightful nights, with their unearthly noises and apparitions. One of the servants saw strange shadows, another saw flames dancing, and a third even insisted that a spook had come to shave him; and what is more, a fat cook was able to repeat whole conversations she had had with the souls of the departed and begged the good doctor to flee the accursed house immediately. Of course she did not tell of the bottles of rum that she had stolen and consumed but the doctor guessed how she had acquired her extraordinary gift of conversing with the denizens of the world beyond, and he laughed more than ever at the fables and stories. Naturally he himself never heard or saw anything unusual. Any knocking, or noises, or rapping he could explain every time as due to rats, mice or wind. Finally he got used to that sort of thing also, and he slept soundly every night, to the great disappointment of his neighbor Radičević, who earnestly hoped that the doctor's experience in the old house would drive him into the camp of the adherents of the fourth dimension. The doctor's quiet nights brought still more disappointment to Baroness Albahic who would ask him every day how he had slept the preceding night, and whether he had seen anything, and who upon receiving a negative answer would frown with displeasure.

So passed about eight months. The doctor's nights continued to be equally quiet; but every morning—for some time—he had felt a sort of spiritual uneasiness, or rather a sort of melancholy that weighed heavily on his serene self. It was a strange, new experience.

Occasionally he would feel an urge to give vent to his tears, as though affected by some great sorrow. During such moments it seemed as though his sunny nature had left him forever. The day's tasks would disperse this feeling, but almost every morning it would come back. He could not explain this new experience. His life passed in a quiet and simple fashion and there was not a single incident in his life that should have disturbed or depressed him. On the contrary everything that happened should have made him contented. The reason then lay within himself. At first he thought of a possible attack of some serious malady; but he dismissed this idea instantly—physically he had rarely felt better. Then he remembered certain forebodings. His departed mother had always insisted that she could foretell the future. At first thought he regarded this idea as so ridiculous and absurd that he rejected it immediately. He, an intelligent man, thoroughly imbued with modern science, could not give himself to such mystic interpretation of phenomena. He simply could not bring himself to believe in presentiments. In the end he ascribed the occurrences to gastric causes. "There must be some disorder in my digestion which deranges the circulation of my blood, and this in turn causes unpleasant dreams which, because of my sound sleeping, leave nothing except this melancholy feeling when I wake up." So argued Doctor Mišić with himself; and with this physiological explanation he was thoroughly satisfied, convinced that he had hit upon the truth, or, as he put it, that he had made a true diagnosis. He now decided to subject himself to a stricter diet. He became very careful of what and when he ate and drank. He was also careful not to overwork. But despite these precautions his inner struggles did not disappear. He then became nervous and excited. Every little thing that fell down made him jump and tremble all over, and he felt an acute pain as if he had received a blow over his temples. The clinking of two glasses together was enough to send a bolt through his head that would daze him. An ever deeper melancholy descended upon his spirit. There were moments in which he was sad to the utmost degree. He was on the verge of bursting into tears. And yet he could not account for such sadness. It had no content or visible form. It was like a hoarse, deep roaring, or a dark impenetrable remoteness.

Mišić became completely changed. His friends noticed the change. It was once the subject of conversation at the home of magnificus Radičević. Doctor Mišić still defended his diagnosis.

"You are mistaken," interrupted the magnificus eagerly. "You cannot explain it in terms of your physiology. You yourself admit that your digestion is in perfect order. Your supposed dreams, then, cannot be caused by indigestion. It is what I have always told you.

The Jabučevac manor is recognized as an excellent medium for communication with a world that is beyond our five senses, and that has more than three dimensions. In that excellent medium you yourself cannot help coming into some sort of rapport with that world. If you had different nerves, and if you were more accessible to the establishment of such a rapport, your impressions would undoubtedly be clearer and stronger. But because you are dense and because you refuse to believe—eh—then from that rapport into which you have entered with the other world nothing remains in your consciousness except this melancholy feeling. If you would yield and believe in that impression—eh—who knows what you could see, learn, and hear."

The doctor had to laugh heartily at Radičević. And the whole group followed his example. Still the conversation continued in the same vein. Mišić, to be sure, did not undertake to refute Radičević; but the parish priest, the Reverend Lacica Kuntek, developed his views concerning the world of spirits, and a lively debate ensued. At last "illustrissimus" Batorić spoke up. As usual he would not suffer a conversation to drift into jocular channels or to become the mere telling of boresome and impossible stories.

"I do not agree with our Škender, Doctor, but I cannot subscribe to your beliefs either! You merely deny the efficacy of premonitions and prophetic dreams. Experience shows that you are wrong. History itself recognizes dreams that have foretold the future. It recognizes premonitions, too. These facts cannot be denied. You explain your melancholy as a mere remnant of an unpleasant dream which is caused by physiological phenomena. I am willing to interpret your melancholy as a fragment of your dream; but I am convinced that a man's soul finds strength in dreams, that in them it sees the world more clearly and penetratingly than it does in its waking hours. To be sure, it acquires this strength only in the most profound of dreams. It may be that you have such dreams, in which something of the future is revealed to you, something which presages evil for you. It is only on rare occasions that dreams leave complete pictures in one's mind; and when they do, the pictures are usually symbolical. You sleep soundly, and such pictures are obliterated from your mind. But then one never can tell. Everything is so speculative! Be it as it may, do not be too much alarmed."

"Do not worry, illustrissime," retorted the doctor, laughing again. "At any rate, I am not going to be frightened by any prophetic dreams. It is possible, however, that I may worry over my nerves and digestion. But I shall try to counteract this by a proper diet."

"All right, then. For that reason the toastmaster must absolve you from the duty of drinking a toast to the Jabučevac ghosts. Mark,

Janko, he is not going to drink with us. Hey, Doctor, it is possible that there is some beauty among the ghosts, and then you may regret that we drank to her health, and that you didn't!" joked the old man.

But the doctor was firm—he did not touch his glass. And when no one had as yet even dreamed of leaving the party, he stole away unobserved and went directly home.

He made his diet even more strict. He cut out his suppers entirely, eating little or nothing before going to bed. This he did because his nervousness and his inner disturbances were growing more and more violent. Together with the inexplicable and groundless melancholy he began to be tortured by a certain indefinable yearning. His soul yearned for something without knowing what, though it seemed to him in a vague way that this something was of an erotic nature. There were moments when he felt in his heart as though he were in love. In his phantasy delicate feminine forms flitted about; and he moved his lips as though to kiss someone. Yet he was positive that none of the neighborhood beauties had ever stirred his imagination.

One night about one o'clock he suddenly awoke from a vivid and clear dream. Immediately he sensed the changed atmosphere but his whole being was pervaded with the sentiments and feelings that he had received in the dream. For a long time after awaking he thought he noticed a strange odor of carbolic acid. This he could not explain. His supplies were stored in the fifth room from his, and during the preceding day he had not used carbolic acid at all. And he could not clearly recall the presence of carbolic acid in his dream; though it did seem to him that the smell of it was a remembrance from the dream.

He had dreamed that he had entered a small, dark, immeasurably cold room. The walls were gray from humidity and were covered with long green spots. How he had come there he could not clearly recall; and the reason for his coming he was utterly unable to guess. He had to wait till his eyes grew accustomed to the darkness in the room. Then from a small round windowpane, up underneath the eaves, descended a wide beam of pale light. He could not say whether it was the light of the moon or of the sun. The beam fell on one side, illumining the furthermost part of the room. There on the stony pavement lay the body of a young girl. It was impossible for him to say whether she was dead or sleeping or perhaps just resting. Then he felt the eyes of the girl fixed upon him. Their gaze was so strange and unusual that he felt uncomfortable and depressed. Yet he could not turn away. Her large eyes were so beautiful and charming, with their calm, penetrating look and long shadowy eyelashes, which seemed covered with a delicate veil, that he could not turn his gaze away from them. The longer he looked the greater was his fascination. And then an immense desire to throw himself on the pavement and to bend down to the girl overcame him. Then something strange happened, something, however, that did not strike him as being strange at all in the dream. Another man came into the room. He looked at him and recognized himself. The newcomer was carrying a knife in his hand. He bent down to the girl and was about to make the customary anatomic incision with which a dissection begins.

"Stop! She is not dead. No! No!" he thundered at the intruder. "Tell me who you are and why you come here when I am here already!"

"You know that our calling is like that of a soldier. Our lives are not our own. I must do my duty."

"But stop! Tell me first, who is this girl? Just look at her! How beautiful she is! Oh, were I ever to love, she would certainly be my choice."

"Ha! Ha! Ha! Don't be a fool!" And then his other self told him rapidly the story of the girl; but the story was utterly incomprehensible to him. Then his other self started to sing an American song. Mišić remembered that he had heard the song once before, in the Anatomy Building in Vienna, from an American colleague who was humming it while dissecting a woman's hand and eating sweets.

"You know English?" he inquired, surprised. But his other self did not answer. Instead, he approached the girl again and lifted the robe that half covered her, and which bore stains of dried blood. Mišić became bewildered—such was the beauty of the body that he beheld! Never in his life had he gazed upon such exquisite loveliness. Only Canova's Psyche could be compared with those delicate, wondrously rounded and uniformly harmonious outlines. The finely shaped head with its luxuriant black hair rested on her left elbow, while her right hand lay on her virginal bosom, underneath her right breast. He could not resist all this magical beauty, despite the fact that he saw his other self suddenly covered all over with blood, as soon as he approached the girl. Now he was alone with the girl, he bent down to her and took her in his arms. He felt a piercing cold surging through his veins, but this did not prevent him from pressing her beautiful body closer to his heart. The girl now threw her arms around his neck and pressed her lips to his. He felt as though her ice-cold kisses were sucking his blood; yet he could not stop. He continued to return her kisses, which seemed to daze him. Suddenly he was no longer in the room. Still locked in her embrace he felt himself being transported somewhere over far-away, boundless waters, sinking deeper into the waves, which appeared thick, yellowish and turbid as the sea when the South wind blows. Immense fright and piercing cold tortured him, yet he still held her in his embrace and returned her kisses. He longed to speak but could not articulate a single word; nor did she utter a syllable. At last he felt such cold that he thought he should freeze. Then he woke up.

The whole dream was stamped vividly on his memory, and he reënacted it mentally. More poignantly than ever he felt his usual spiritual uneasiness. Almost timidly he looked about the room. It lay before him silent and dark. The cabinets and chairs loomed in dim outline, mere round, black objects. Through the window curtains a narrow moonbeam found its way into the room, falling vertically on the center of the floor. The clock on the wall was invisible, but its slow, harsh ticking was audible. The alarm clock on the night cabinet near the bed was producing a loud, unpleasant noise. Mišić turned toward it. The phosphorescent hands and numerals showed that it was ten minutes past one. He turned toward the wall and fell asleep again. Shortly afterwards he woke up. He thought it was morning already—his slumber seemed so long! He looked at the clock. It was only sixteen minutes past one. In his dream the short minutes had seemed like ten hours. He had dreamed again of the same girl. But this time he saw her in the middle of some vast desert plain. She met him with the same rigid look; and as soon as he drew near her she embraced him with both arms, and then began to kiss or rather to suck him.

Against his will and yet with pleasure and delight he gave himself over to her kisses, which were still cold—cold as ice. And suddenly across the vast plain from all sides began to flow filthy puddle water, which surrounded him and the girl. Still he was not afraid, but continued to kiss her and caress her body, beautiful as that of Hebe. And it seemed to him that he was singing to her a mighty dithyramb in which he compared her beautiful form to lilies in a garden, to birds in a forest and to silvery fishes in water. And accompanied by his singing, the lilies, the birds and the fishes swam about her bosom, her neck and shoulders, her finely shaped elbows and her thighs, gliding through the water in luxuriant garlands. The array increased so greatly that an immense quantity of wreaths, of all sorts of prodigious creatures, surrounded both him and her, veering around them, making silvery waves back and forth. And from the scales of the fishes, from the feathers of the birds, from the petals of the flowers and from the waves emanated a peculiar bluish phosphorescent light, which illumined the farthermost end of the train, where additional golden and red fishes were joining the procession, appearing as so many emeralds, topazes and rubies. "Venus Anadyomene!" he exulted triumphantly amidst the roaring waves, kissing her cold neck and pressing his breast to her bosom; while she, mute and motionless, clung round his neck and continued sucking him with her kisses rather than kissing him. Thereupon he found himself with her upon a shell as large as a canoe, garlanded with cypress wreaths. Giant fishes and monsters of the deep were pulling the shell on and on, executing graceful voluptuous movements in the water as they proceeded. He did not care, did not ask where he was going. Hours and hours he sailed, always seeing before him imposing coral cliffs, fathomless depths, and beautiful water fauna, with species of flowers such as he had never seen; and all of these were illumined by a magic but melancholy light. Suddenly the shell changed into a wooden vessel. At first he could not tell what kind of a vessel it was, but later he divined that it was a coffin. A sweet, pleasing peace, and a feeling of happiness and indescribable comfort descended upon him, while her body, still more beautiful, still more charming, rested at his side. God knows how long that lasted. He had no means of measuring time, nor did he care to.

All at once the coffin hit a cliff, and, all alone, he fell deeper and deeper into the abyss. An inexplicable fear dominated him; and then he woke up.

He did not fall asleep till morning. He was greatly excited and irritated. At times the opinions expressed by Radičević and Batorić occurred to him. To be sure, he still had enough control over his intellect to resist their influence, yet he felt a certain uneasiness. It seemed to him that something was hovering in the air and then stealthily climbing the wall. He thought he could distinguish a very delicate fluttering, at times similar to the vibration of violin strings, at times to the dying chords of a far, far away song or music. And on all sides an invisible hammer seemed to be pounding upon some hard metallic object. The picture of the dream girl was even now floating before his eyes vividly and harmoniously, whether he kept them open or closed. He was still under the spell of her divine beauty. Oh, even now, in his waking moments, how clearly he remembered every line, every feature. Even now his hands move avidly to touch that perfect beauty.

"If I could only find such beauty in real life!" he exclaimed aloud several times. And the thought flashed through his head, why was he not a painter or a sculptor in order to present to the outside world that charming apparition.

Towards morning he fell asleep again. He slept quietly and

soundly. It was ten o'clock when he awoke, and the room was filled with daylight. Although he had to go to work at once, since in the corridor and in the antechamber patients were waiting, he could not dismiss his dream from his thoughts. Somehow it perturbed him; and every moment he remembered how Radičević had explained it.

"Bah! What stupidity!" he would interrupt himself, only to recall and ponder upon Batorić's contention. He was acquainted to a certain extent with the philosophy of Schopenhauer, whose theory of dreams was not unknown to him. Of course he would not admit that Batorić was right, but no longer did he retain his former sovereign calm—the calm of the modern materialist. "After all, no one can tell!" he exclaimed involuntarily, as he wrote out a prescription for a villager who insisted that he was afflicted with some frightful disease.

Yet he still could not escape the picture of the dream girl. He had a number of women patients and he could not help making comparisons between their visible outlines and those that had appeared before him in his dream.

During the rest of the day the image of the beautiful dream creature kept coming back upon his memory. In the evening he did not go to pay his usual visits to his neighbors; instead he went into the garden to take a walk. He hoped that the fresh evening air would soothe and calm him; yet something made him yearn to be alone and to muse on the girl of his dream. The garden was vast and extended far into the hillside. Old fruit trees gave it in places the air of a forest. There were other trees also: tall lindens, birches, firs, and weeping willows; so that immediately after sunset the whole garden was inlaid with deep shadows. The narrow and grass-covered paths could hardly be distinguished. On one side of the garden stood a half-demolished gardener's cottage. From it extended a long but narrow vista of cornel and hazel wood, which led to an artificial hill where a Chinese pavilion lay in complete ruin. The doctor moved absent-mindedly in that direction. In the gray twilight there loomed up in the distance the round, stupid outline of a Chinese head with a pointed hat, which was placed on the peak of the roof. Mišić could not repress a smile; he then went to the pavilion, from which he hoped to see a beautiful panorama. From there he could see the whole garden and part of the plain that extended toward the brook. It was now growing dark, and the country around presented a disagreeable aspect in the gloomy semi-gray darkness in which objects can still be clearly distinguished, though they lack the charm of the daylight. Here and there a swallow was flying; and bats and June beetles were gliding through the air.

Crows and ravens gathered round the tops of the trees, preferring the tall poplars. In the deep, narrow moat, just beneath the pavilion, all covered up with needle-furze, thick weeds, and still thicker briers, something stirred, making a rustling noise. Mišić trembled despite himself, without thinking of anything definite. He was still excessively nervous. Sitting on a broken bench in the pavilion, he was driven to think of his dream and particularly of the girl whom he had beheld in it.

"If she were only alive—here—in the garden—before me—little Mignon!" he mused tenderly, recalling to his mind the charming little creature that Goethe's genius had created. He felt as though his dream girl were a similar mysterious being from some far-away land.

"But from where?" he asked himself audibly, at the same time convinced of the foolishness of the question. Still some strange and mystic power took possession of him, and instantly he believed in his heart that his dream girl really lived, and that there was some connection between her and him. He gazed into the distance. Suddenly he thought he heard something stir and hover over the bushes, down in the remotest corner of the chasm. He grew rigid and he felt shudders running through his whole body.

"Oh, I must be ill. My nerves are completely shattered. It is because of them that all this nonsense is happening to me," he was saying to himself; and at the same time he fancied he saw a shadow flash by him—or what was it! He looked around. Everything was still, calm, in deathlike silence. Not a leaf on the nearby trees rustled. Only up above, far, far away in the air, a bird was flying leisurely toward the west; but because of the semi-darkness he could not recognize it. The doctor left the pavilion in ill humor and distractedly descended the path of hazel and cornel wood. There everything was quiet and calm—only here and there some belated thrush or squirrel was arranging its bed among the thickly interwoven branches of the trees. In this stillness the doctor, despite his desire and his fixed purpose to think of nothing except his patients, again recalled to his mind the girl from his dream. And in a moment he fell into a reverie. He saw his beauty in various circumstances, romantic or commonplace, but always clearly and distinctly as he had done in his dream. There were moments when he saw not only parts of the phantom or a vaguely outlined whole, as is usual in reverie, but her entire body clearly outlined—all he had to do was to touch her with his finger tips. Then his heart was filled with tenderness. For a moment he gazed at the form of his imagination, if we may call it such, and then felt a great yearning to behold her alive, now, before him. He was dominated by an enthusiasm for the beauty that he beheld in his thoughts. Never had his æsthetic instinct been awakened and satisfied as it now was by this elusive phantom of his fancy. He admired her beautiful oval face and luxuriant, lusterless black tresses, her perfectly moulded shoulders and her delicate virginal bosom; and then her graceful waist with the charmingly curved lines from her back to her thighs, and then those marvelous limbs, so well rounded and yet so delicately fashioned. Oh, he was aflame, trembling with passion—forgetting that it was all merely his imagination, not reality.

Complete darkness had come on. No objects could be perceived in the woods. He turned back to the pavilion. As soon as he arrived there his former fear returned. Timidly he looked around him several times. The immense stillness of the evening grew more and more intense about him. All around reigned a most profound silence. Not even a cricket in the grass could be heard chirping. The doctor could almost hear the beating of the blood in his temples.

All at once he thought he heard a whisper or a hiss behind him. He turned around, but could see nothing. The moon had just risen above the forest and a faint beam illumined the pavilion and its Chinese head, the face of which seemed to radiate mockery and malice. In a moment the moonlight spread over everything. The sky was no longer gray, but dark blue, with only a few stars twinkling. Near the moon floated a dark round cloud. The edge which was nearer the moon seemed aflame with a brilliant golden fire. The doctor glanced at the cloud and then relapsed into his musing. He was awakened by a louder hissing or whispering. He was convinced that he had heard his name spoken. He jumped from the bench; and his eyes rested on the ravine near the moat. Unquestionably he could see some object down there. He thought it was the same apparition that he had seen in his dream. It seemed to him that she was motioning to him with her hand. Her face he could not clearly distinguish, yet he thought that it was sad and unhappy and that she was invoking his aid.

He stepped forward, but immediately regained his senses. "Oh, I must be insane. It is my accursed nerves again!" he moaned desperately, clasping his burning forehead with both his hands. He could feel the blood surging through his veins.

With hasty steps he left the pavilion, but ashamed of himself he turned toward the moat. Across the tall, dewy grass he descended to the place where he had seen the apparition. A frog leaped from beneath his feet. He started. When he arrived there everything was as usual. A lilac in full bloom, flooded with the moonlight, solved the riddle of the apparition.

"So that's what it was!" he cried triumphantly. And then and there he decided to take a cold shower before going to bed that night.

That night he did not dream. He slept soundly. When he woke up in the morning the sun was high in the heavens. His usual melancholy had also disappeared.

"Eureka!" he exulted, ascribing his success to the cold shower. Immediately he decided to adopt that mode of treatment. "I was right. Everything was due to my shattered nerves!" But after dinner he was actually depressed because he had not dreamed of the beautiful girl. A pleasing and irresistible wish to see her—were it only in his dreams—took possession of his soul. When he realized that if his dreams ceased her image would disappear forever from his heart, he felt as if he had lost a very dear friend.

Eight days passed and the dream did not recur. The doctor almost regretted the fact. He had not ascribed to the dream any fatal significance, anyhow, and his desire to see the lovely girl again was overwhelming. If he could only see such marvelous perfection once more! Until now he had told no one of his dreams. Some force that he himself could not have explained, restrained him. When he thought that everything was over, he related the whole dream to a group of people at a supper party given by Batorić in Brezovica. Enthusiastically he described the beauty of the dream girl.

"Fine finaliter," he jokingly imitated the mode of conversation of his neighbors, "there are qualities of a painter or a sculptor hidden in me. And yet, behold, I am only a doctor! Really I have missed my true calling," concluded the doctor in a jocular tone.

Magnificus Radičević only shook his head and requested that the doctor repeat the incident of the garden.

"But I am telling you, it was only my nerves. All that sort of thing comes from excitability," explained Mišić.

"Yes, yes, you are right," interrupted illustrissimus Batorić. "I should say that the incident in the garden was due to your nerves; but your dream was an entirely different matter. You know the verses of our old Horace, *Post mediam noctem, cum somnia vera.* And do not forget that the old Latins were a brainy lot, and that they always hit upon the truth. *Ad proposita,* they had a wonderful book. A certain Artemidorus wrote it, and called it, I believe, *Ankirokritikon.* As a young man once I had it in my hands. It belonged to my godfather, the old Count Keglević. If you could get hold of it, clarissime, and read it, perhaps it would give you the key to your dream.

The doctor only smiled; and throughout the supper he kept to his strict diet, despite numerous temptations to violate it.

A few nights later he dreamed the same dream. Again he saw the same beautiful body of the girl. This time he dreamed that he was still a student at the University of Vienna, and in the Anatomy Building. The attendant told him that he had a whole corpse at his disposal; and added that it was through his, the attendant's, good offices that the body was obtained; and that consequently he deserved a tip, as the other students were envious of Mišić's good luck. "Watch out, Doctor, that something doesn't happen to you. You might lose your head over her, she is so beautiful," the attendant said to him. When he stepped to the dissecting board, he saw her entirely naked. He recognized her, but could not remember where he had seen her. Enchanted by her beauty, it was long before he could bring himself to use his knife. He felt distressed at the prospect of cutting out of so perfect a form the breast which was to afford him material for his chapter on anatomy. He could not see his way clear to proceed.

He suddenly became unable to move. His hands and feet seemed petrified. His eyes bulged out; and then everything went blank. From an awesome distance he heard certain Latin conversations of which he could understand neither the content nor the purpose. He knew only that it was Latin and that it tortured and pained him seriously. In one word, he was terrified. Affrighted, he woke up. He looked at the phosphorescent clock. It indicated ten minutes past one.

"Post mediam noctem, cum somnia vera," were his first horrified words. And again he felt the usual melancholy and uneasiness.

"To see her in such a terrible condition! my little beauty!" he whispered almost sorrowfully. "And really may there not be something behind all this? What does this incessant renewal of the same apparition mean? Finally, why does the situation always develop in the same fashion? Why is it that my feelings are wrought up to so high a pitch by a mere apparition in a dream—by a mere phantom of my imagination? Is it not strange that a creature of my fancy should enchant me far more than a real woman ever has done?" the doctor asked himself. He did not wish to invoke the aid of his intellect or of the postulates of his science. Instead, with an absorbed delight, he gave himself over to these meditations, deriving a great joy from fancying that the marvelous girl was not an ephemeral creation of his imagination, but a real being, no matter of what sort.

"But why do I always dream of her in such horrifying circumstances?" he would interrupt himself in his leisurely meditations. And in his heart there would settle a chill like that of a serpent; and he would relapse into his melancholy attitude.

From that night on, his dreadful dreams recurred frequently, and he always saw the same girl, and always in some frightful situation. And after every such dream he would wake up terribly frightened. If he slept through without waking up, the morning would still bring him the usual melancholy and oppressive feeling, and he would have a premonition of something terrible.

But besides these gruesome dreams he had still more frequently erotic dreams, in which he always had to deal with the fair girlish phantom. He had numberless trysts in unknown places, and these trysts were filled with such extraordinary dramatic incidents as he had never—so far as he knew—experienced in real life. Scenes occurred in which most ardent declarations of love took place; and again others in which torturing jealousy held sway. Frequently he saw himself in a dual rôle. And his two selves clashed in jealous encounters. But the girl he always beheld in her perfect beauty, always veiled with the poesy of sadness and misfortune.

These dreams became so dear to him that he truly yearned for them. In order to insure her appearance during the night, he would force himself in the evening to think of her as intensely as possible. But presently he noticed that just at those times when he had mused on the phantom especially long and earnestly he would not dream of her. He never discussed his dreams with any one. He even sought to avoid such discussions. Whenever Radičević or Batorić asked him any questions concerning his experiences he would merely shake his head or smile and at once divert the conversation into some other channel. He himself did not know what to think of the whole affair. He ardently desired, however, that the image of the girl should forever remain fixed in his memory. As a boy he had studied drawing and he now attempted to draw the figure of his apparition, but after a quarter of an hour he had to throw away his pencil. He contrived another means. He started a diary, and in it he accurately noted every dream.

One evening, exhausted by the hard work of the day, he went to bed a trifle earlier than usual. Outside a storm was brewing. It was thundering in the distance and the moonlight sky was covered with black clouds. Here and there a jagged thunderbolt flashed. The doctor, thinking of his nervousness and fearing that the thunder and lightning might interfere with his sleep, got up, lowered the Venetian blinds and closed the shutters.

It was not long before he fell asleep. He dreamed that he was sleeping there in his bed, from which he could barely distinguish the objects in the dark room, and see through the narrow slits of the shutters the bluish flashing of lightning. His man-servant entered the neighboring room with a half-burned candle in his hand. He saw him open the cupboard and remove from it a bottle of his finest cognac, tuck it under his arm, and then tiptoe out of the room. The doctor, still in his bed, saw him in the corridor, then on the ground floor, and then entering his own room, where a group of men and women were waiting for him. Mišić did not care to follow the servant any longer, nor did he marvel in the least at his ability to see everything from his bed. His glance now wandered outside, and he saw rain pouring down heavily. There on the street he saw a carriage—perhaps a farmer's—going at a dizzy pace. He could see still farther, much farther, God knows how far. Then he saw on a wide public road a lonely structure, which was low but long. Immediately he guessed that it was a tavern. In front of the house stood a crowd of men who looked like carters; and inside a large smoky room was filled with carters, farmers, and nondescripts. A corpulent tavern keeper and his thin wife, who was as dirty as the maid, a young Carinthian girl, were making their way among the customers, continually passing wine, cigars, and whiskey. In the corner, near the stove, sat a lone man, stooping over. He wore a long overcoat that reached to the ground. The raiment was so worn out that it was impossible to tell its original color. On his knees rested a violin. His long curly hair fell over his dark, wearied, and weather-beaten face, which was of an unusual sallow color. His wretched face was overgrown with a long black beard; and as his head was bowed deeply, his unkempt beard fell half-way down his breast. Upon someone's motioning or calling to him, he adjusted the violin, stood up, and began to play. Long, sorrowful chords swelled through the room and then gradually, with a gentle, moaning tremolo, died away amid the uproar of drunken voices. The musician now turned toward someone and motioned sadly with his head. Then from somewhere—from behind a cabinet in the corner, it seemed—appeared a young girl in a short pink circus dress with blue ribbons. She placed herself near the fiddler, with her face turned toward him, and began to sing. It was a beautifully soft, divine voice. It started gently, very gently, then with a mighty crescendo swelled into an enchanting melody of now delicate, now strong notes, and finally in a profound sigh died away with magic sweetness.

Dr. Mišić understood neither the words nor the song, nor did he recognize the melody; he only knew that he was listening to something that he had never heard before, so beautiful, so majestic, so perfect was her singing. He could not see the face of the singer. But when, toward the end of the song, the drunken rabble began to clamor and shout that they did not want any of those sad, goody-goody songs, but that instead the "gipsy" should sing a gay song, one of "ours," the girl turned toward the "audience." Her oval face almost morbidly pale, her large dark eyes, her luxuriant black tresses, her delicate swan-like neck, her whole being, assured him that she was the stranger from his dreams. He was dreadfully depressed and sad because he could not get up from his bed. Ah! she appeared far more beautiful now than ever before! Even now her face was veiled with a sort of inexplicable sadness and her eyes had a certain melancholy look; but from her whole being emanated fresh youthfulness. Ah! she was so charming, so wonderful in her timid, frightened, almost childlike attitude, with her soft smiles and the bewildered look in her tearful eyes, shaded with their long eyelashes! Again she sang, and again her song thrilled with a sad resonance still more heartrending than before. While she sang silence reigned everywhere. The most drunken drivers propped their unsteady heads with their elbows and listened with open mouths. Others, who were still able to stand on their feet, stepped nearer and encircled the singer, gazed stupidly at her, and despite their befogged brains, nodded in approval and dried their tears. When the last notes had ceased to vibrate, a voice rose in the opposite corner: "Hey, I don't want any more of those wailing songs; they give me a pain in my breast, my throat. Sing us something jolly, witch!" And a huge tramp jumped from his seat like a mad lynx, breaking all the glasses around him, and staggered drunkenly toward the musician.

"Sing us something jolly!" echoed others, and like a ball they rolled toward the wretched fiddler.

"Lay off, you filthy dogs! Let her be. Let her sing as she has been singing! It is beautiful! What do you want here anyway! Sing on!" protested those who had gathered around the singer.

"No, no!" and it became pandemonium as fists swung furiously. The poor fiddler's violin was smashed to pieces. Dejectedly he seized the girl by the arm and made for the door. At that moment a bottle whizzed through the air and hit the girl right on her temple. She fell down, a crumpled mass, without uttering a single sound. Dr. Mišić, terrified, emitted a piercing cry—and then awoke.

He was so excited that he could not close his eyes again. —"Whence these terrible, strange pictures?" he asked himself frantically, suspecting that they might be the first symptoms of insanity. "And how clear it all was, how vivid and distinctly outlined, just like an experience of real life. This time there was not a single fantastic motif. An absolute fact! I can hardly believe that it was only a dream. It was as though I were viewing a scene from real life! Something serious is the matter with me. I shall have to go to Vienna, for observation by the professors. Oh, it would be horrible if I were to go insane!"

And he fell into a black despair. He decided firmly not to indulge in any fanciful meditations about the bewitching beauty of the girl. "Such meditations cause my dreams; these with their deceitful reality go quite beyond the true nature of dreams and are manifestations of a deranged spirit. Ugh! . . . ." He could lie in bed no longer. He got up and paced nervously up and down the room in his night-shirt. Then obeying a mysterious impulse he went into the neighboring room and opened the cupboard. His glance fell upon the cognac shelf. He was absolutely astounded and had to draw back a step or two. The very bottle of which he had dreamed had disappeared. The first thing he did was to walk towards the servant's room; he did not mind the theft, but he wanted to get to the bottom of this affair. From the corridor he could hear the drunken song that issued from the servants' quarters on the ground floor. He had dreamed of that, too. A feeling of amazement descended upon him. Almost frightened, he went downstairs. On the first step it occurred to him: "Oh, I heard the drunken song through my sleep, and that is how my dream created the picture that I saw!" And he slapped his forehead, smiled reassuringly and returned to his room. "Ultimately, or rather *fine finaliter,* chances are that I shall become another magnificus Škender."

Passing the cupboard he remembered the cognac. "Oh, that's a mere trifle,—just a coincidence. Perhaps I noticed yesterday that the bottle wasn't there and then never gave it another thought till I saw the scene in my dream."

He then went to bed, calmed.

The next day at noon, just as he was finishing his work in the office, a messenger came from the district court. He bore an official summons ordering the doctor to appear at the courthouse to join a commission of experts that was to investigate a case of murder that had occurred somewhere in a distant town on the boundary of the district. Ordinarily the doctor would have received such a summons with indifference. This time, however, he immediately thought of his dream. "There was some truth in it," he whispered as he perused the document. But immediately he called himself a fool. "With my excitability I am growing almost childish." And he really was excited. The dream, a sleepless night, and his tense condition, which had existed for a whole week, all contributed to make him more nervous than usual.

His hands fairly trembled as he was packing in his case the instruments necessary for a dissection. Three times he had to return from his carriage to the office to get things that he had forgotten and that were indispensable.

When he reached the courthouse the commission was gone. The judge, with a clerk and an older doctor, had left early in order to reach the morgue as soon as possible. Word had been left for him to follow them.

It was a hot August afternoon. All along the road the carriage raised veritable clouds of thick, yellowish dust. The air was heavy and oppressive and prevented free breathing. Mišić was impatient to reach his destination and to escape the inconveniences of the drive; and yet whenever he thought of arriving there, an inexplicable fear and terror took possession of him. He was utterly unable to explain his state of mind. But the strange similarity between his dream and the case upon which he was called to officiate constantly preyed upon his subconsciousness.

"After all . . . . . oh . . . . . who could believe it for a single moment! Nothing! Nothing! At any rate such things are dangerous —they trouble our brains. One thing only is clear to me—a man can never escape superstition!" the doctor reflected, attempting to drive away his thoughts.

The ride lasted about two hours. The town constable who awaited the doctor's arrival took him to the morgue in the cemetery, where the investigating commission was already at work. There he found a great many people gathered round the table that stood outside the morgue. At the table sat a clerk who was taking down the testimony of witnesses. The doctor threw only a hurried glance at the crowd. Strangely enough it seemed to him that all the faces there were familiar to him. However, he did not have time to ponder over that. The judge stepped up to him immediately and, indicating the door of the morgue, asked him to perform the autopsy while he was examining the witnesses.

"Murder—a gipsy murdered. Go ahead, Doctor, and finish up everything; then you can dictate your report. Let's not waste too much time. You, as the junior doctor, will do the dissecting. Isn't that so, my dear Dr. Aschbayer?"

"Quite so, quite so. My respected colleague may proceed," retorted the senior doctor, a man of advanced years and extraordinary obesity. "I've had plenty of that sort of thing. And I have a headache—I could not stand it inside. I will sign everything you wish. In the meanwhile I am going to the village to see if I can find a glass of good wine. —Undoubtedly, colleague, you can do everything necessary without my aid. Anyhow, it is a very clear case—a fatal blow on the left temple, I think; and the skull is broken above the ear. Yes, yes, a clear case. Then . . . I'll see you again! I shall return before you've finished the dissecting. Your Honor has nothing against my departure!"

And the old Doctor rolled out of the crowd, and with his goose step descended to the village.

Dr. Mišić prepared his instruments, ordered water to be brought to the morgue and, accompanied by the constable and the sexton, went inside. The beam of light that entered through a small window above the door dimly illumined the scene. The place was narrow, and the walls were black and green from humidity. The air inside was musty. There was a slightly perceptible odor of a corpse. In the center stood a crude, clumsy table; and on it lay a body which was covered with a long soiled robe in such a way that no part of it could be seen—only a pair of dusty and much-worn shoes protruded from the lower end. The upper end of the robe, near the head, was bloodstained.

Dr. Mišić felt his usual composure deserting him. Continually his dream of last night kept coming back to his mind; and now, seeing the morgue and the bloodstains, he recalled his other dreams also.

"If under this robe lay . . . she! Oh, that would be too horrible!" he said to himself, suffering more from the thought that she was dead than from the presentiment that his dream was true. His feelings were like those of a lover who fears for the life of his belovèd. On similar occasions he himself would have undertaken to undress the corpse, for he was anxious not to let the awkward hands of untrained villagers touch the rigid limbs of the dead body. Now was he either unwilling or unable to follow his customary procedure. Instead he ordered the sexton to do the undressing. For his own part he turned toward the door, looked outside, and listened to the questions of the judge and the answers of the witnesses.

"I could not tell exactly how many of us there were; no one could. Yes, the room was filled with people," answered a voice. "All of a sudden a noise and a cry arose and the young people began to fight. Who can tell how and why! The devil himself seemed to be mixed up in it. The crowd was drunk; and it would be impossible to tell who struck the blow. I did not—I could swear it on the Crucifix—I never touched anybody—I did not."

"Oh—Oh!" wailed a shrill voice on the side, "you all are guilty. Oh God! to kill such a child! They've taken away my only support. Oh, wretched old me! Where shall I turn now? Please, please, illustrious, merciful court, arrest all of them; and make them pay me, pay me plenty. My poor, hapless child! They killed her as they would a cat. Oh! They broke my violin, too—my old Italian violin! No concert player ever had a better one!"

The voice somehow sounded familiar to Mišić, and he wanted to go out and see the wailing old man; but something held him back and he remained in his place.

"We have finished," announced the sexton and the constable behind his back. The doctor started, and avoiding any glance at the table, withdrew from the door and bent over his instrument case. Outside, the wailing of the old man grew louder and louder. Although there was nothing to select, the doctor remained bent over for a long time, picking and choosing among the knives, scissors and lancets.

"Daylight won't last forever," remarked the sexton, to remind the doctor that it was about time to start.

Mišić bent over with a sigh, then with a supreme effort he stepped to the table, still forbearing to look in the direction of the corpse.

"Bah! What stupid thoughts are entering my mind! I am not Redičević!" he mumbled angrily, drawing very close to the table.

"Yes, it is . . . it is she!" he ejaculated almost aloud, drawing back two paces. His arms fell to his sides, and his right hand clasped the blade of the knife, so that he felt a twinge of pain. On the table lay the body of a beautiful young girl. Her soft and delicate face, wearing a frightened and suffering expression, seemed to gaze at the doctor, and her large dark eyes were wide open. On her long eyelashes and thick brows some dust had gathered. Her black luxuriant tresses fell in disorder over the table to the floor. Above her left ear a quantity of dried blood had transformed one lock into a hard ball.

"No, no, it cannot be she!" the doctor stammered to himself, after a long pause. "It must be a hallucination, as it was in the garden when I took a blossoming lilac for a girl. My nerves, my nerves!" and he grasped his forehead.

But the longer he gazed the surer he was that the body was identical with the one that he had seen in his dreams.

"There is no doubt—the same lines—the same face that I have seen so many times in my dreams. It is she. It is she!" he moaned pitiably and his heart was afflicted by a great pain and a boundless sorrow, and his eyes were moist with tears.

"It is she!" he whispered hoarsely, scarcely able to breathe, and gazing at her beautiful form, which was just slightly rigid and not yet entirely suffused with the paleness of death. He recognized every line. There was the same insignificant black scar above the right thigh. Even her right hand lay near her right breast, as he had seen it in the first dream. He trembled and felt a great fear. It seemed as though a fatal, mysterious cloud were hovering over him, enveloping him in the terrible shadow of the world beyond where human intelligence is powerless.

"Then dreams do not lie," he spoke aloud, without paying any attention to the two men present. "It is the same body, and in exactly the same circumstances as in my dream. And then the witness said that there was a scuffle. But no! All this may be a mere coincidence. Perhaps I do not see clearly. Sick nerves! I always dream the same apparition, and now I see it everywhere. But . . ." He interrupted himself and jumped feverishly toward the sexton, and asked him to describe the body. The sexton eyed him suspiciously, then distorted his mouth with a stupid laugh, turned toward the constable and scratched his head above his ear.

"But, can't you see her, Doctor? Hm . . . She is beautiful. It's a pity she got killed. A mere child."

"But tell me what kind of hair she has! Is her body stout? Is it? . . . Speak up!"

"For God's sake, Doctor, she has black hair. And her body . . . how could I describe it? . . . She is young and beautiful. . . . She is not fat."

"Is there a scar above her thigh?"

"Yes, of course, there is. How can you doubt it? There, see it!"

"Then I saw all right!" the doctor said to himself. "It is she. It is she!"

And he no longer thought of his dream. He merely gazed upon the beautiful body. He suddenly felt a need of being alone; and almost rudely he ordered the sexton and the constable to leave the room.

Now he directed a long, long glance upon the dead girl. The beauty of her graceful figure again rose before his eyes, as in his dreams. An enormous sorrow, a saintly pity, and a black despair filled his soul. "How beautiful, how wonderful she is! By her beauty she deserves naught but happiness. But now, alas, there she lies, a dead body! Why could not the fates have been kinder to her?" And in his mind he delved into the history of the poor vagabond songstress, whose destiny was not satisfied with her wretched life on the street, and with her continuous contact with poverty, sin, and grief, but had to punish her with so cruel and so early a death! The doctor trembled with horror. Then his erotic dreams arose in his memory. It seemed to him that they were real; and that like a lover he was standing before the corpse of his belovèd, bewailing her loss. He cursed Fate for playing such a cruel trick upon him. The girl had conquered his heart and soul, and yet in real life he was permitted to behold merely her dead body. An immense, tender affection pervaded his whole being, and he felt a desire to press his lips against those of the corpse. Fantastic thoughts flitted through his brain; and in a strange ecstasy he began to whisper to her that she belonged to him, that she was destined for him, and that his obstinate dreaming of her was not a mere trifle.

"Yes, yes, between our souls there existed a communion through which they overcame all physical obstacles and found each other. She is mine! She is mine!"

He bent down to her and kissed her cold lips. At first the unpleasant cold touch and the repelling odor terrified him. But after again beholding her magnificent and delicate beauty, his former ecstasy and affection returned, and he felt quite ashamed of himself for yielding even for a moment to a feeling of repulsion for his belovèd, though she was dead. And again he began to kiss the corpse but not only on her face; he showered with kisses her tresses, her neck, her bosom, and her hands. When he came to himself he started up and freed himself from the strange embrace. His soul was now possessed by a terrific, indescribable pain. The whole tragedy of that wasted young life, so beautiful and marvelous, as well as the still greater tragedy of his own heart and soul, became apparent to him. He wept bitterly. Profuse tears rolled down his face, which was distorted and quivering with pain.

It was a terrible, terrible moment for him!

"Well, Doctor, have you started?" asked the judge from the entrance. "I've finished the chief part of my work."

And he began to recite the findings concerning the murder. It was the same act of which the doctor had dreamed. The judge was followed by the father of the murdered girl. The doctor could not help shivering again when he saw him. He was of almost exactly the same appearance as the musician of the dream.

"What is the matter with you, Doctor? You look pale! You look . . ." remarked the judge upon seeing the changed and agitated appearance of the doctor.

"Nothing—nothing.—It is long since I have done any dissecting."

"If you feel ill, I will send for Dr. Aschbayer. He is old, it is true, but still if it is necessary he will have to perform the dissection."

"No, no!" exclaimed the doctor. The idea of someone else dissecting her body horrified him. "I must do it.—Let me perform at least this service for her," he said to himself, almost insanely.

The old musician in the meanwhile had slunk into a corner, where he continually groaned and cried. He was bewailing the loss of his child and his violin. The judge wanted to send him out, but he raised his hand and begged that he be allowed to remain inside. The doctor, however, would not agree; but requested that everybody leave the room, with the exception of the sexton, whom he needed to hold the vessel of water.

Now he was alone. With a great moral effort he attempted to be calm. And in fact he was quite steady while he removed his coat, rolled up his sleeves, and once more took hold of his instruments.

But, alas, the first incision across her forehead caused him frightful moral suffering. That fine soft forehead, that delicate face which had captivated him with its beauty and charm in those wondrously sweet dreams, he had now to destroy. And after he had cut the skin and was ready to saw off the cranium, he had to stop for a moment and go out for a breath of fresh air.

Despite all his efforts he was unable to conquer himself. His whole body was quivering from excitement, severe suffering, and sorrow. It was only his unusual skill as a surgeon that enabled him to continue the dissection. But when he was about to cut open her breast and abdomen his forces began to desert him, and the incision that he made was not the proper one. He was perspiring profusely all over his forehead and his body. He could hardly distinguish objects before him. After he had removed her heart he felt a terrific pain. A dizziness descended upon him. Then he reeled and fell helpless over the corpse, his arms crossed.

"For God's sake, Doctor, be careful that you do not cut yourself," exclaimed the sexton, observing that the knife in the doctor's right hand had plunged into him somewhere under his left shoulder. The doctor did not hear him. Dazed, almost senseless, he arose in a moment and continued his work unconsciously, almost mechanically.

Never in his life had it taken him so long to perform an autopsy. When he had finished he went out and called the clerk to take down his report. At first his voice shook slightly, but gradually he regained his self-control, and when Dr. Aschbayer arrived, Mišić was dictating in a firm and sure voice.

While signing the report a drop of blood suddenly fell on the paper from underneath his sleeve.

"What is that?" queried Dr. Aschbayer in surprise.

"I don't know," replied Mišić. "I washed myself well. I have no idea where the blood comes from."

"But, good God, is it possible that you have cut yourself? God, that would be terrible!"

"I do not remember having done so," answered Mišić, fairly alarmed.

"Yes you did—there—the blood is still dripping. Oh, good God Almighty, you have poisoned yourself!" and the old doctor quickly took off Mišić's coat and rolled up his shirt sleeve. On the left upper arm, quite near the shoulder, there appeared a slight cut of some length.

"Alas, how did it happen?—so high? It would be bad enough if it were on your hands, your fingers, but so high! How in thunder could you reach so high with your knife? It is almost impossible for one to cut himself there."

The sexton observed that he had seen the knife rip into the doctor's shoulder when he swooned and fell down.

"And you, man alive, you did not say anything? Fool—fool, don't you know that this is not an ordinary wound, but poison, death, unless there is immediate treatment! And it is almost two hours now since this happened," lamented Aschbayer.

Then he proceeded to search Mišić's case for materials used in rendering first aid on such occasions. But his search revealed the fact that there was no alcohol, or caustic, or nitric acid—in short that there was nothing. In his confusion at the time of leaving, Mišić had forgotten the small case in which he kept such things.

"God, what shall we do now?" cried the old man; while Mišić stood motionless, as if petrified. "And it is too late to suck the wound, too late!"

"Too late!" echoed Mišić, speaking in a hoarse and solemn voice, more to himself than to others. He felt as though he were under the influence of some mighty and absolute law which functioned mercilessly and against whose will there could be no struggle, no recourse. The meaning of his dream now dawned upon him.

"This is then what the rigid body, the coffin, the drowning in the frightful stream, and the bloodsucking kisses of the girl in my dream portended. Death was awaiting me—hence my melancholy. In my dream my soul foresaw everything. It was fated to be!" Mišić whispered to himself without observing or caring what was happening about him. His whole being was pervaded by an immense apathy. He was convinced that the whole life of man, even in its most minute details, was nothing but an uninterrupted series of absolutely preordained events. Now he understood how his soul, weeks and weeks ahead of time, could presage what was going to happen. At this moment he felt and perceived its mystic nature. His mechanical and chemical understanding of the universe and of himself came to naught, and in his soul he felt that there was something else besides the mere physiological processes of the human brain. This new understanding was not a disappointment to him. On the contrary he felt bigger and stronger, and the thought of dying did not terrify him. He fell into a sort of mystic ecstasy which lifted his spirit and made him believe that death was not the end but the beginning of progress towards true perfection. And here he thought of the dead girl. A warm, ardent belief that he should see her again entered into his heart.

"We must hurry home," Dr. Aschbayer aroused him from his meditation. "From there we'll send immediately to Zagreb for doctors. The need is great—you know it best—what is the use concealing it. You know yourself what the poison of a corpse means. Your arm will have to be amputated at the shoulder. That's your only salvation."

"You think so? Hm . . . I don't know," retorted Mišić, thinking of his dream. But he made no further remarks. At home he made no objection to the sending of a carriage to Zagreb for a famous surgeon. He did not seem to care about anything.

That night he lapsed into a fever; his poisoned wound was inflamed. At first the inflammation had only reached the joint of the shoulder. But the next morning when the surgeon and his assistant arrived, the whole shoulder was inflamed. There was no doubt that his blood was poisoned. Amputation would have been purposeless now.

"Medical science is powerless here. Send for a priest. Telegraph his relatives," the surgeon said to Aschbayer; and after receiving his fee he hurried back to the city, where urgent cases were awaiting him.

Mišić passed from one fever into another. Very seldom did he regain consciousness. The pain increased with great speed and unabated fury. He was delirious. And in his fevered mind he was carrying on a happy love affair with the hapless girl. He lived through days, months, years, of an idyllic love. Nay, it was a veritable eternity that he lived through during a few short hours.

When the physical end approached, he regained consciousness. A bright summer sun was flooding the room. Near the bed sat Dr. Aschbayer and old Batorić.

"Truly I am not sorry to go," continued the doomed man. He told the truth. He felt elated and far, far away from everything that surrounded him. He was unable to understand how it was possible for him to have any love for his recent life or to see any sense in it. So strange, so distant and indifferent was everything worldly to him now. Not even the golden sunbeams moved him, nor did he for a moment regret that in a short time he should be deprived of their brilliancy forever.

Suddenly his mind became unusually clear. Every thought that came to him appeared clear and exact, without any ambiguity and doubt. And his thoughts flowed with a rapidity in comparison with which electricity is nothing. Almost all his knowledge passed before his mind with such accuracy, clearness, and completeness as never before. He remembered long-forgotten things from his primary school, every page of the books he had studied—as if he were studying them now. Then he felt a strange change in his inner being. His whole life from his early childhood was now revealed to him. The most insignificant things, trifles, the playthings of his childhood, senseless jokes, and incidents—all passed before him. And it was not as though he were forming pictures, visualizing the incidents—it seemed to him that he was living his past life all over again. He was unaware of any physical measure of time and space and he saw no difference between the realities of his past life and his fateful dream. That also was present to him and he viewed it with the same sensations. Then a sweet, resplendent enchantment took possession of his soul and the wondrous figure of the young girl stood before him.

"All things with which our souls commune are real for us. And now I am able to see that such things alone are truly ours. They do not leave us even at the time of our death!" he spoke aloud, interrupting his thoughts.

"Oh, how my blood burns!" He straightened himself in his anguish, wishing to change his position. But his strength failed him and his head sank into the pillow.

He was dead.

Translated from the Croatian
by John J. Batistich and
George R. Noyes

Jean Lorrain

1855-1906

Pseudonym of Paul Duval, French journalist and writer, who toward the end of his life systematically abused narcotics. His best-known works are Monsieur de Bougrelon *and* Monsieur de Phocas. *His strongest qualities can be seen in a collection of shorter works,* Poussières de Paris.

THE HOLES IN THE MASK

The charms of horror tempt only the strong.

Baudelaire.

I

"Want to see something?" my friend de Jakels had said to me. "Very well. Get yourself a domino and a black velvet mask—a rather elegant black satin domino—put on some pumps and, for this occasion, black silk stockings, and wait for me at home on Tuesday towards half past ten; I'll come to fetch you."

The following Tuesday, wrapped in the rustling folds of a long cape, a velvet mask with satin flap tied behind my ears, I was waiting for my friend de Jakels in my bachelor's apartment in the Rue Taitbout, while warming my feet—irritated and shivering from their unaccustomed contact with silk—over the hot coals of the fireplace. From the boulevard rose a medley of horns and the excited cries of a Carnival evening.

How strange and even disquieting as time drew on, I mused, was the lonely watch of this masked figure slouched in an armchair, in the chiaroscuro of this ground-floor room crowded with knickknacks and deadened by draperies. The mirrors hanging on the heavy walls reflected the tall flames of a petroleum lamp and the flickering of two long, slender, very white, almost funereal candles and . . . no sign of de Jakels! The cries of maskers ringing in the distance only heightened the hostility of this silence; the two candles were burning so straight that a fit of irritation finally seized me and, suddenly frightened by those three lights, I rose to blow one of them out.

Just then, one of the door-curtains drew aside and de Jakels entered.

De Jakels? I had heard neither a ring nor the sound of the door. How then did he enter my apartment? I have often pondered over this since then; yet de Jakels was here before me. De Jakels? I should say a long domino, a tall dark shape, muffled and masked as I was.

"Are you ready?" inquired his voice, which was so altered that I could not recognize it. "My carriage is here, let us go."

I had heard neither his carriage drive up nor stop beneath my windows. Into what nightmare, into what gloom and into what mystery was I beginning to sink?

"It's the hood which is stopping your ears; you aren't used to a mask," de Jakels—who had pierced my silence—reflected aloud. He had every divining power that night and, turning up my domino, he satisfied himself as to the fineness of my silk stockings and my slender shoes.

That gesture reassured me. It had to be de Jakels and no one else speaking to me beneath that domino. No one else would have been concerned with the request which de Jakels had made of me one week earlier.

"All right, off we go!" ordered his voice and, with a rustling of silk and satin, we rushed into the passage of the carriage entrance, rather like, it seemed to me, two enormous bats with our hoods billowing out, suddenly blown over our dominos.

Where had this strong wind come from, this strange blast of air? The temperature of that Mardi Gras night was so humid and yet so mild.

II

Where were we driving now, crammed into the shadows of this extraordinarily quiet cab, whose wheels, just as the hooves of the horse, made no sound on the wooden pavement of the streets and the macadam of the deserted avenues?

Where were we going along the river and those unfamiliar steep banks, here and there barely illuminated by the torch lantern of an antique street-lamp? We had long since lost sight of the fantastic silhouette of Notre Dame standing out on the other bank against a leaden sky. Quai Saint-Michel, Quai de la Tournelle, now Quai Bercy—we were far from the Opéra, the Rues Drouot and Le Peletier, and the center of the city. We were not even headed for Bullier, where shameful vices hold their sessions and, escaping under a mask, whirl almost diabolically, flaunting themselves impudently on Mardi Gras nights; my companion remained silent.

Along the taciturn and pale Seine, beneath the piles of bridges which now appeared less and less frequently, along those quays planted with tall, lean trees whose boughs were spread out against the livid sky like the fingers of death, I was seized with an irrational fear, a fear aggravated by de Jakels' inexplicable silence; I ended by doubting his presence and believing I was with a stranger. My companion's hand had grasped mine and, though slack and without force, held it in a vice which was crushing my fingers. That hand of power and determination riveted my words in my throat, and under its clasp I felt all desire to rebel melt and dissolve inside me. Now we were driving outside the walls, along wide streets bordered by hedges and dreary fronts of wine shops, inns at the customs gates closed long ago; we were speeding along under the moon, which had finally grazed a floating pile of clouds and seemed to throw, over this ambiguous suburban scene, a wrinkled cloth of salt. At that moment, I thought I heard the horses' hooves resounding on the road surfaces, and the wheels of the carriage, no longer phantoms, squeaking among the broken stones and pebbles of the road.

"There it is!" murmured my companion's voice. "We are there; we can get out." And as I stammered a timid, "Where are we?" he continued, "Barrière d'Italie, outside the walls. We took the longest but safest way. Tomorrow morning we'll go back by a different route."

The horses stopped and de Jakels released me to open the carriage door and offer me his hand.

III

A large, very high-ceilinged hall, its walls rough-plastered with lime, inside shutters sealing the windows hermetically and, along the entire length of the room, tables with tin goblets fastened down with chains. At the rear, up three steps, was a zinc counter crowded with liquors and bottles bearing the colorful labels of legendary wine merchants; inside, the gas light was hissing tall and bright. One might say that the hall was that of a typical merchant on the outskirts whose business was prospering, but it was more spacious and neater.

"Above all, not a word to anyone. Don't speak to anybody, nor reply to them. They would see that you are not one of them, and we might be placed in a very unpleasant position. At least they know me." And de Jakels pushed me into the hall.

A few scattered masqueraders were drinking. As we came in, the manager of the place rose and, dragging his feet heavily, came toward us as though to block our way. Without saying a word, de Jakels lifted the hems of our two dominos and showed him our feet wearing fine pumps: this was no doubt the *Open sesame!* of this curious establishment. The boss shuffled back to his counter and I noticed that, oddly, he too was masked, but with rough cardboard comically colored to imitate a human face.

The two waiters, two giants whose shirtsleeves were rolled up over their hairy wrestlers' biceps, were silently making their rounds, they like the other guests invisible under the same frightful masks.

The few guests in disguise sitting around the tables drinking wore velvet and satin masks. Except for an enormous cuirassier in uniform, a brutal-looking sort with a heavy jaw and a tawny mustache who was drinking with his face uncovered, a vague look already in his eyes, none of the creatures in that place had human features. In one corner, two large men wearing blouses and velvet caps, with black satin masks, made a puzzling appearance in their suspicious elegance; for their blouses were of light blue silk and from the bottom of their too-new trousers peeked narrow feminine toes in silk stockings and pumps. Nearly hypnotized, I would have continued to gaze at that spectacle if de Jakels had not swept me off toward the back of the hall to a glass door covered by a red curtain. *Entrance to ballroom,* read the sign over that door in flowery letters made by an amateur painter; a city policeman stood guard next to it. That at least was a comfort, but brushing against his hand as I went by, I noticed it to be made of wax, as was his pink face bristling with a false mustache. I had the horrible impression that the one creature whose presence would have reassured me in this mysterious place was a dummy.

IV

How many hours was it that I wandered alone amidst these silent maskers, in this shed with arches like a church, for it was indeed a church, an abandoned and converted church, this vast hall with its ogival windows, most of them half walled in, between their foliage-decorated columns daubed with a thick yellowish coating, which covered up the sculptured flowers on the capitals.

What a strange ball, where no one was dancing, and where there was no orchestra! De Jakels had disappeared and I was alone, abandoned in the midst of this crowd of strangers. An old wrought-iron chandelier suspended from the arch flamed tall and bright, lighting up the dusty slabs, some of which, carved up with inscriptions, covered perhaps tombs. In the back, at the spot where the altar had surely reigned, mangers and racks ran along halfway up the wall, while in the corners lay stacks of harnesses and halters: the ballroom was a stable. Here and there, large barbershop mirrors framed in gilt paper reflected and cross-reflected the masqueraders' mute parade; or rather, they no longer reflected it, for now the guests were all seated, lined up motionless on both sides of the former church, hidden up to their shoulders behind the former stalls of the choir.

There they sat, without a word, absolutely motionless, as though they had withdrawn into mystery under long cloaks of silvery cloth, a dull, reflectionless silver; for there were no longer dominos, nor blue silk blouses, nor Columbines, nor Pierrots, nor grotesque disguises, but all the maskers were similar, hooded in the same robe of green—a sallow green as though dipped in gold—with long, black sleeves, and all of them with dark green hoods and, in the cavity inside the hood, the two eye-holes of their silver cloak.

They resembled lepers' chalky faces of ancient lazarettos, and their black-gloved hands held long stems of black lilies with pale leaves; and their hoods, like that of Dante, were crowned with black lilies.

And all these cloaked figures sat there in silence with the motionless attitudes of specters while, above their funereal crowns, the window arches, in which patches of white moonlit sky stood out, capped them with transparent miters.

I felt my reason foundering in terror; the supernatural enveloped me: that rigidity, the stillness of all those masked beings. What were they? Another instant of suspense and I would go mad! I could stand it no longer and, feverish with anguish, I drew near one of the maskers and abruptly lifted the cloak.

Oh horror! There was nothing there, nothing at all. My haggard eyes fell only upon the hollow space in the cowl; the robe, the cloak were empty. That living something was but shadow and emptiness.

Insane with terror, I wrested off the cloak of the masker sitting in the adjoining stall: the green velvet hood was empty, as were the hoods of the other maskers seated along the walls. They all were as shadows, all of them were nothingness.

And in the lofty hall, the gas blazed still brighter, almost whistling; through the broken panes of the ogives, the moonlight came piercing, almost dazzling me. A feeling of dread seized me among all those hollow beings with their shadowy appearance of ghosts. A ghastly doubt clutched my heart at the sight of all these empty masks.

What if I too were like them, what if I too had ceased to exist, and, under my mask, there was nothing, nothing but emptiness! I dashed to one of the mirrors. A creature out of a dream was standing before me, with a dark green hood, crowned with black lilies, masked with silver.

And I was that masker, for I recognized my gesture in the hand lifting the cloak and, gaping with terror, I uttered a great cry, for there was nothing under the mask of silvery cloth, nothing in the oval of the cowl except the hollow of the cloth doubled over nothingness; I was dead and I. . .

"And you have been drinking ether again," grumbled de Jakels' voice in my ear. "An odd way to deceive your boredom while waiting for me."

I was stretched out in the middle of the room, my body having slipped to the rug and my head resting against the armchair, and de Jakels, in evening clothes under a monk's robe, was giving orders feverishly to my bewildered valet, while the two lighted candles, having burned to their end, burst their sconces and awoke me. . . None too soon!

Translated from the French by Roger J. Moore

Rudyard Kipling

1865-1936

English novelist, short-story writer, and poet, born in Bombay. His best-known works include The Jungle Book, Kim, *and* Just So Stories.

THE BRUSHWOOD BOY

> Girls and boys, come out to play:
> The moon is shining as bright as day!
> Leave your supper and leave your sleep,
> And come with your playfellows out in the street!
> Up the ladder and down the wall—

A child of three sat up in his crib and screamed at the top of his voice, his fists clinched and his eyes full of terror. At first no one heard, for his nursery was in the west wing, and the nurse was talking to a gardener among the laurels. Then the housekeeper passed that way, and hurried to soothe him. He was her special pet, and she disapproved of the nurse.

"What was it, then? What was it, then? There's nothing to frighten him, Georgie dear."

"It was—it was a policeman! He was on the Down—I saw him! He came in. Jane *said* he would."

"Policemen don't come into houses, dearie. Turn over, and take my hand."

"I saw him—on the Down. He came here. Where is your hand, Harper?"

The housekeeper waited till the sobs changed to the regular breathing of sleep before she stole out.

"Jane, what nonsense have you been telling Master Georgie about policemen?"

"I haven't told him anything."

"You have. He's been dreaming about them."

"We met Tisdall on Dowhead when we were in the donkey-cart this morning. P'r'aps that's what put it into his head."

"Oh! Now you are n't going to frighten the child into fits with your silly tales, and the master know nothing about it. If ever I catch you again," etc.

A child of six was telling himself stories as he lay in bed. It was a new power, and he kept it a secret. A month before it had occurred to him to carry on a nursery tale left unfinished by his mother, and he was delighted to find the tale as it came out of his own head just as surprising as though he were listening to it "all new from the beginning." There was a prince in that tale, and he killed dragons, but only for one night. Ever afterwards Georgie dubbed himself prince, pasha, giant-killer, and all the rest (you see, he could not tell any one, for fear of being laughed at), and his tales faded gradually into dreamland, where adventures were so many that he could not recall the half of them. They all began in the same way, or, as Georgie explained to the shadows of the night-light, there was "the same starting-off place"—a pile of brushwood stacked somewhere near a beach; and round this pile Georgie found himself running races with little boys and girls. These ended, ships ran high up the dry land and opened into cardboard boxes; or gilt-and-green iron railings that surrounded beautiful gardens turned all soft and could be walked through and overthrown so long as he remembered it was only a dream. He could never hold that knowledge more than a few seconds ere things became real, and instead of pushing down houses full of grown-up people (a just revenge), he sat miserably upon gigantic door-steps trying to sing the multiplication-table up to four times six.

The princess of his tales was a person of wonderful beauty (she came from the old illustrated edition of Grimm, now out of print), and as she always applauded Georgie's valour among the dragons and buffaloes, he gave her the two finest names he had ever heard in his life—Annie and Louise, pronounced "Annie*an*louise." When the dreams swamped the stories, she would change into one of the little girls round the brushwood-pile, still keeping her title and crown. She saw Georgie drown once in a dream-sea by the beach (it was the day after he had been taken to bathe in a real sea by his nurse); and he said as he sank: "Poor Annie*an*louise! She'll be sorry for me now!" But "Annie*an*louise," walking slowly on the beach, called, " 'Ha! Ha!' said the duck, laughing," which to a waking mind might not seem to bear on the situation. It consoled Georgie at once, and must have been some kind of spell, for it raised the bottom of the deep, and he waded out with a twelve-inch flower-pot on each foot. As he was strictly forbidden to meddle with flower-pots in real life, he felt triumphantly wicked.

The movements of the grown-ups, whom Georgie tolerated, but did not pretend to understand, removed his world, when he was seven years old, to a place called "Oxford-on-a-visit." Here were huge buildings surrounded by vast prairies, with streets of infinite length, and, above all, something called the "buttery," which Georgie was dying to see, because he knew it must be greasy, and therefore delightful. He perceived how correct were his judgments when his nurse led him through a stone arch into the presence of an enormously fat man, who asked him if he would like some bread and cheese. Georgie was used to eat all round the clock, so he took what "buttery" gave him, and would have taken some brown liquid called "auditale" but that his nurse led him away to an afternoon performance of a thing called "Pepper's Ghost." This was intensely thrilling. People's heads came off and flew all over the stage, and skeletons danced bone by bone, while Mr. Pepper himself, beyond question a man of the worst, waved his arms and flapped a long gown, and in a deep bass voice (Georgie had never heard a man sing before) told of his sorrows unspeakable. Some grown-up or other tried to explain that the illusion was made with mirrors, and that there was no need to be frightened. Georgie did not know what illusions were, but he did know that a mirror was the looking-glass with the ivory handle on his mother's dressing-table. Therefore the "grown-up" was "just saying things" after the distressing custom of "grown-ups," and Georgie cast about for amusement between scenes. Next to him sat a little girl dressed all in black, her hair combed off her forehead exactly like the girl in the book called "Alice in Wonderland," which had been given him on his last birthday. The little girl looked at Georgie, and Georgie looked at her. There seemed to be no need of any further introduction.

"I've got a cut on my thumb," said he. It was the first work of his first real knife, a savage triangular hack, and he esteemed it a most valuable possession.

"I'm tho thorry!" she lisped. "Let me look—pleathe."

"There's a di-ack-lum plaster on, but it's all raw under," Georgie answered, complying.

"Dothent it hurt?"—her grey eyes were full of pity and interest.

"Awf'ly. Perhaps it will give me lockjaw."

"It lookth very horrid. I'm *tho* thorry!" She put a forefinger to his hand, and held her head sidewise for a better view.

Here the nurse turned, and shook him severely. "You mustn't talk to strange little girls, Master Georgie."

"She is n't strange. She's very nice. I like her, an' I've showed her my new cut."

"The idea! You change places with me."

She moved him over, and shut out the little girl from his view, while the grown-up behind renewed the futile explanations.

"I am *not* afraid, truly," said the boy, wriggling in despair; "but why don't you go to sleep in the afternoons, same as Provost of Oriel?"

Georgie had been introduced to a grown-up of that name, who slept in his presence without apology. Georgie understood that he was the most important grown-up in Oxford; hence he strove to gild his rebuke with flatteries. This grown-up did not seem to like it, but he collapsed, and Georgie lay back in his seat, silent and enraptured. Mr. Pepper was singing again, and the deep, ringing voice, the red fire, and the misty, waving gown all seemed to be mixed up with the little girl who had been so kind about his cut. When the performance was ended she nodded to Georgie, and Georgie nodded in return. He spoke no more than was necessary till bedtime, but meditated on new colors and sounds and lights and music and things as far as he understood them; the deep-mouthed agony of Mr. Pepper mingling with the little girl's lisp. That night he made a new tale, from which he shamelessly removed the Rapunzel-Rapunzel-let-down-your-hair princess, gold crown, Grimm edition, and all, and put a new Annie*an*louise in her place. So it was perfectly right and natural that when he came to the brushwood-pile he should find her waiting for him, her hair combed off her forehead more like Alice in Wonderland than ever, and the races and adventures began.

Ten years at an English public school do not encourage dreaming. Georgie won his growth and chest measurement, and a few other things which did not appear in the bills, under a system of cricket, foot-ball, and paper-chases, from four to five days a week, which provided for three lawful cuts of a ground-ash if any boy absented himself from these entertainments. He became a rumple-collared, dusty-hatted fag of the Lower Third, and a light half-back at Little Side foot-ball; was pushed and prodded through the slack back-waters of the Lower Fourth, where the raffle of a school generally accumulates; won his "second-fifteen" cap at foot-ball, enjoyed the dignity of a study with two companions in it, and began to look forward to office as a sub-prefect. At last he blossomed into full glory as head of the school, ex-officio captain of the games; head of his house, where he and his lieutenants preserved discipline and decency among seventy boys from twelve to seventeen; general arbiter in the quarrels that spring up among the touchy Sixth—and intimate friend and ally of the Head himself. When he stepped forth in the black jersey, white knickers, and black stockings of the First Fifteen, the new match-ball under his arm, and his old and frayed cap at the back of his head, the small fry of the lower forms stood apart and worshipped, and the "new caps" of the team talked to him ostentatiously, that the world might see. And so, in summer, when he came back to the pavilion after a slow but eminently safe game, it mattered not whether he had made nothing or, as once happened, a hundred and three, the school shouted just the same, and women-folk who had come to look at the match looked at Cottar—Cottar, *major;* "that's Cottar!" Above all, he was responsible for that thing called the tone of the school, and few realise with what passionate devotion a certain type of boy throws himself into this work. Home was a far-away country, full of ponies and fishing and shooting, and men-visitors who interfered with one's plans; but school was the real world, where things of vital importance happened, and crises arose that must be dealt with promptly and quietly. Not for nothing was it written, "Let the Consuls look to it that the Republic takes no harm," and Georgie was glad to be back in authority when the holidays ended. Behind him, but not too near, was the wise and temperate Head, now suggesting the wisdom of the serpent, now counselling the mildness of the dove; leading him on to see, more by half-hints than by any direct word, how boys and men are all of a piece, and how he who can handle the one will assuredly in time control the other.

For the rest, the school was not encouraged to dwell on its emotions, but rather to keep in hard condition, to avoid false quantities, and to enter the army direct, without the help of the expensive London crammer, under whose roof young blood learns too much. Cottar, *major,* went the way of hundreds before him. The Head gave him six months' final polish, taught him what kind of answers best please a certain kind of examiners, and handed him over to the properly constituted authorities, who passed him into Sandhurst. Here he had sense enough to see that he was in the Lower Third once more, and behaved with respect toward his seniors, till they in turn respected him, and he was promoted to the rank of corporal, and sat in authority over mixed peoples with all the vices of men and boys combined. His reward was another string of athletic cups, a good-conduct sword, and, at last, Her Majesty's commission as a subaltern in a first-class line regiment. He did not know that he bore with him from school and college a character worth much fine gold, but was pleased to find his mess so kindly. He had plenty of money of his own; his training had set the public-school mask upon his face, and had taught him how many were the "things no fellow can do." By virtue of the same training he kept his pores open and his mouth shut.

The regular working of the Empire shifted his world to India, where he tasted utter loneliness in subaltern's quarters,—one room and one bullock-trunk,—and, with his mess, learned the new life from the beginning. But there were horses in the land—ponies at reasonable price; there was polo for such as could afford it; there were the disreputable remnants of a pack of hounds; and Cottar worried his way along without too much despair. It dawned on him that a regiment in India was nearer the chance of active service than he had conceived, and that a man might as well study his profession. A major of the new school backed this idea with enthusiasm, and he and Cottar, accumulated a library of military works, and read and argued and disputed far into the nights. But the adjutant said the old thing: "Get to know your men, young un, and they'll follow you anywhere. That's all you want—know your men." Cottar thought he knew them fairly well at cricket and the regimental sports, but he never realised the true inwardness of them till he was sent off with a detachment of twenty to sit down in a mud fort near a rushing river which was spanned by a bridge of boats. When the floods came they went forth and hunted strayed pontoons along the banks. Otherwise there was nothing to do, and the men got drunk, gambled, and quarreled. They were a sickly crew, for a junior subaltern is by custom saddled with the worst men. Cottar endured their rioting as long as he could, and then sent down-country for a dozen pairs of boxing-gloves.

"I wouldn't blame you for fightin'," said he, "if you only knew how to use your hands; but you don't. Take these things, and I'll show you." The men appreciated his efforts. Now, instead of blaspheming and swearing at a comrade, and threatening to shoot him, they could take him apart, and soothe themselves to exhaustion. As one explained whom Cottar found with a shut eye and a diamond-shaped mouth spitting blood through an embrasure: "We tried it with the gloves, sir, for twenty minutes, and *that* done us no good, sir. Then we took off the gloves and tried it that way for another twenty minutes, same as you showed us, sir, an' that done us a world o' good. 'T wasn't fightin', sir; there was a bet on."

Cottar dared not laugh, but he invited his men to other sports, such as racing across country in shirt and trousers after a trail of torn paper, and to single-stick in the evenings, till the native population, who had a lust for sport in every form, wished to know whether the white men understood wrestling. They sent in an ambassador, who took the soldiers by the neck and threw them about the dust; and the entire command were all for this new game. They spent money on learning new falls and holds, which was better than buying other doubtful commodities; and the peasantry grinned five deep round the tournaments.

That detachment, who had gone up in bullock-carts, returned to headquarters at an average rate of thirty miles a day, fair heel-and-toe; no sick, no prisoners, and no court martials pending. They scattered themselves among their friends, singing the praises of their lieutenant and looking for causes of offense.

"How did you do it, young un?" the adjutant asked.

"Oh, I sweated the beef off 'em, and then I sweated some muscle on to 'em. It was rather a lark."

"If that's your way of lookin' at it, we can give you all the larks you want. Young Davies isn't feelin' quite fit, and he's next for detachment duty. Care to go for him?"

" 'Sure he would n't mind? I don't want to shove myself forward, you know."

"You needn't bother on Davies's account. We'll give you the sweepin's of the corps, and you can see what you can make of 'em."

"All right," said Cottar. "It's better fun than loafin' about cantonments."

"Rummy thing," said the adjutant, after Cottar had returned to his wilderness with twenty other devils worse than the first. "If Cottar only knew it, half the women in the station would give their eyes—confound 'em!—to have the young un in tow."

"That accounts for Mrs. Elery sayin' I was workin' my nice new boy too hard," said a wing commander.

"Oh, yes; and 'Why doesn't he come to the bandstand in the evenings?' and 'Can't I get him to make up a four at tennis with the Hammon girls?' " the adjutant snorted. "Look at young Davies makin' an ass of himself over mutton-dressed-as-lamb old enough to be his mother!"

"No one can accuse young Cottar of runnin' after women, white *or* black," the major replied thoughtfully. "But, then, that's the kind that generally goes the worst mucker in the end."

"Not Cottar. I've only run across one of his muster before—a fellow called Ingles, in South Africa. He was just the same hard-trained, athletic-sports build of animal. Always kept himself in the pink of condition. Did n't do him much good, though. 'Shot at Wesselstroom the week before Majuba. Wonder how the young un will lick his detachment into shape."

Cottar turned up six weeks later, on foot, with his pupils. He never told his experiences, but the men spoke enthusiastically, and fragments of it leaked back to the colonel through sergeants, bâtmen, and the like.

There was great jealousy between the first and second detachments, but the men united in adoring Cottar, and their way of showing it was by sparing him all the trouble that men know how to make for an unloved officer. He sought popularity as little as he had sought it at school, and therefore it came to him. He favoured no one—not even when the company sloven pulled the company cricket-match out of the fire with an unexpected forty-three at the last moment. There was very little getting round him, for he seemed to know by instinct exactly when and where to head off a malingerer; but he did not forget that the difference between a dazed and sulky junior of the upper school and a bewildered, browbeaten lump of a private fresh from the depot was very small indeed. The sergeants, seeing these things, told him secrets generally hid from young officers. His words were quoted as barrack authority on bets in canteen and at tea; and the veriest shrew of the corps, bursting with charges against other women who had used the cooking-ranges out of turn, forbore to speak when Cottar, as the regulations ordained, asked of a morning if there were "any complaints."

"I'm full o' complaints," said Mrs. Corporal Morrison, "an' I'd kill O'Halloran's fat sow of a wife any day, but ye know how it is. 'E puts 'is head just inside the door, an' looks down 'is blessed nose so bashful, an' 'e whispers, 'Any complaints?' Ye can't complain after that. *I* want to kiss him. Some day I think I will. Heigh-ho! she'll be a lucky woman that gets Young Innocence. See 'im now, girls. Do ye blame me?"

Cottar was cantering across to polo, and he looked a very satisfactory figure of a man as he gave easily to the first excited bucks of his pony, and slipped over a low mud wall to the practice-ground. There were more than Mrs. Corporal Morrison who felt as she did. But Cottar was busy for eleven hours of the day. He did not care to have his tennis spoiled by petticoats in the court; and after one long afternoon at a garden-party, he explained to his major that this sort of thing was "futile piffle," and the major laughed. Theirs was not a married mess, except for the colonel's wife, and Cottar stood in awe of the good lady. She said "my regiment," and the world knows what that means. None the less, when they wanted her to give away the prizes after a shooting-match, and she refused because one of the prize-winners was married to a girl who had made a jest of her behind her broad back, the mess ordered Cottar to "tackle her," in his best calling-kit. This he did, simply and laboriously, and she gave way altogether.

"She only wanted to know the facts of the case," he explained. "I just told her, and she saw at once."

"Ye-es," said the adjutant. "I expect that's what she did. Comin' to the Fusiliers' dance to-night, Galahad?"

"No, thanks. I've got a fight on with the major." The virtuous apprentice sat up till midnight in the major's quarters, with a stop-watch and a pair of compasses, shifting little painted lead-blocks about a four-inch map.

Then he turned in and slept the sleep of innocence, which is full of healthy dreams. One peculiarity of his dreams he noticed at the beginning of his second hot weather. Two or three times a month they duplicated or ran in series. He would find himself sliding into dreamland by the same road—a road that ran along a beach near a pile of brushwood. To the right lay the sea, sometimes at full tide, sometimes withdrawn to the very horizon; but he knew it for the same sea. By that road he would travel over a swell of rising ground covered with short, withered grass, into valleys of wonder and unreason. Beyond the ridge, which was crowned with some sort of street-lamp, anything was possible; but up to the lamp it seemed to him that he knew the road as well as he knew the parade-ground. He learned to look forward to the place; for, once there, he was sure of a good night's rest, and Indian hot weather can be rather trying. First, shadowy under closing eyelids, would come the outline of the brushwood-pile, next the white sand of the beach-road, almost overhanging the black, changeful sea; then the turn inland and uphill to the single light. When he was unrestful for any reason, he would tell himself how he was sure to get there—sure to get there—if he shut his eyes and surrendered to the drift of things. But one night after a foolishly hard hour's polo (the thermometer was 94° in his quarters at ten o'clock), sleep stood away from him altogether, though he did his best to find the well-known road, the point where true sleep began. At last he saw the brushwood-pile, and hurried along to the ridge, for behind him he felt was the wide-awake, sultry world. He reached the lamp in safety, tingling with drowsiness, when a policeman—a common country policeman—sprang up before him and touched him on the shoulder ere he could dive into the dim valley below. He was filled with terror,—the hopeless terror of dreams,—for the policeman said, in the awful, distinct voice of dream-people, "I am Policeman Day coming back from the City of Sleep. You come with me." Georgie knew it was true—that just beyond him in the valley lay the lights of the City of Sleep, where he would have been sheltered, and that this Policeman-Thing had full power and authority to head him back to miserable wakefulness. He found himself looking at the moonlight on the wall, dripping with fright; and he never overcame that horror, though he met the Policeman several times that hot weather, and his coming was the forerunner of a bad night.

But other dreams—perfectly absurd ones—filled him with an incommunicable delight. All those that he remembered began by the brushwood-pile. For instance, he found a small clockwork steamer (he had noticed it many nights before) lying by the sea-road, and stepped into it, whereupon it moved with surpassing swiftness over an absolutely level sea. This was glorious, for he felt he was exploring great matters; and it stopped by a lily carved in stone, which, most naturally, floated on the water. Seeing the lily was labelled "Hong-Kong," Georgie said: "Of course. This is precisely what I expected Hong-Kong would be like. How magnificent!" Thousands of miles farther on it halted at yet another stone lily, labelled "Java"; and this, again, delighted him hugely, because he knew that now he was at the world's end. But the little boat ran on and on till it lay in a deep fresh-water lock, the sides of which were carven marble, green with moss. Lily-pads lay on the water, and reeds arched above. Some one moved among the reeds—some one whom Georgie knew he had travelled to this world's end to reach. Therefore everything was entirely well with him. He was unspeakably happy, and vaulted over the ship's side to find this person. When his feet touched that still water, it changed, with the rustle of unrolling maps, to nothing less than a sixth quarter of the globe, beyond the most remote imagining of man—a place where islands were coloured yellow and blue, their lettering strung across their faces. They gave on unknown seas, and Georgie's urgent desire was to return swiftly across this floating atlas to known bearings. He told himself repeatedly that it was no good to hurry; but still he hurried desperately, and the islands slipped and slid under his feet, the straits yawned and widened, till he found himself utterly lost in the world's fourth dimension, with no hope of return. Yet only a little distance away he could see the old world with the rivers and mountain-chains marked according to the Sandhurst rules of map-making. Then that person for whom he had come to the Lily Lock (that was its name) ran up across unexplored territories, and showed him a way. They fled hand in hand till they reached a road that spanned ravines, and ran along the edge of precipices, and was tunnelled through mountains. "This goes to our brushwood-pile," said his companion; and all his trouble was at an end. He took a pony, because he understood that this was the Thirty-Mile Ride and he must ride swiftly, and raced through the clattering tunnels and round the curves, always downhill, till he heard the sea to his left, and saw it raging under a full moon, against sandy cliffs. It was heavy going, but he recognized the nature of the country, the dark-purple downs inland, and the bents that whistled in the wind. The road was eaten away in places, and the sea lashed at him—black, foamless tongues of smooth and glossy rollers; but he was sure that there was less danger from the sea than from "Them," whoever "They" were, inland to his right. He knew, too, that he would be safe if he could reach the down with the lamp on it. This came as he expected: he saw the one light a mile ahead along the beach, dismounted, turned to the right, walked quietly over to the brushwood-pile, found the little steamer had returned to the beach whence he had unmoored it, and—must have fallen asleep, for he could remember no more.

"I'm gettin' the hang of the geography of that place," he said to himself, as he shaved next morning. "I must have made some sort of circle. Let's see. The Thirty-Mile Ride (now how the deuce did I know it was called the Thirty-Mile Ride?) joins the sea-road beyond the first down where the lamp is. And that atlas-country lies at the back of the Thirty-Mile Ride, somewhere out to the right beyond the hills and tunnels. Rummy things, dreams. 'Wonder what makes mine fit into each other so?"

He continued on his solid way through the recurring duties of the seasons. The regiment was shifted to another station, and he enjoyed road-marching for two months, with a good deal of mixed shooting thrown in, and when they reached their new cantonments he became a member of the local Tent Club, and chased the mighty boar on horseback with a short stabbing-spear. There he met the *mahseer* of the Poonch, beside whom the tarpon is as a herring, and he who lands him can say that he is a fisherman. This was as new and as fascinating as the big-game shooting that fell to his portion, when he had himself photographed for the mother's benefit, sitting on the flank of his first tiger.

Then the adjutant was promoted, and Cottar rejoiced with him, for he admired the adjutant greatly, and marvelled who might be big enough to fill his place; so that he nearly collapsed when the mantle fell on his own shoulders, and the colonel said a few sweet things that made him blush. An adjutant's position does not differ materially from that of head of the school, and Cottar stood in the same relation to the colonel as he had to his old Head in England. Only, tempers wear out in hot weather, and things were said and done that tried him sorely, and he made glorious blunders, from which the regimental sergeant-major pulled him with a loyal soul and a shut mouth. Slovens and incompetents raged against him; the weak-minded strove to lure him from the ways of justice; the small-minded—yea, men whom Cottar believed would never do "things no fellow can do"—imputed motives mean and circuitous to actions that he had not spent a thought upon; and he tasted injustice, and it made him very sick. But his consolation came on parade, when he looked down the full companies, and reflected how few were in hospital or cells, and wondered when the time would come to try the machine of his love and labour.

But they needed and expected the whole of a man's working-day, and maybe three or four hours of the night. Curiously enough, he never dreamed about the regiment as he was popularly supposed to. The mind, set free from the day's doings, generally ceased working altogether, or, if it moved at all, carried him along the old beach-road to the downs, the lamp-post, and, once in a while, to terrible Policeman Day. The second time that he returned to the world's lost continent (this was a dream that repeated itself again and again, with variations, on the same ground) he knew that if he only sat still the person from the Lily Lock would help him, and he was not disappointed. Sometimes he was trapped in mines of vast depth hollowed out of the heart of the world, where men in torment chanted echoing songs; and he heard this person coming along through the galleries, and everything was made safe and delightful. They met again in low-roofed Indian railway-carriages that halted in a garden surrounded by gilt-and-green railings, where a mob of stony white people, all unfriendly, sat at breakfast-tables covered with roses, and separated Georgie from his companion, while underground voices sang deep-voiced songs. Georgie was filled with enormous despair till they two met again. They foregathered in the middle of an endless, hot tropic night, and crept into a huge house that stood, he knew, somewhere north of the railway-station where the people ate among the roses. It was surrounded with gardens, all moist and dripping; and in one room, reached through leagues of whitewashed passages, a Sick Thing lay in bed. Now the least noise, Georgie knew, would unchain some waiting horror, and his companion knew it, too; but when their eyes met across the bed, Georgie was disgusted to see that she was a child—a little girl in strapped shoes, with her black hair combed back from her forehead.

"What disgraceful folly!" he thought. "Now she could do nothing whatever if Its head came off."

Then the Thing coughed, and the ceiling shattered down in plaster on the mosquito-netting, and "They" rushed in from all quarters. He dragged the child through the stifling garden, voices chanting behind them, and they rode the Thirty-Mile Ride under whip and spur along the sandy beach by the booming sea, till they came to the downs, the lamp-post, and the brushwood-pile, which was safety. Very often dreams would break up about them in this fashion, and they would be separated, to endure awful adventures alone. But the most amusing times were when he and she had a clear understanding that it was all make-believe, and walked through mile-wide roaring rivers without even taking off their shoes, or set light to populous cities to see how they would burn, and were rude as any children to the vague shadows met in their rambles. Later in the night they were sure to suffer for this, either at the hands of the Railway People eating among the roses, or in the tropic uplands at the far end of the Thirty-Mile Ride. Together, this did no much affright them; but often Georgie would hear her shrill cry of "Boy! Boy!" half a world away, and hurry to her rescue before "They" maltreated her.

He and she explored the dark-purple downs as far inland from the brushwood-pile as they dared, but that was always a dangerous matter. The interior was filled with "Them," and "They" went about singing in the hollows, and Georgie and she felt safer on or near the seaboard. So thoroughly had he come to know the place of his dreams that even waking he accepted it as a real country, and made a rough sketch of it. He kept his own counsel, of course; but the permanence of the land puzzled him. His ordinary dreams were as formless and as fleeting as any healthy dreams could be, but once at the brushwood-pile he moved within known limits and could see where he was going. There were months at a time when nothing notable crossed his sleep. Then the dreams would come in a batch of five or six, and next morning the map that he kept in his writing-case would be written up to date, for Georgie was a most methodical person. There was, indeed, a danger—his seniors said so—of his developing into a regular "Auntie Fuss" of an adjutant, and when an officer once takes to old-maidism there is more hope for the virgin of seventy than for him.

But fate sent the change that was needed, in the shape of a little winter campaign on the Border, which, after the manner of little campaigns, flashed out into a very ugly war; and Cottar's regiment was chosen among the first.

"Now," said a major, "this'll shake the cobwebs out of us all—especially you, Galahad; and we can see what your hen-with-one-chick attitude has done for the regiment."

Cottar nearly wept with joy as the campaign went forward. They were fit—physically fit beyond the other troops; they were good children in camp, wet or dry, fed or unfed; and they followed their officers with the quick suppleness and trained obedience of a first-class foot-ball fifteen. They were cut off from their apology for a base, and cheerfully cut their way back to it again; they crowned and cleaned out hills full of the enemy with the precision of well-broken dogs of chase; and in the hour of retreat, when, hampered with the sick and wounded of the column, they were persecuted down eleven miles of waterless valley, they, serving as rearguard, covered themselves with a great glory in the eyes of fellow-professionals. Any regiment can advance, but few know how to retreat with a sting in the tail. Then they turned to made roads, most often under fire, and dismantled some inconvenient mud redoubts. They were the last corps to be withdrawn when the rubbish of the campaign was all swept up; and after a month in standing camp, which tries morals severely, they departed to their own place in column of fours, singing:

" 'E's goin' to do without 'em—
Don't want 'em any more;
'E's goin' to do without 'em,
As 'e's often done before.

'E's goin' to be a martyr
On a 'ighly novel plan,
An' all the boys and girls will say,
'Ow! what a nice young man—man—man!
Ow! what a nice young man! ' "

There came out a "Gazette" in which Cottar found that he had been behaving with "courage and coolness and discretion" in all his capacities; that he had assisted the wounded under fire, and blown in a gate, also under fire. Net result, his captaincy and a brevet majority, coupled with the Distinguished Service Order.

As to his wounded, he explained that they were both heavy men, whom he could lift more easily than any one else. "Otherwise, of course, I should have sent out one of my men; and, of course, about that gate business, we were safe the minute we were well under the walls." But this did not prevent his men from cheering him furiously whenever they saw him, or the mess from giving him a dinner on the eve of his departure to England. (A year's leave was among the things he had "snaffled out of the campaign," to use his own words.) The doctor, who had taken quite as much as was good for him, quoted poetry about "a good blade carving the casques of men," and so on, and everybody told Cottar that he was an excellent person; but when he rose to make his maiden speech they shouted so that he was understood to say, "It isn't any use tryin' to speak with you chaps rottin' me like this. Let's have some pool."

It is not unpleasant to spend eight-and-twenty days in an easy-going steamer on warm waters, in the company of a woman who lets you see that you are head and shoulders superior to the rest of the world, even though that woman may be, and most often is, ten counted years your senior. P. O. boats are not lighted with the disgustful particularity of Atlantic liners. There is more phosphorescence at the bows, and greater silence and darkness by the hand-steering gear aft.

Awful things might have happened to Georgie but for the little fact that he had never studied the first principles of the game he was expected to play. So when Mrs. Zuleika, at Aden, told him how motherly an interest she felt in his welfare, medals, brevet, and all, Georgie took her at the foot of the letter, and promptly talked of his own mother, three hundred miles nearer each day, of his home, and so forth, all the way up the Red Sea. It was much easier than he had supposed to converse with a woman for an hour at a time. Then Mrs. Zuleika, turning from parental affection, spoke of love in the abstract as a thing not unworthy of study, and in discreet twilights after dinner demanded confidences. Georgie would have been delighted to supply them, but he had none, and did not know it was his duty to manufacture them. Mrs. Zuleika expressed surprise and unbelief, and asked those questions which deep asks of deep. She learned all that was necessary to conviction, and, being very much a woman, resumed (Georgie never knew that she had abandoned) the motherly attitude.

"Do you know," she said, somewhere in the Mediterranean, "I think you're the very dearest boy I have ever met in my life, and I'd like you to remember me a little. You will when you are older, but I want you to remember me now. You'll make some girl very happy."

"Oh! Hope so," said Georgie, gravely; "but there's heaps of time for marryin' an' all that sort of thing, ain't there?"

"That depends. Here are your bean-bags for the Ladies' Competition. I think I'm growing too old to care for these *tamashas*."

They were getting up sports, and Georgie was on the committee. He never noticed how perfectly the bags were sewn, but another woman did, and smiled—once. He liked Mrs. Zuleika greatly. She was a bit old, of course, but uncommonly nice. There was no nonsense about her.

A few nights after they passed Gibraltar his dream returned to him. She who waited by the brushwood-pile was no longer a little girl, but a woman with black hair that grew into a "widow's peak," combed back from her forehead. He knew her for the child in black, the companion of the last six years, and, as it had been in the time of the meetings on the Lost Continent, he was filled with delight unspeakable. "They," for some dreamland reason, were friendly or had gone away that night, and the two flitted together over all their country, from the brushwood-pile up the Thirty-Mile Ride, till they saw the House of the Sick Thing, a pin-point in the distance to the left; stamped through the Railway Waiting-room where the roses lay on the spread breakfast-tables; and returned, by the ford and the city they had once burned for sport, to the great swells of the downs under the lamp-post. Wherever they moved a strong singing followed them underground, but this night there was no panic. All the land was empty except for themselves, and at the last (they were sitting by the lamp-post hand in hand) she turned and kissed him. He woke with a start, staring at the waving curtain of the cabin door; he could almost have sworn that the kiss was real.

Next morning the ship was rolling in a Biscay sea, and people were not happy; but as Georgie came to breakfast, shaven, tubbed, and smelling of soap, several turned to look at him because of the light in his eyes and the splendour of his countenance.

"Well, you look beastly fit," snapped a neighbour. "Any one left you a legacy in the middle of the Bay?"

Georgie reached for the curry, with a seraphic grin. "I suppose it's the gettin' so near home, and all that. I do feel rather festive this mornin'. 'Rolls a bit, doesn't she?"

Mrs. Zuleika stayed in her cabin till the end of the voyage, when she left without bidding him farewell, and wept passionately on the dock-head for pure joy of meeting her children, who, she had often said, were so like their father.

Georgie headed for his own country, wild with delight of his first long furlough after the lean seasons. Nothing was changed in that orderly life, from the coachman who met him at the station to the white peacock that stormed at the carriage from the stone wall above the shaven lawns. The house took toll of him with due regard to precedence—first the mother; then the father; then the housekeeper, who wept and praised God; then the butler, and so on down to the under-keeper, who had been dog-boy in Georgie's youth, and called him "Master Georgie," and was reproved by the groom who had taught Georgie to ride.

"Not a thing changed," he sighed contentedly, when the three of them sat down to dinner in the late sunlight, while the rabbits crept out upon the lawn below the cedars, and the big trout in the ponds by the home paddock rose for their evening meal.

"*Our* changes are all over, dear," cooed the mother; "and now I am getting used to your size and your tan (you're very brown, Georgie), I see you haven't changed in the least. You're exactly like the pater."

The father beamed on this man after his own heart, —"youngest major in the army, and should have had the V. C., sir,"—and the butler listened with his professional mask off when Master Georgie spoke of war as it is waged to-day, and his father cross-questioned.

They went out on the terrace to smoke among the roses, and the shadow of the old house lay long across the wonderful English foliage, which is the only living green in the world.

"Perfect! By Jove, it's perfect!" Georgie was looking at the round-bosomed woods beyond the home paddock, where the white pheasant boxes were ranged; and the golden air was full of a hundred sacred scents and sounds. Georgie felt his father's arm tighten in his.

"It's not half bad—but *hodie mihi, cras tibi,* isn't it? I suppose you'll be turning up some fine day with a girl under your arm, if you haven't one now, eh?"

"You can make your mind easy, sir. I haven't one."

"Not in all these years?" said the mother.

"I hadn't time, mummy. They keep a man pretty busy, these days, in the service, and most of our mess are unmarried, too."

"But you must have met hundreds in society—at balls, and so on?"

"I'm like the Tenth, mummy: I don't dance."

"Don't dance! What have you been doing with yourself, then—backing other men's bills?" said the father.

"Oh, yes; I've done a little of that too; but you see, as things are now, a man has all his work cut out for him to keep abreast of his profession, and my days were always too full to let me lark about half the night."

"Hmm!"—suspiciously.

"It's never too late to learn. We ought to give some kind of house-warming for the people about, now you've come back. Unless you want to go straight up to town, dear!"

"No. I don't want anything better than this. Let's sit still and enjoy ourselves. I suppose there will be something for me to ride if I look for it?"

"Seeing I've been kept down to the old brown pair for the last six weeks because all the others were being got ready for Master Georgie, I should say there might be," the father chuckled. "They're reminding me in a hundred ways that I must take the second place now."

"Brutes!"

"The pater doesn't mean it, dear; but every one has been trying to make your home-coming a success; and you *do* like it, don't you?"

"Perfect! Perfect! There's no place like England—when you've done your work."

"That's the proper way to look at it, my son."

And so up and down the flagged walk till their shadows grew long in the moonlight, and the mother went indoors and played such songs as a small boy once clamoured for, and the squat silver candle-sticks were brought in, and Georgie climbed to the two rooms in the west wing that had been his nursery and his playroom in the beginning. Then who should come to tuck him up for the night but the mother? And she sat down on the bed, and they talked for a long hour, as mother and son should, if there is to be any future for the Empire. With a simple woman's deep guile she asked questions and suggested answers that should have waked some sign in the face on the pillow, and there was neither quiver of eyelid nor quickening of breath, neither evasion nor delay in reply. So she blessed him and kissed him on the mouth, which is not always a mother's property, and said something to her husband later, at which he laughed profane and incredulous laughs.

All the establishment waited on Georgie next morning, from the tallest six-year-old, "with a mouth like a kid glove, Master Georgie," to the under-keeper strolling carelessly along the horizon, Georgie's pet rod in his hand, and "There's a four-pounder risin' below the lasher. You don't 'ave 'em in Injia, Mast—Major Georgie." It was all beautiful beyond telling, even thought the mother insisted on taking him out in the landau (the leather had the hot Sunday smell of his youth) and showing him off to her friends at all the houses for six miles round; and the pater bore him up to town and a lunch at the club, where he introduced him, quite carelessly, to not less than thirty ancient warriors whose sons were not the youngest majors in the army and had not the D. S. O. After that it was Georgie's turn; and remembering his friends, he filled up the house with that kind of officer who live in cheap lodgings at Southsea or Montpelier Square, Brompton—good men all, but not well off. The mother perceived that they needed girls to play with; and as there was no scarcity of girls, the house hummed like a dovecote in spring. They tore up the place for amateur theatricals; they disappeared in the gardens when they ought to have been rehearsing; they swept off every available horse and vehicle, especially the governess-cart and the fat pony; they fell into the trout-ponds; they picnicked and they tennised; and they sat on gates in the twilight, two by two, and Georgie found that he was not in the least necessary to their entertainment.

"My word!" said he, when he saw the last of their dear backs. "They told me they've enjoyed 'emselves, but they haven't done half the things they said they would."

"I know they've enjoyed themselves—immensely," said the mother. "You're a public benefactor, dear."

"Now we can be quiet again, can't we?"

"Oh, quite. I've a very dear friend of mine that I want you to know. She couldn't come with the house so full, because she's an invalid, and she was away when you first came. She's a Mrs. Lacy."

"Lacy! I don't remember the name about here."

"No; they came after you went to India—from Oxford. Her husband died there, and she lost some money, I believe. They bought The Firs on the Bassett Road. She's a very sweet woman, and we're very fond of them both."

"She's a widow, didn't you say?"

"She has a daughter. Surely I said so, dear?"

"Does she fall into trout-ponds, and gas and giggle, and 'Oh, Major Cottah!' and all that sort of thing?"

"No, indeed. She's a very quiet girl, and very musical. She always came over here with her music-books—composing, you know; and she generally works all day, so you won't—"

" 'Talking about Miriam?" said the pater, coming up. The mother edged toward him within elbow-reach. There was no finesse about Georgie's father. "Oh, Miriam's a dear girl. Plays beautifully. Rides beautifully, too, She's a regular pet of the household. Used to call me—" The elbow went home, and ignorant but obedient always, the pater shut himself off.

"What used she to call you, sir?"

"All sorts of pet names. I'm very fond of Miriam."

"Sounds Jewish—Miriam."

"Jew! You'll be calling yourself a Jew next. She's one of the Herefordshire Lacys. When her aunt dies—" Again the elbow.

"Oh, you won't see anything of her, Georgie. She's busy with her music or her mother all day. Besides, you're going up to town tomorrow, aren't you? I thought you said something about an Institute meeting?" The mother spoke.

"Go up to town *now!* What nonsense!" Once more the pater was shut off.

"I had some idea of it, but I'm not quite sure," said the son of the house. Why did the mother try to get him away because a musical girl and her invalid parent were expected? He did not approve of unknown females calling his father pet names. He would observe these pushing persons who had been only seven years in the county.

All of which the delighted mother read in his countenance, herself keeping an air of sweet disinterestedness.

"They'll be here this evening for dinner. I'm sending the carriage over for them, and they won't stay more than a week."

"Perhaps I shall go up to town. I don't quite know yet." Georgie moved away irresolutely. There was a lecture at the United Services Institute on the supply of ammunition in the field, and the one man whose theories most irritated Major Cottar would deliver it. A heated discussion was sure to follow, and perhaps he might find himself moved to speak. He took his rod that afternoon and went down to thrash it out among the trout.

"Good sport, dear!" said the mother, from the terrace.

" 'Fraid it won't be, mummy. All those men from town, and the girls particularly, have put every trout off his feed for weeks. There isn't one of 'em that cares for fishin'—really. Fancy stampin' and shoutin' on the bank, and tellin' every fish for half a mile exactly what you're goin' to do, and then chuckin' a brute of a fly at him! By Jove, it would scare *me* if I was a trout!"

But things were not as bad as he had expected. The black gnat was on the water, and the water was strictly preserved. A three-quarter-pounder at the second cast set him for the campaign, and he worked down-stream, crouching behind the reed and meadow-sweet; creeping between a hornbeam hedge and a foot-wide strip of bank, where he could see the trout, but where they could not distinguish him from the background; lying almost on his stomach to switch the blue-upright sidewise through the checkered shadows of a gravelly ripple under overarching trees. But he had known every inch of the water since he was four feet high. The aged and astute between sunk roots, with the large and fat that lay in the frothy scum below some strong rush of water, sucking as lazily as carp, came to trouble in their turn, at the hand that imitated so delicately the flicker and wimple of an egg-dropping fly. Consequently, Georgie found himself five miles from home when he ought to have been dressing for dinner. The housekeeper had taken good care that her boy should not go empty, and before he changed to the white moth he sat down to excellent claret with sandwiches of potted egg and things that adoring women make and men never notice. Then back, to surprise the otter grubbing for fresh-water mussels, the rabbits on the edge of the beechwoods foraging in the clover, and the policeman-like white owl stooping to the little field-mice, till the moon was strong, and he took his rod apart, and went home through well-remembered gaps in the hedges. He fetched a compass round the house, for, though he might have broken every law of the establishment every hour, the law of his boyhood was unbreakable: after fishing you went in by the south garden back-door, cleaned up in the outer scullery, and did not present yourself to your elders and your betters till you had washed and changed.

"Half-past ten, by Jove! Well, we'll make the sport an excuse. They wouldn't want to see me the first evening, at any rate. Gone to bed, probably." He skirted by the open French windows of the drawing-room. "No, they haven't. They look very comfy in there."

He could see his father in his own particular chair, the mother in hers, and the back of a girl at the piano by the big potpourri-jar. The gardens looked half divine in the moonlight, and he turned down through the roses to finish his pipe.

A prelude ended, and there floated out a voice of the kind that in his childhood he used to call "creamy"—a full, true contralto; and this is the song that he heard, every syllable of it:

Over the edge of the purple down,
    Where the single lamplight gleams,
Know ye the road to the Merciful Town
    That is hard by the Sea of Dreams—

Where the poor may lay their wrongs away,
And the sick may forget to weep?
But we—pity us! Oh, pity us!
We wakeful; ah, pity us!—
We must go back with Policeman Day—
Back from the City of Sleep!

Weary they turn from the scroll and crown,
Fetter and prayer and plough—
They that go up to the Merciful Town,
For her gates are closing now.
It is their right in the Baths of Night
Body and soul to steep:
But we—pity us! ah, pity us!
We wakeful; oh, pity us!—
We must go back with Policeman Day—
Back from the City of Sleep!

Over the edge of the purple down,
Ere the tender dreams begin,
Look—we may look—at the Merciful Town,
But we may not enter in!
Outcasts all, from her guarded wall
Back to our watch we creep:
We—pity us! ah, pity us!
We wakeful; oh, pity us!—
We that go back from Policeman Day—
Back from the City of Sleep!

At the last echo he was aware that his mouth was dry and unknown pulses were beating in the roof of it. The housekeeper, who would have it that he must have fallen in and caught a chill, was waiting to catch him on the stairs, and, since he neither saw nor answered her, carried a wild tale abroad that brought his mother knocking at the door.

"Anything happened, dear? Harper said she thought you weren't—"

"No; it's nothing. I'm all right, mummy. *Please* don't bother."

He did not recognise his own voice, but that was a small matter beside what he was considering. Obviously, most obviously, the whole coincidence was crazy lunacy. He proved it to the satisfaction of Major George Cottar, who was going up to town to-morrow to hear a lecture on the supply of ammunition in the field; and having so proved it, the soul and brain and heart and body of Georgie cried joyously: "That's the Lily Lock girl—the Lost Continent girl—the Thirty-Mile Ride girl—the Brushwood girl! *I* know her!"

He waked, stiff and cramped in his chair, to reconsider the situation by sunlight, when it did not appear normal. But a man must eat, and he went to breakfast, his heart between his teeth, holding himself severely in hand.

"Late as usual," said the mother. " 'My boy, Miss Lacy."

A tall girl in black raised her eyes to his, and Georgie's life training deserted him—just as soon as he realised that she did not know. He stared coolly and critically. There was the abundant black hair, growing in a widow's peak, turned back from the forehead, with that peculiar ripple over the right ear; there were the grey eyes set a little close together; the short upper lip, resolute chin, and the known poise of the head. There was also the small well-cut mouth that had kissed him.

"Georgie—*dear!*" said the mother, amazedly, for Miriam was flushing under the stare.

"I—I beg your pardon!" he gulped. "I don't know whether the mother has told you, but I'm rather an idiot at times, specially before I've had my breakfast. It's—it's a family failing."

He turned to explore among the hot-water dishes on the sideboard, rejoicing that she did not know—she did not know.

His conversation for the rest of the meal was mildly insane, though the mother thought she had never seen her boy look half so handsome. How could any girl, least of all one of Miriam's discernment, forbear to fall down and worship? But deeply Miriam was displeased. She had never been stared at in that fashion before, and promptly retired into her shell when Georgie announced that he had changed his mind about going to town, and would stay to play with Miss Lacy if she had nothing better to do.

"Oh, but don't let me throw you out. I'm at work. I've things to do all the morning."

"What possessed Georgie to behave so oddly?" the mother sighed to herself. "Miriam's a bundle of feelings—like her mother."

"You compose—don't you? Must be a fine thing to be able to do that. ["Pig—oh, pig!" thought Miriam.] I think I heard you singin' when I came in last night after fishin'. All about a Sea of Dreams, wasn't it? [Miriam shuddered to the core of the soul that afflicted her.] Awfully pretty song. How d'you think of such things?"

"You only composed the music, dear, didn't you?"

"The words too. I'm sure of it," said Georgie, with a sparkling eye. No; she did not know.

"Yeth; I wrote the words too." Miriam spoke slowly, for she knew she lisped when she was nervous.

"Now how *could* you tell, Georgie?" said the mother, as delighted as though the youngest major in the army were ten years old, showing off before company.

"I was sure of it, somehow. Oh, there are heaps of things about me, mummy, that you don't understand. Looks as if it were goin' to be a hot day—for England. Would you care for a ride this afternoon, Miss Lacy? We can start out after tea, if you'd like it."

Miriam could not in decency refuse, but any woman might see she was not filled with delight.

"That will be very nice, if you take the Bassett Road. It will save me sending Martin down to the village," said the mother, filling in gaps.

Like all good managers, the mother had her one weakness—a mania for little strategies that should economise horses and vehicles. Her men-folk complained that she turned them into common carriers, and there was a legend in the family that she had once said to the pater on the morning of a meet: "If you *should* kill near Bassett, dear, and if it isn't too late, would you mind just popping over and matching me this?"

"I knew that was coming. You'd never miss a chance, mother. If it's a fish or a trunk I won't." Georgie laughed.

"It's only a duck. They can do it up very neatly at Mallett's, said the mother, simply. "You won't mind, will you? We'll have a scratch dinner at nine, because it's so hot."

The long summer day dragged itself out for centuries; but at last there was tea on the lawn, and Miriam appeared.

She was in the saddle before he could offer to help, with the clean spring of the child who mounted the pony for the Thirty-Mile Ride. The day held mercilessly, though Georgie got down thrice to look for imaginary stones in Rufus's foot. One cannot say even simple things in broad light, and this that Georgie meditated was not simple. So he spoke seldom, and Miriam was divided between relief and scorn. It annoyed her that the great hulking thing should know she had written the words of the song overnight; for though a maiden may sing her most secret fancies aloud, she does not care to have them trampled over by the male Philistine. They rode into the little red-brick street of Bassett, and Georgie made untold fuss over the disposition of that duck. It must go in just such a package, and be fastened to the saddle in just such a manner, though eight o'clock had struck and they were miles from dinner.

"We must be quick!" said Miriam, bored and angry.

"There's no great hurry; but we can cut over Dowhead Down, and let 'em out on the grass. That will save us half an hour."

The horses capered on the short, sweet-smelling turf, and the delaying shadows gathered in the valley as they cantered over the great dun down that overhangs Basset and the Western coaching-road. Insensibly the pace quickened without thought of mole-hills; Rufus, gentleman that he was, waiting on Miriam's Dandy till they should have cleared the rise. Then down the two-mile slope they raced together, the wind whistling in their ears, to the steady throb of eight hoofs and the light click-click of the shifting bits.

"Oh, that was glorious!" Miriam cried, reining in. "Dandy and I are old friends, but I don't think we've ever gone better together."

"No; but you've gone quicker, once or twice."

"Really? When?"

Georgie moistened his lips. "Don't you remember the Thirty-Mile Ride—with me—when 'They' were after us—on the beach-road, with the sea to the left—going toward the lamp-post on the downs?"

The girl gasped. "What—what do you mean?" she said hysterically.

"The Thirty-Mile Ride, and—and all the rest of it."

"You mean—? I didn't sing anything about the Thirty-Mile Ride. I know I didn't. I have never told a living soul."

"You told about Policeman Day, and the lamp at the top of the down, and the City of Sleep. It's all joins on, you know—it's the same country—and it was easy enough to see where you had been."

"Good God!—It joins on—of course it does; but—I have been—you have been— Oh, let's walk, please, or I shall fall off!"

Georgie ranged alongside, and laid a hand that shook below her bridle-hand, pulling Dandy into a walk. Miriam was sobbing as he had seen a man sob under the touch of the bullet.

"It's all right—it's all right," he whispered feebly. "Only—only it's true, you know."

"True! Am I mad?"

"Not unless I'm mad as well. *Do* try to think a minute quietly. How could any one conceivably know anything about the Thirty-Mile Ride having anything to do with you, unless he had been there?"

"But where? But *where?* Tell me!"

"There—wherever it may be—in our country, I suppose. Do you remember the first time you rode it—the Thirty-Mile Ride, I mean? You must."

"It was all dreams—all dreams!"

"Yes, but tell, please; because I know."

"Let me think. I—we were on no account to make any noise—on no account to make any noise." She was staring between Dandy's ears with eyes that did not see, and a suffocating heart.

"Because 'It' was dying in the big house?" Georgie went on, reining in again.

"There was a garden with green-and-gilt railings—all hot. Do *you* remember?"

"I ought to. I was sitting on the other side of the bed before 'It' coughed and 'They' came in."

"You!"—the deep voice was unnaturally full and strong, and the girl's wide-opened eyes burned in the dusk as she stared him through and through. "Then you're the Boy—my Brushwood Boy, and I've known you all my life!"

She fell forward on Dandy's neck. Georgie forced himself out of the weakness that was overmastering his limbs, and slid an arm round her waist. The head dropped on his shoulder, and he found himself with parched lips saying things that up till then he believed existed only in printed works of fiction. Mercifully the horses were quiet. She made no attempt to draw herself away when she recovered, but lay still, whispering, "Of course you're the Boy, and I didn't know—I didn't know."

"I knew last night; and when I saw you at breakfast—"

"Oh, *that* was why! I wondered at the time. You would, of course."

"I could n't speak before this. Keep your head where it is, dear. It's all right now—all right now, is n't it?"

"But how was it *I* didn't know—after all these years and years? I remember—oh, what lots of things I remember!"

"Tell me some. I'll look after the horses."

"I remember waiting for you when the steamer came in. Do you?"

"At the Lily Lock, beyond Hong-Kong and Java?"

"Do *you* call it that, too?"

"You told me it was when I was lost in the continent. That was you that showed me the way through the mountains?"

"When the islands slid? It must have been, because you're the only one I remember. All the others were 'Them.'

"Awful brutes they were, too."

"I remember showing you the Thirty-Mile Ride the first time. You ride just as you used to—then. You *are* you!"

"That's odd. I thought that of you this afternoon. Isn't it wonderful?"

"What does it all mean? Why should you and I of the millions of people in the world have this—this thing between us? What does it mean? I'm frightened."

"This!" said Georgie. The horses quickened their pace. They thought they had heard an order. "Perhaps when we die we may find out more, but it means this now."

There was no answer. What could she say? As the world went,

they had known each other rather less than eight and a half hours, but the matter was one that did not concern the world. There was a very long silence, while the breath in their nostrils drew cold and sharp as it might have been a fume of ether.

"That's the second," Georgie whispered. "You remember, don't you?"

"It's not!"—furiously. "It's not!"

"On the downs the other night—months ago. You were just as you are now, and we went over the country for miles and miles."

"It was all empty, too. They had gone away. Nobody frightened us. I wonder why, Boy?"

"Oh, if you remember *that,* you must remember the rest. Confess!"

"I remember lots of things, but I *know* I didn't. I never have—till just now."

"You *did,* dear."

"I know I didn't, because—oh, it's no use keeping anything back! —because I truthfully meant to."

"And truthfully did."

"No; meant to; but some one else came by."

"There wasn't any one else. There never has been."

"There was—there always is. It was another woman—out there on the sea. I saw her. It was the 26th of May. I've got it written down somewhere."

"Oh, *you*'ve kept a record of your dreams, too? That's odd about the other woman, because I happened to be on the sea just then."

"I was right. How do I know what you've done when you were awake—and I thought it was only *you!*"

"You never were more wrong in your life. What a little temper you've got! Listen to me a minute, dear." And Georgie, though he knew it not, committed black perjury. "It—it isn't the kind of thing one says to any one, because they'd laugh; but on my word and honour, darling, I've never been kissed by a living soul outside my own people in all my life. Don't laugh, dear. I wouldn't tell any one but you, but it's the solemn truth."

"I knew! You are you. Oh, I *knew* you'd come some day; but I didn't know you were you in the least till you spoke."

"Then give me another."

"And you never cared or looked anywhere? Why, all the round world must have loved you from the very minute they saw you, Boy."

"They kept it to themselves if they did. No; I never cared."

"And we shall be late for dinner—horribly late. Oh, how can I look at you in the light before your mother—and mine!"

"We'll play you're Miss Lacy till the proper time comes. What's the shortest limit for people to get engaged? S'pose we have got to go through all the fuss of an engagement, haven't we?"

"Oh, I don't want to talk about that. It's so commonplace. I've thought of something that you don't know. I'm sure of it. What's my name?"

"Miri—no, it isn't, by Jove! Wait half a second, and it'll come back to me. You aren't—you can't? Why, *those* old tales—before I went to school! I've never thought of 'em from that day to this. Are you the original, only Annie*an*louise?"

"It was what you always called me ever since the beginning. Oh! We've turned into the avenue, and we must be an hour late."

"What does it matter? The chain goes as far back as those days? It must, of course—of course it must. I've got to ride around with this pestilent old bird—confound him!"

" ' "Ha! ha!" said the duck, laughing'—do you remember *that?*"

"Yes, I do—flower-pots on my feet, and all. We've been together all this while; and I've got to say good-bye to you till dinner. *Sure* I'll see you at dinner-time? *Sure* you won't sneak up to your room, darling, and leave me all the evening? Good-bye, dear—good-bye."

"Good-bye, Boy, good-bye. Mind the arch! Don't let Rufus bolt into his stables. Good-bye. Yes, I'll come down to dinner; but—what shall I do when I see you in the light!"

H. G. Wells

1866-1946

English novelist and essayist, the author of numerous works of science-fiction and social criticism. His best-known works are The Time Machine, The War of the Worlds, Tono-Bungay, *and* The Outline of History.

THE DOOR IN THE WALL

I

One confidential evening, not three months ago, Lionel Wallace told me this story of the Door in the Wall. And at the time I thought that so far as he was concerned it was a true story.

He told it me with such a direct simplicity of conviction that I could not do otherwise than believe in him. But in the morning, in my own flat, I woke to a different atmosphere, and as I lay in bed and recalled the things he had told me, stripped of the glamour of his earnest slow voice, denuded of the focussed shaded table light, the shadowy atmosphere that wrapped about him and the pleasant bright things, the dessert and glasses and napery of the dinner we had shared, making them for the time a bright little world quite cut off from every-day realities, I saw it all as frankly incredible. "He was mystifying!" I said, and then: "How well he did it! . . . . . It isn't quite the thing I should have expected him, of all people, to do well."

Afterwards, as I sat up in bed and sipped my morning tea, I found myself trying to account for the flavour of reality that perplexed me in his impossible reminiscences, by supposing they did in some way suggest, present, convey—I hardly know which word to use—experiences it was otherwise impossible to tell.

Well, I don't resort to that explanation now. I have got over my intervening doubts. I believe now, as I believed at the moment of telling, that Wallace did to the very best of his ability strip the truth of his secret for me. But whether he himself saw, or only thought he saw, whether he himself was the possessor of an inestimable privilege, or the victim of a fantastic dream, I cannot pretend to guess. Even the facts of his death, which ended my doubts forever, throw no light on that. That much the reader must judge for himself.

I forget now what chance comment or criticism of mine moved so reticent a man to confide in me. He was, I think, defending himself against an imputation of slackness and unreliability I had made in relation to a great public movement in which he had disappointed me. But he plunged suddenly. "I have," he said, "a preoccupation—"

"I know," he went on, after a pause that he devoted to the study of his cigar ash, "I have been negligent. The fact is—it isn't a case of ghosts or apparitions—but—it's an odd thing to tell of, Redmond—I am haunted. I am haunted by something—that rather takes the light out of things, that fills me with longings . . . ."

He paused, checked by that English shyness that so often overcomes us when we would speak of moving or grave or beautiful things. "You were at Saint Athelstan's all through," he said, and for a moment that seemed to me quite irrelevant. "Well"—and he paused. Then very haltingly at first, but afterwards more easily, he began to tell of the thing that was hidden in his life, the haunting memory of a beauty and a happiness that filled his heart with insatiable longings that made all the interests and spectacle of worldly life seem dull and tedious and vain to him.

Now that I have the clue to it, the thing seems written visibly in his face. I have a photograph in which that look of detachment has been caught and intensified. It reminds me of what a woman once said of him—a woman who had loved him greatly. "Suddenly," she said, "the interest goes out of him. He forgets you. He doesn't care a rap for you—under his very nose . . . . ."

Yet the interest was not always out of him, and when he was holding his attention to a thing Wallace could contrive to be an extremely successful man. His career, indeed, is set with successes. He left me behind him long ago; he soared up over my head, and cut a figure in the world that I couldn't cut—anyhow. He was still a year short of forty, and they say now that he would have been in office and very probably in the new Cabinet if he had lived. At school he always beat me without effort—as it were by nature. We were at school together at Saint Athelstan's College in West Kensington for almost all our school time. He came into the school as my co-equal, but he left far above me, in a blaze of scholarships and brilliant performance. Yet I think I made a fair average running. And it was at school I heard first of the Door in the Wall—that I was to hear of a second time only a month before his death.

To him at least the Door in the Wall was a real door leading through a real wall to immortal realities. Of that I am now quite assured.

And it came into his life early, when he was a little fellow between five and six. I remember how, as he sat making his confession to me with a slow gravity, he reasoned and reckoned the date of it. "There was," he said, "a crimson Virginia creeper in it—all one bright uniform crimson in a clear amber sunshine against a white wall. That came into the impression somehow, though I don't clearly remember how, and there were horse-chestnut leaves upon the clean pavement outside the green door. They were blotched yellow and green, you know, not brown nor dirty, so that they must have been new fallen. I take it that means October. I look out for horse-chestnut leaves every year, and I ought to know.

"If I'm right in that, I was about five years and four months old."

He was, he said, rather a precocious little boy—he learned to talk at an abnormally early age, and he was so sane and "old-fashioned," as people say, that he was permitted an amount of initiative that most children scarcely attain by seven or eight. His mother died when he was born, and he was under the less vigilant and authoritative care of a nursery governess. His father was a stern, preoccupied lawyer, who gave him little attention, and expected great things of him. For all his brightness he found life a little grey and dull, I think. And one day he wandered.

He could not recall the particular neglect that enabled him to get away, nor the course he took among the West Kensington roads. All that had faded among the incurable blurs of memory. But the white wall and the green door stood out quite distinctly.

As his memory of that remote childish experience ran, he did at the very first sight of that door experience a peculiar emotion, an attraction, a desire to get to the door and open it and walk in. And at the same time he had the clearest conviction that either it was unwise or it was wrong of him—he could not tell which—to yield to this attraction. He insisted upon it as a curious thing that he knew from the very beginning—unless memory has played him the queerest trick—that the door was unfastened, and that he could go in as he chose.

I seem to see the figure of that little boy, drawn and repelled. And it was very clear in his mind, too, though why it should be so was never explained, that his father would be very angry if he went through that door.

Wallace described all these moments of hesitation to me with the utmost particularity. He went right past the door, and then, with his hands in his pockets, and making an infantile attempt to whistle, strolled right along beyond the end of the wall. There he recalls a number of mean, dirty shops, and particularly that of a plumber and decorator, with a dusty disorder of earthenware pipes, sheet lead ball taps, pattern books of wall paper, and tins of enamel. He stood pretending to examine these things, and coveting, passionately desiring the green door.

Then, he said, he had a gust of emotion. He made a run for it, lest hesitation should grip him again, he went plump with outstretched hand through the green door and let it slam behind him. And so, in a trice, he came into the garden that has haunted all his life.

It was very difficult for Wallace to give me his full sense of that garden into which he came.

There was something in the very air of it that exhilarated, that gave one a sense of lightness and good happening and well being;

there was something in the sight of it that made all its colour clean and perfect and subtly luminous. In the instant of coming into it one was exquisitely glad—as only in rare moments and when one is young and joyful one can be glad in this world. And everything was beautiful there . . . . .

Wallace mused before he went on telling me. "You see," he said, with the doubtful inflection of a man who pauses at incredible things, "there were two great panthers there . . . Yes, spotted panthers. And I was not afraid. There was a long wide path with marble-edged flower borders on either side, and these two huge velvety beasts were playing there with a ball. One looked up and came towards me, a little curious as it seemed. It came right up to me, rubbed its soft round ear very gently against the small hand I held out and purred. It was, I tell you, an enchanted garden. I know. And the size? Oh! it stretched far and wide, this way and that. I believe there were hills far away. Heaven knows where West Kensington had suddenly got to! And somehow it was just like coming home.

"You know, in the very moment the door swung to behind me, I forgot the road with its fallen chestnut leaves, its cabs and tradesmen's carts, I forgot the sort of gravitational pull back to the discipline and obedience of home, I forgot all hesitations and fear, forgot discretion, forgot all the intimate realities of this life. I became in a moment a very glad and wonder-happy little boy—in another world. It was a world with a different quality, a warmer, more penetrating and mellower light, with a faint clear gladness in its air, and wisps of sun-touched cloud in the blueness of its sky. And before me ran this long wide path, invitingly, with weedless beds on either side, rich with untended flowers, and these two great panthers. I put my little hands fearlessly on their soft fur, and caressed their round ears and the sensitive corners under their ears, and played with them, and it was as though they welcomed me home. There was a keen sense of home-coming in my mind, and when presently a tall, fair girl appeared in the pathway and came to meet me, smiling, and said 'Well?' to me, and lifted me, and kissed me, and put me down, and led me by the hand, there was no amazement, but only an impression of delightful rightness, of being reminded of happy things that had in some strange way been overlooked. There were broad steps, I remember, that came into view between spikes of delphinium, and up these we went to a great avenue between very old and shady dark trees. All down this avenue, you know, between the red chapped stems, were marble seats of honour and statuary, and very tame and friendly white doves . . . . .

"And along this avenue my girl-friend led me, looking down—I recall the pleasant lines, the finely-modelled chin of her sweet kind face—asking me questions in a soft, agreeable voice, and telling me things, pleasant things I know, though what they were I was never able to recall . . . And presently a little Capuchin monkey, very clean, with a fur of ruddy brown and kindly hazel eyes, came down a tree to us and ran beside me, looking up at me and grinning, and presently leapt to my shoulder. So we went on our way in great happiness . . . ."

He paused.

"Go on," I said.

"I remember little things. We passed an old man musing among laurels, I remember, and a place gay with paroquets, and came through a broad shaded colonnade to a spacious cool palace, full of pleasant fountains, full of beautiful things, full of the quality and promise of heart's desire. And there were many things and many people, some that still seem to stand out clearly and some that are a little vague, but all these people were beautiful and kind. In some way—I don't know how—it was conveyed to me that they all were kind to me, glad to have me there, and filling me with gladness by their gestures, by the touch of their hands, by the welcome and love in their eyes. Yes—"

He mused for a while. "Playmates I found there. That was very much to me, because I was a lonely little boy. They played delightful games in a grass-covered court where there was a sun-dial set about with flowers. And as one played one loved . . . .

"But—it's odd—there's a gap in my memory. I don't remember the games we played. I never remembered. Afterwards, as a child, I spent long hours trying, even with tears, to recall the form of that happiness. I wanted to play it all over again—in my nursery—by myself. No! All I remember is the happiness and two dear playfellows who were most with me . . . . Then presently came a sombre dark woman, with a grave, pale face and dreamy eyes, a sombre woman wearing a soft long robe of pale purple, who carried a book and beckoned and took me aside with her into a gallery above a hall—though my playmates were loth to have me go, and ceased their game and stood watching as I was carried away. 'Come back to us!' they cried. 'Come back to us soon!' I looked up at her face, but she heeded them not at all. Her face was very gentle and grave. She took me to a seat in the gallery, and I stood beside her, ready to look at her book as she opened it upon her knee. The pages fell open. She pointed, and I looked, marvelling, for in the living pages of that book I saw myself; it was a story about myself, and in it were all the things that had happened to me since ever I was born . . . .

"It was wonderful to me, because the pages of that book were not pictures, you understand, but realities."

Wallace paused gravely—looking at me doubtfully.

"Go on," I said. "I understand."

"They were realities—yes, they must have been; people moved and things came and went in them; my dear mother, whom I had near forgotten; then my father, stern and upright, the servants, the nursery, all the familiar things of home. Then the front door and the busy streets, with traffic to and fro: I looked and marvelled, and looked half doubtfully again into the woman's face and turned the pages over, skipping this and that, to see more of this book, and more, and so at last I came to myself hovering and hesitating outside the green door in the long white wall, and felt again the conflict and the fear.

" 'And next?' I cried, and would have turned on, but the cool hand of the grave woman delayed me.

" 'Next?' I insisted, and struggled gently with her hand, pulling up her fingers with all my childish strength and as she yielded and the page came over she bent down upon me like a shadow and kissed my brow.

"But the page did not show the enchanted garden, nor the panthers, nor the girl who had led me by the hand, nor the playfellows who had been so loth to let me go. It showed a long grey street in West Kensington, on that chill hour of afternoon before the lamps are lit, and I was there, a wretched little figure, weeping aloud, for all that I could do to restrain myself, and I was weeping because I could not return to my dear playfellows who had called after me, 'Come back to us! Come back to us soon!' I was there. This was no page in a book, but harsh reality; that enchanted place and the restraining hand of the grave mother at whose knee I stood had gone—whither have they gone?"

He halted again, and remained for a time, staring into the fire.

"Oh! the wretchedness of that return!" he murmured.

"Well?" I said after a minute or so.

"Poor little wretch I was—brought back to this grey world again! As I realised the fulness of what had happened to me, I gave way to quite ungovernable grief. And the shame and humiliation of that public weeping and my disgraceful home-coming remain with me still. I see again the benevolent-looking old gentleman in gold spectacles who stopped and spoke to me—prodding me first with his umbrella. 'Poor little chap,' said he; 'and are you lost then?'—and me a London boy of five and more! And he must needs bring in a kindly young policeman and make a crowd of me, and so march me home. Sobbing, conspicuous and frightened, I came from the enchanted garden to the steps of my father's house.

"That is as well as I can remember my vision of that garden—the garden that haunts me still. Of course, I can convey nothing of that indescribable quality of translucent unreality, that difference from the common things of experience that hung about it all; but that—that is what happened. If it was a dream, I am sure it was a day-time and altogether extraordinary dream . . . . . . H'm!—naturally there followed a terrible questioning, by my aunt, my father, the nurse, the governess—everyone. . . .

"I tried to tell them, and my father gave me my first thrashing for telling lies. When afterwards I tried to tell my aunt, she punished me again for my wicked persistence. Then, as I said, everyone was forbidden to listen to me, to hear a word about it. Even my fairy tale books were taken away from me for a time—because I was 'too imaginative.' Eh? Yes, they did that! My father belonged to the old school . . . . . And my story was driven back upon myself. I whispered it to my pillow—my pillow that was often damp and salt to my whispering lips with childish tears. And I added always to my official and less fervent prayers this one heartfelt request: 'Please God I may dream of the garden. Oh! take me back to my garden! Take me back to my garden!'

"I dreamt often of the garden. I may have added to it, I may have changed it; I do not know . . . . . All this you understand is an attempt to reconstruct from fragmentary memories a very early experience. Between that and the other consecutive memories of my boyhood there is a gulf. A time came when it seemed impossible I should ever speak of that wonder glimpse again."

I asked an obvious question.

"No," he said. "I don't remember that I ever attempted to find my way back to the garden in those early years. This seems odd to me now, but I think that very probably a closer watch was kept on my movements after this misadventure to prevent my going astray. No, it wasn't until you knew me that I tried for the garden again. And I believe there was a period—incredible as it seems now—when I forgot the garden altogether—when I was about eight or nine it may have been. Do you remember me as a kid at Saint Athelstan's?"

"Rather!"

"I didn't show any signs did I in those days of having a secret dream?"

II

He looked up with a sudden smile.

"Did you ever play North-West Passage with me? . . . . . No, of course you didn't come my way!"

"It was the sort of game," he went on, "that every imaginative child plays all day. The idea was the discovery of a North-West Passage to school. The way to school was plain enough; the game consisted in finding some way that wasn't plain, starting off ten minutes early in some almost hopeless direction, and working one's way round through unaccustomed streets to my goal. And one day I got entangled among some rather low-class streets on the other side of Campden Hill, and I began to think that for once the game would be against me and that I should get to school late. I tried rather desperately a street that seemed a *cul de sac,* and found a passage at the end. I hurried through that with renewed hope. 'I shall do it yet,' I said, and passed a row of frowsy little shops that were inexplicably familiar to me, and behold! there was my long white wall and the green door that led to the enchanted garden!

"The thing whacked upon me suddenly. Then, after all, that garden, that wonderful garden, wasn't a dream!" . . . .

He paused.

"I suppose my second experience with the green door marks the world of difference there is between the busy life of a schoolboy and the infinite leisure of a child. Anyhow, this second time I didn't for a moment think of going in straight away. You see . . . For one thing my mind was full of the idea of getting to school in time—set on not breaking my record for punctuality. I must surely have felt *some* little desire at least to try the door—yes, I must have felt that . . . . . But I seem to remember the attraction of the door mainly as another obstacle to my overmastering determination to get to school. I was immediately interested by this discovery I had made, of course—I went on with my mind full of it—but I went on. It didn't check me. I ran past tugging out my watch, found I had ten minutes still to spare, and then I was going downhill into familiar surroundings. I got to school, breathless, it is true, and wet with perspiration, but in time. I can remember hanging up my coat and hat . . . Went right by it and left it behind me. Odd, eh?"

He looked at me thoughtfully. "Of course, I didn't know then that it wouldn't always be there. School boys have limited imaginations. I suppose I thought it was an awfully jolly thing to have it there, to know my way back to it, but there was the school tugging at me. I expect I was a good deal distraught and inattentive that morning, recalling what I could of the beautiful strange people I should presently see again. Oddly enough I had no doubt in my mind that they would be glad to see me . . . Yes, I must have thought of the garden that morning just as a jolly sort of place to which one might resort in the interludes of a strenuous scholastic career.

"I didn't go that day at all. The next day was a half holiday, and that may have weighed with me. Perhaps, too, my state of inattention brought down impositions upon me and docked the margin of time necessary for the detour. I don't know. What I do know is that in the meantime the enchanted garden was so much upon my mind that I could not keep it to myself.

"I told—What was his name?—a ferrety-looking youngster we used to call Squiff."

"Young Hopkins," said I.

"Hopkins it was. I did not like telling him, I had a feeling that in some way it was against the rules to tell him, but I did. He was walking part of the way home with me; he was talkative, and if we had not talked about the enchanted garden we should have talked of something else, and it was intolerable to me to think about any other subject. So I blabbed.

"Well, he told my secret. The next day in the play interval I found myself surrounded by half a dozen bigger boys, half teasing and wholly curious to hear more of the enchanted garden. There was that big Fawcett—you remember him?—and Carnaby and Morley Reynolds. You weren't there by any chance? No, I think I should have remembered if you were . . . . .

"A boy is a creature of odd feelings. I was, I really believe, in spite of my secret self-disgust, a little flattered to have the attention of these big fellows. I remember particularly a moment of pleasure caused by the praise of Crawshaw—you remember Crawshaw major, the son of Crawshaw the composer?—who said it was the best lie he had ever heard. But at the same time there was a really painful undertow of shame at telling what I felt was indeed a sacred secret. That beast Fawcett made a joke about the girl in green—."

Wallace's voice sank with the keen memory of that shame. "I pretended not to hear," he said. "Well, then Carnaby suddenly called me a young liar and disputed with me when I said the thing was true. I said I knew where to find the green door, could lead them all there in ten minutes. Carnaby became outrageously virtuous, and said I'd have to—and bear out my words or suffer. Did you ever have Carnaby twist your arm? Then perhaps you'll understand how it went with me. I swore my story was true. There was nobody in the school then to save a chap from Carnaby though Crawshaw put in a word or so. Carnaby had got his game. I grew excited and red-eared, and a little frightened, I behaved altogether like a silly little chap, and the outcome of it all was that instead of starting alone for my enchanted garden, I led the way presently—cheeks flushed, ears hot, eyes smarting, and my soul one burning misery and shame—for a party of six mocking, curious and threatening schoolfellows.

"We never found the white wall and the green door . . ."

"You mean?—"

"I mean I couldn't find it. I would have found it if I could.

"And afterwards when I could go alone I couldn't find it. I never found it. I seem now to have been always looking for it through my school-boy days, but I've never come upon it again."

"Did the fellows—make it disagreeable?"

"Beastly . . . . . Carnaby held a council over me for wanton lying. I remember how I sneaked home and upstairs to hide the marks of my blubbering. But when I cried myself to sleep at last it wasn't for Carnaby, but for the garden, for the beautiful afternoon I had hoped for, for the sweet friendly women and the waiting playfellows and the game I had hoped to learn again, that beautiful forgotten game . . . . .

"I believed firmly that if I had not told— . . . . . I had bad times after that—crying at night and wool-gathering by day. For two terms I slackened and had bad reports. Do you remember? Of course you would! It was *you*—your beating me in mathematics that brought me back to the grind again."

III

For a time my friend stared silently into the red heart of the fire. Then he said: "I never saw it again until I was seventeen.

"It leapt upon me for the third time—as I was driving to Paddington on my way to Oxford and a scholarship. I had just one momentary glimpse. I was leaning over the apron of my hansom smoking a cigarette, and no doubt thinking myself no end of a man of the world, and suddenly there was the door, the wall, the dear sense of unforgettable and still attainable things.

"We clattered by—I too taken by surprise to stop my cab until we were well past and round a corner. Then I had a queer moment, a double and divergent movement of my will: I tapped the little door in the roof of the cab, and brought my arm down to pull out my watch. 'Yes, sir!' said the cabman, smartly. 'Er—well—it's nothing,' I cried. '*My* mistake! We haven't much time! Go on!' and he went on . . .

"I got my scholarship. And the night after I was told of that I sat over my fire in my little upper room, my study, in my father's house, with his praise—his rare praise—and his sound counsels ringing in my ears, and I smoked my favourite pipe—the formidable bulldog of adolescence—and thought of that door in the long white wall. 'If I had stopped,' I thought, 'I should have missed my scholarship, I should have missed Oxford—muddled all the fine career before me! I begin to see things better!' I fell musing deeply, but I did not doubt then this career of mine was a thing that merited sacrifice.

"Those dear friends and that clear atmosphere seemed very sweet to me, very fine, but remote. My grip was fixing now upon the world. I saw another door opening—the door of my career."

He stared again into the fire. Its red lights picked out a stubborn strength in his face for just one flickering moment, and then it vanished again.

"Well," he said and sighed, "I have served that career. I have done—much work, much hard work. But I have dreamt of the enchanted garden a thousand dreams, and seen its door, or at least glimpsed its door, four times since then. Yes—four times. For a while this world was so bright and interesting, seemed so full of meaning and opportunity that the half-effaced charm of the garden was by comparison gentle and remote. Who wants to pat panthers on the way to dinner with pretty women and distinguished men? I came down to London from Oxford, a man of bold promise that I have done something to redeem. Something—and yet there have been disappointments . . . . .

"Twice I have been in love—I will not dwell on that—but once, as I went to someone who, I know, doubted whether I dared to come, I took a short cut at a venture through an unfrequented road near Earl's Court, and so happened on a white wall and a familiar green door. 'Odd!' said I to myself, 'but I thought this place was on Campden Hill. It's the place I never could find somehow—like counting Stonehenge—the place of that queer day dream of mine.' And I went by it intent upon my purpose. It had no appeal to me that afternoon.

"I had just a moment's impulse to try the door, three steps aside were needed at the most—though I was sure enough in my heart that it would open to me—and then I thought that doing so might delay me on the way to that appointment in which I thought my honour was involved. Afterwards I was sorry for my punctuality—I might at least have peeped in, I thought, and waved a hand to those panthers, but I knew enough by this time not to seek again belatedly that which is not found by seeking. Yes, that time made me very sorry . . . . .

"Years of hard work after that and never a sight of the door. It's only recently it has come back to me. With it there has come a sense as though some thin tarnish had spread itself over my world. I began to think of it as a sorrowful and bitter thing that I should never see that door again. Perhaps I was suffering a little from overwork—perhaps it was what I've heard spoken of as the feeling of forty. I don't know. But certainly the keen brightness that makes effort easy has gone out of things recently, and that just at a time with all these new political developments—when I ought to be working. Odd, isn't it? But I do begin to find life toilsome, its rewards, as I come near them, cheap. I began a little while ago to want the garden quite badly. Yes—and I've seen it three times."

"The garden?"

"No—the door! And I haven't gone in!"

He leaned over the table to me, with an enormous sorrow in his voice as he spoke. "Thrice I had my chance—*thrice!* If ever that door offers itself to me again, I swore, I will go in out of this dust and heat, out of this dry glitter of vanity, out of these toilsome futilities. I will go and never return. This time I will stay . . . . . I swore it and when the time came—*I didn't go.*

"Three times in one year have I passed that door and failed to enter. Three times in the last year.

"The first time was on the night of the snatch division on the Tenants' Redemption Bill, on which the Government was saved by a majority of three. You remember? No one on our side—perhaps very few on the opposite side—expected the end that night. Then the debate collapsed like eggshells. I and Hotchkiss were dining with his cousin at Brentford, we were both unpaired, and we were called up by telephone, and set off at once in his cousin's motor. We got in barely in time, and on the way we passed my wall and door—livid in the moonlight, blotched with hot yellow as the glare of our lamps lit it, but unmistakable. 'My God!' cried I. 'What?' said Hotchkiss. 'Nothing!' I answered, and the moment passed.

" 'I've made a great sacrifice,' I told the whip as I got in. 'They all have,' he said, and hurried by.

"I do not see how I could have done otherwise then. And the next occasion was as I rushed to my father's bedside to bid that stern old man farewell. Then, too, the claims of life were imperative. But the third time was different; it happened a week ago. It fills me with hot remorse to recall it. I was with Gurker and Ralphs—it's no secret now you know that I've had my talk with Gurker. We had been dining at Frobisher's, and the talk had become intimate between us. The question of my place in the reconstructed ministry lay always just over the boundary of the discussion. Yes—yes. That's all settled. It needn't be talked about yet, but there's no reason to keep a secret from you . . . . . Yes—thanks! thanks! But let me tell you my story.

"Then, on that night things were very much in the air. My position was a very delicate one. I was keenly anxious to get some definite word from Gurker, but was hampered by Ralphs' presence. I was using the best power of my brain to keep that light and careless talk not too obviously directed to the point that concerns me. I had to.

Ralphs' behaviour since has more than justified my caution . . . . Ralphs, I knew, would leave us beyond the Kensington High Street, and then I could surprise Gurker by a sudden frankness. One has sometimes to resort to these little devices. . . . And then it was that in the margin of my field of vision I became aware once more of the white wall, the green door before us down the road.

"We passed it talking. I passed it. I can still see the shadow of Gurker's marked profile, his opera hat tilted forward over his prominent nose, the many folds of his neck wrap going before my shadow and Ralphs' as we sauntered past.

"I passed within twenty inches of the door. 'If I say good-night to them, and go in,' I asked myself, 'what will happen?' And I was all a-tingle for that word with Gurker.

"I could not answer that question in the tangle of my other problems. 'They will think me mad,' I thought. 'And suppose I vanish now!—Amazing disappearance of a prominent politician!' That weighed with me. A thousand inconceivably petty worldlinesses weighed with me in that crisis."

Then he turned on me with a sorrowful smile, and, speaking slowly; "Here I am!" he said.

"Here I am!" he repeated, "and my chance has gone from me. Three times in one year the door has been offered me—the door that goes into peace, into delight, into a beauty beyond dreaming, a kindness no man on earth can know. And I have rejected it, Redmond, and it has gone—"

"How do you know?"

"I know. I know. I am left now to work it out, to stick to the tasks that held me so strongly when my moments came. You say, I have success—this vulgar, tawdry, irksome, envied thing. I have it." He had a walnut in his big hand. "If that was my success," he said, and crushed it, and held it out for me to see.

"Let me tell you something, Redmond. This loss is destroying me. For two months, for ten weeks nearly now, I have done no work at all, except the most necessary and urgent duties. My soul is full of inappeasable regrets. At nights—when it is less likely I shall be recognised—I go out. I wander. Yes. I wonder what people would think of that if they knew. A Cabinet Minister, the responsible head of that most vital of all departments, wandering alone—grieving—sometimes near audibly lamenting—for a door, for a garden!"

IV

I can see now his rather pallid face, and the unfamiliar sombre fire that had come into his eyes. I see him very vividly to-night. I sit recalling his words, his tones, and last evening's *Westminster Gazette* still lies on my sofa, containing the notice of his death. At lunch to-day the club was busy with him and the strange riddle of his fate.

They found his body very early yesterday morning in a deep excavation near East Kensington Station. It is one of two shafts that have been made in connection with an extension of the railway southward. It is protected from the intrusion of the public by a hoarding upon the high road, in which a small doorway has been cut for the convenience of some of the workmen who live in that direction. The doorway was left unfastened through a misunderstanding between two gangers, and through it he made his way . . . . .

My mind is darkened with questions and riddles.

It would seem he walked all the way from the House that night—he has frequently walked home during the past Session—and so it is I figure his dark form coming along the late and empty streets, wrapped up, intent. And then did the pale electric lights near the station cheat the rough planking into a semblance of white? Did that fatal unfastened door awaken some memory?

Was there, after all, ever any green door in the wall at all?

I do not know. I have told his story as he told it to me. There are times when I believe that Wallace was no more than the victim of the coincidence between a rare but not unprecedented type of hallucination and a careless trap, but that indeed is not my profoundest belief. You may think me superstitious if you will, and foolish; but, indeed, I am more than half convinced that he had in truth, an abnormal gift, and a sense, something—I know not what—that in the guise of wall and door offered him an outlet, a secret and peculiar passage of escape into another and altogether more beautiful world. At any rate, you will say, it betrayed him in the end. But did it betray him? There you touch the inmost mystery of these dreamers, these men of vision and the imagination. We see our world fair and common, the hoarding and the pit. By our daylight standard he walked out of security into darkness, danger and death. But did he see like that?

Oliver Onions

1873-1961

Pseudonym of George Oliver, English writer born in Bradford, Yorkshire. He is particularly known for the Story of Louie *and* Mushroom Town. *The selection below is taken from his* Collected Ghost Stories, *published in 1935.*

PHANTAS

"For, barring all pother,
With this, or the other,
Still Britons are Lords of the Main."
The Chapter of Admirals

I

As Abel Keeling lay on the galleon's deck, held from rolling down it only by his own weight and the sun-blackened hand that lay outstretched upon the planks, his gaze wandered, but ever returned to the bell that hung, jammed with the dangerous heel-over of the vessel, in the small ornamental belfry immediately abaft the mainmast. The bell was of cast bronze, with half-obliterated bosses upon it that had been the heads of cherubs; but wind and salt spray had given it a thick incrustation of bright, beautiful, lichenous green. It was this colour that Abel Keeling's eyes liked.

For wherever else on the galleon his eyes rested they found only whiteness—the whiteness of extreme eld. There were slightly varying degrees in her whiteness; here she was of a white that glistened like salt-granules, there of a greyish chalky white, and again her whiteness had the yellowish cast of decay; but everywhere it was the mild, disquieting whiteness of materials out of which the life had departed. Her cordage was bleached as old straw is bleached, and half her ropes kept their shape little more firmly than the ash of a string keeps its shape after the fire has passed; her pallid timbers were white and clean as bones found in sand; and even the wild frankincense with which (for lack of tar, at her last touching of land) she had been pitched, had dried to a pale hard gum that sparkled like quartz in her open seams. The sun was yet so pale a buckler of silver through the still white mists that not a cord or timber cast a shadow; and only Abel Keeling's face and hands were black, carked and cinder-black from exposure to his pitiless rays.

The galleon was the *Mary of the Tower,* and she had a frightful list to starboard. So canted was she that her mainyard dipped one of its steel sickles into the glassy water, and, had her foremast remained, or more than the broken stump of her bonventure mizen, she must have turned over completely. Many days ago they had stripped the mainyard of its course, and had passed the sail under the *Mary's* bottom, in the hope that it would stop the lead. This it had partly done as long as the galleon had continued to glide one way; then, without coming about, she had begun to glide the other, the ropes had parted, and she had dragged the sail after her, leaving a broad tarnish on the silver sea.

For it was broadside that the galleon glided, almost imperceptibly, ever sucking down. She glided as if a loadstone drew her, and, at first, Abel Keeling had thought it was a loadstone, pulling at her iron, drawing her through the pearly mists that lay like face-cloths to the water and hid at a short distance the tarnish left by the sail. But later he had known that it was no loadstone drawing at her iron. The motion was due—must be due—to the absolute deadness of the calm in that silent, sinister, three-miles-broad waterway. With the eye of his mind he saw that loadstone now as he lay against a gun-truck, all but toppling down the deck. Soon that would happen again which had happened for five days past. He would hear again the chattering of monkeys and the screaming of parrots, the mat of green and yellow weeds would creep in towards the *Mary* over the quicksilver sea, once more the sheer wall of rock would rise, and the men would run. . . .

But no; the men would not run this time to drop the fenders. There were no men left to do so, unless Bligh was still alive. Perhaps Bligh was still alive. He had walked half-way down the quarter-deck steps a little before the sudden nightfall of the day before, had then fallen and lain for a minute (dead, Abel Keeling had supposed, watching him from his place by the gun-truck), and had then got up again and tottered forward to the forecastle, his tall figure swaying, and his long arms waving. Abel Keeling had not seen him since. Most likely, he had died in the forecastle during the night. If he had not been dead he would have come aft again for water. . . .

At the remembrance of the water Abel Keeling lifted his head. The strands of lean muscle about his emaciated mouth worked, and he made a little pressure of his sun-blackened hand on the deck, as if to verify its steepness and his own balance. The mainmast was some seven or eight yards away. . . . He put one stiff leg under him and began, seated as he was, to make shuffling movements down the slope.

To the mainmast, near the belfry, was affixed his contrivance for catching water. It consisted of a collar of rope set lower at one side than at the other (but that had been before the mast had steeved so many degrees away from the zenith), and tallowed beneath. The mists lingered later in that gully of a strait than they did on the open ocean, and the collar of rope served as a collector for the dews that condensed on the masts. The drops fell into a small earthen pipkin placed on the deck beneath it.

Abel Keeling reached the pipkin and looked into it. It was nearly a third full of fresh water. Good. If Bligh, the mate, was dead, so much the more water for Abel Keeling, master of the *Mary of the Tower*. He dipped two fingers into the pipkin and put them into his mouth. This he did several times. He did not dare to raise the pipkin to his black and broken lips for dread of a remembered agony, he could not have told how many days ago, when a devil had whispered to him, and he had gulped down the contents of the pipkin in the morning, and for the rest of the day had gone waterless. . . . Again he moistened his fingers and sucked them; then he lay sprawling against the mast, idly watching the drops of water as they fell.

It was odd how the drops formed. Slowly they collected at the edge of the tallowed collar, trembled in their fullness for an instant, and fell, another beginning the process instantly. It amused Abel Keeling to watch them. Why (he wondered) were all the drops the same size? What cause and compulsion did they obey that they never varied, and what frail tenuity held the little globules intact? It must be due to some Cause. . . . He remembered that the aromatic gum of the wild frankincense with which they had parcelled the seams had hung on the buckets in great sluggish gouts, obedient to a different compulsion; oil was different again, and so were juices and balsams. Only quicksilver (perhaps the heavy and motionless sea put him in mind of quicksilver) seemed obedient to no law. . . . Why was it so?

Bligh, of course, would have had his explanation: it was the Hand of God. That sufficed for Bligh, who had gone forward the evening before, and whom Abel Keeling now seemed vaguely and as at a distance to remember as the deep-voiced fanatic who had sung his hymns as, man by man, he had committed the bodies of the ship's company to the deep. Bligh was that sort of man; accepted things without question; was content to take things as they were and be ready with the fenders when the wall of rock rose out of the opalescent mists. Bligh, too, like the waterdrops, had his Law, that was his and nobody else's. . . .

There floated down from some rotten rope up aloft a flake of scurf, that settled in the pipkin. Abel Keeling watched it dully as it settled towards the pipkin's rim. When presently he again dipped his fingers into the vessel the water ran into a little vortex, drawing the flake with it. The water settled again; and again the minute flake, determined towards the rim and adhered there, as if the rim had power to draw it. . . .

It was exactly so that the galleon was gliding towards the wall of rock, the yellow and green weeds, and the monkeys and parrots. Put out into mid-water again (while there had been men to put her out) she had glided to the other wall. One force drew the chip in the pipkin and the ship over the tranced sea. It was the Hand of God, said Bligh. . . .

Abel Keeling, his mind now noting minute things and now clouded with torpor, did not at first hear a voice that was quakingly lifted up over by the forecastle—a voice that drew nearer, to an accompaniment of swirling water.

"O Thou, that Jonas in the fish
Three days didst keep from pain,
Which was a figure of Thy death
And rising up again——"

It was Bligh, singing one of his hymns:

"O Thou, that Noah keptst from flood
And Abram, day by day,
As he along through Egypt passed
Didst guide him in the way——"

The voice ceased, leaving the pious period uncompleted. Bligh was alive, at any rate. . . . Abel Keeling resumed his fitful musing.

Yes, that was the Law of Bligh's life, to call things the Hand of God; but Abel Keeling's Law was different; no better, no worse, only different. The Hand of God, that drew chips and galleons, must work by some method; and Abel Keeling's eyes were dully on the pipkin again as if he sought the method there. . . .

Then conscious thought left him for a space, and when he resumed it was without obvious connection.

Oars, of course, were the thing. With oars, men could laugh at calms. Oars, that only pinnaces and galliasses now used, had had their advantages. But oars (which was to say a method, for you could say if you liked that the Hand of God grasped the oar-loom, as the Breath of God filled the sail)—oars were antiquated, belonged to the past, and meant a throwing-over of all that was good and new and a return to fine lines, a battle-formation abreast to give effect to the shock of the ram, and a day or two at sea and then to port again for provisions. Oars . . . no. Abel Keeling was one of the new men, the men who swore by the line-ahead, the broadside fire of sakers and demi-cannon, and weeks and months without a landfall. Perhaps one day the wits of such men as he would devise a craft, not oar-driven (because oars could not penetrate into the remote seas of the world)—not sail-driven (because men who trusted to sails found themselves in an airless, three-mile strait, suspended motionless between cloud and water, ever gliding to a wall of rock)—but a ship . . . a ship. . . .

"To Noah and his sons with him
God spake, and thus said He:
A cov'nant set I up with you
And your posterity——"

It was Bligh again, wandering somewhere in the waist. Abel Keeling's mind was once more a blank. Then slowly, slowly, as the water drops collected on the collar of rope, his thought took shape again.

A galliasse? No, not a galliasse. The galliasse made shift to be two things, and was neither. This ship, that the hand of man should one day make for the Hand of God to manage, should be a ship that should take and conserve the force of the wind, take it and store it as she stored her victuals; at rest when she wished, going ahead when she wished; turning the forces both of calm and storm against themselves. For, of course, her force must be wind —stored wind—a bag of the winds, as the children's tale had it— wind probably directed upon the water astern, driving it away and urging forward the ship, acting by reaction. She would have a wind-chamber, into which wind would be pumped with pumps. Bligh would call that equally the Hand of God, this driving-force of the ship of the future that Abel Keeling dimly foreshadowed as he lay between the mainmast and the belfry, turning his eyes now and then from ashy white timbers to the vivid green bronze-rust of the bell above him. . . .

Bligh's face, liver-coloured with the sun and ravaged from inwards by the faith that consumed him, appeared at the head of the quarter-deck steps. His voice beat uncontrolledly out.

"And in the earth here is no place
Of refuge to be found,
Nor in the deep and water-course
That passeth under ground——"

II

Bligh's eyes were lidded, as if in contemplation of his inner ecstasy. His head was thrown back, and his brows worked up and down tormentedly. His wide mouth remained open as his hymn was suddenly interrupted on the long-drawn note. From somewhere in the shimmering mists the note was taken up, and there drummed and rang and reverberated through the strait a windy, hoarse, and dismal bellow, alarming and sustained. A tremor rang through Bligh. Moving like a sightless man, he stumbled forward from the head of the quarter-deck steps, and Abel Keeling was aware of his gaunt figure behind him, taller for the steepness of the deck. As that vast empty sound died away, Bligh laughed in his mania.

"Lord hath the grave's wide mouth a tongue to praise Thee? Lo, again——"

Again the cavernous sound possessed the air, louder and nearer. Through it came another sound, a slow throb, throb—throb, throb—— Again the sounds ceased.

"Even Leviathan lifted up his voice in praise!" Bligh sobbed.

Abel Keeling did not raise his head. There had returned to him the memory of that day when, before the morning mists had lifted from the strait, he had emptied the pipkin of the water that was the allowance until night should fall again. During that agony of thirst he had seen shapes and heard sounds with other than his mortal eyes and ears, and even in the moments that had alternated with his lightness, when he had known these to be hallucinations, they had come again. He had heard the bells on a Sunday in his own Kentish home, the calling of children at play, the unconcerned singing of men at their daily labour, and the laughter and gossip of the women as they had spread the linen on the hedge or distributed bread upon the platters. These voices had rung in his brain, interrupted now and then by the groans of Bligh and of two other men who had been alive then. Some of the voices he had heard had been silent on earth this many a long year, but Abel Keeling, thirst-tortured, had heard them, even as he was now hearing that vacant moaning with the intermittent throbbing that filled the strait with alarm. . . .

"Praise Him, praise Him, praise Him!" Bligh was calling deliriously.

Then a bell seemed to sound in Abel Keeling's ears, and, as if something in the mechanism of his brain had slipped, another picture rose in his fancy—the scene when the *Mary of the Tower* had put out, to a bravery of swinging bells and shrill fifes and valiant trumpets. She had not been a leper-white galleon then. The scroll-work on her prow had twinkled with gilding; her belfry and stern-galleries and elaborate lanterns had flashed in the sun with gold; and her fighting-tops and the warpavesse about her waist had been gay with painted coats and scutcheons. To her sails had been stitched gaudy ramping lions of scarlet say, and from her mainyard, now dipping in the water, had hung the broad two-tailed pennant with the Virgin and Child embroidered upon it. . . .

Then suddenly a voice about him seemed to be saying, *"And a half-seven—and a half-seven—"* and in a twink the picture in Abel Keeling's brain changed again. He was at home again, instructing his son, young Abel, in the casting of the lead from the skiff they had pulled out of the harbour.

"And a half-seven!" the boy seemed to be calling.

Abel Keeling's blackened lips muttered: "Excellently well cast, Abel, excellently well cast!"

"And a half-seven—and a half-seven—seven—seven——"

"Ah," Abel Keeling murmured, "that last was not a clear cast—give me the line—thus it should go . . . ay, so. . . . Soon you shall sail the seas with me in the *Mary of the Tower*. You are already perfect in the stars and the motions of the planets; to-morrow I will instruct you in the use of the backstaff. . . ."

For a minute or two he continued to mutter; then he dozed. When again he came to semi-consciousness it was once more to the sound of bells, at first faint, then louder, and finally becoming a noisy clamour immediately above his head. It was Bligh. Bligh, in a fresh attack of delirium, had seized the bell-lanyard and was ringing the bell insanely. The cord broke in his fingers, but he thrust at the bell with his hand, and again called aloud.

"Upon an harp and an instrument of ten strings . . . let Heaven and Earth praise Thy Name! . . ."

He continued to call aloud, and to beat on the bronze-rusted bell.

"Ship ahoy! What ship's that?"

One would have said that a veritable hail had come out of the mists; but Abel Keeling knew those hails that came out of the mists. They came from ships which were not there. "Ay, ay, keep a good look-out, and have a care to your lode-manage," he muttered again to his son. . . .

But, as sometimes a sleeper sits up in his dream, or rises from his couch and walks, so all of a sudden Abel Keeling found himself on his hands and knees on the deck, looking back over his shoulder. In some deep-seated region of his consciousness he was dimly aware that the cant of the deck had become more perilous, but his brain received the intelligence and forgot it again. He was looking out into the bright and baffling mists. The buckler of the sun was of a more ardent silver; the sea below it was lost in brilliant evaporation; and between them, suspended in the haze, no more substantial than the vague darknesses that float before dazzled eyes, a pyramidal phantom-shape hung. Abel Keeling passed his hand over his eyes, but when he removed it the shape was still there, gliding slowly towards the *Mary's* quarter. Its form changed as he watched it. The spirit-grey shape that had been a pyramid seemed to dissolve into four upright members, slightly graduated in tallness, that nearest the *Mary's* stern the tallest and that to the left the lowest. It might have been the shadow of the gigantic set of reed-pipes on which that vacant mournful note had been sounded.

And as he looked, with fooled eyes, again his ears became fooled: *"Ahoy there! What ship's that? Are you a ship? . . . Here, give me that trumpet——"* Then a metallic barking. *"Ahoy there! What the devil are you? Didn't you ring a bell? Ring it again, or blow a blast or something, and go dead slow!"*

All this came, as it were, indistinctly, and through a sort of high singing in Abel Keeling's own ears. Then he fancied a short bewildered laugh, followed by a colloquy from somewhere between sea and sky.

"Here, Ward, just pinch me, will you? Tell me what you see there. I want to know if I'm awake."

"See where?"

"There, on the starboard bow. (Stop that ventilating fan; I can't hear myself think.) See anything? Don't tell me it's that damned Dutchman—don't pitch me that old Vanderdecken tale—give me an easy one first, some thing about a sea-serpent. . . . You did hear that bell, didn't you?"

"Shut up a minute—listen——"

Again Bligh's voice was lifted up.

"This is the cov'nant that I make:
From henceforth nevermore
Will I again the world destroy
With water, as before."

Bligh's voice died away again in Abel Keeling's ears.

"Oh—my—fat—Aunt—Julia!" the voice that seemed to come from between sea and sky sounded again. Then it spoke more loudly. *"I say,"* it began with careful politeness, *"if you are a ship, do you mind telling us where the masquerade is to be? Our wireless is out of order, and we hadn't heard of it. . . . Oh, you do see it, Ward, don't you? . . . Please, please tell us what the hell you are!"*

Again Abel Keeling had moved as a sleep-walker moves. He had raised himself up by the belfry timbers, and Bligh had sunk in a heap on the deck. Abel Keeling's movement overturned the pipkin, which raced the little trickle of its contents down the deck and lodged where the still and brimming sea made, as it were, a chain with the carved balustrade of the quarter-deck—one link a still gleaming edge, then a dark baluster, and then another gleaming link. For one moment only Abel Keeling found himself noticing that that which had driven Bligh aft had been the rising of the water in the waist as the galleon settled by the head—the waist was now entirely submerged; then once more he was absorbed in his dream, its voices, and its shape in the mist, which had again taken the form of a pyramid before his eyeballs.

"*Of course,*" a voice seemed to be complaining anew, and still through that confused dinning in Abel Keeling's ears, "*we can't turn a four-inch on it. . . . And, of course, Ward, I don't believe in 'em. D'you hear, Ward? I don't believe in 'em, I say. . . . Shall we call down to old A.B.? This might interest His Scientific Skippership. . . .*"

"*Oh, lower a boat and pull out to it—into it—over it—through it——*"

"*Look at our chaps crowded on the barbette yonder. They've seen it. Better not give an order you know won't be obeyed. . . .*"

Abel Keeling, cramped against the antique belfry, had begun to find his dream interesting. For, though he did not know her build, that mirage was the shape of a ship. No doubt it was projected from his brooding on ships of half an hour before; and that was odd. . . . But perhaps, after all, it was not very odd. He knew that she did not really exist; only the appearance of her existed; but things had to exist like that before they really existed. Before the *Mary of the Tower* had existed she had been a shape in some man's imagination; before that, some dreamer had dreamed the form of a ship with oars; and before that, far away in the dawn and infancy of the world, some seer had seen in a vision the raft before man had ventured to push out over the water on his two planks. And since this shape that rode before Abel Keeling's eyes was a shape in his, Abel Keeling's dream, he, Abel Keeling, was the master of it. His own brooding brain had contrived her, and she was launched upon the illimitable ocean of his own mind. . . .

"And I will not unmindful be
Of this, My cov'nant, passed
Twixt Me and you and every flesh
Whiles that the world should last,"

sang Bligh, rapt. . . .

But as a dreamer, even in his dream, will scratch upon the wall by his couch some key or word to put him in mind of his vision on the morrow when it has left him, so Abel Keeling found himself seeking some sign to be a proof to those to whom no vision is vouchsafed. Even Bligh sought that—could not be silent in his bliss, but lay on the deck there, uttering great passionate Amens and praising his Maker, as he said, upon an harp and an instrument of ten strings. So with Abel Keeling. It would be the Amen of his life to have praised God, not upon a harp, but upon a ship that should carry her own power, that should store wind or its equivalent as she stored her victuals, that should be something wrested from the chaos of uninvention and ordered and disciplined and subordinated to Abel Keeling's will. . . . And there she was, that ship-shaped thing of spirit-grey, with the four pipes that resembled a phantom organ now broadside and of equal length. And the ghost-crew of that ship were speaking again. . . .

The interrupted silver chain by the quarter-deck balustrade had now become continuous, and the balusters made a herring-bone over their own motionless reflections. The spilt water from the pipkin had dried, and the pipkin was not to be seen. Abel Keeling stood beside the mast, erect as God made man to go. With his leathery hand he smote upon the bell. He waited for the space of a minute, and then cried:

"Ahoy! . . . Ship ahoy! . . . What ship's that?"

III

We are not conscious in a dream that we are playing a game, the beginning and end of which are in ourselves. In this dream of Abel Keeling's a voice replied:

"Hallo, it's found its tongue. . . . Ahoy there! What are you?"

Loudly and in a clear voice Abel Keeling called: "Are you a ship?"

With a nervous giggle the answer came:

"We are a ship, aren't we, Ward? I hardly feel sure. . . . Yes, of course, we're a ship. No question about us. The question is what the dickens you are."

Not all the words these voices used were intelligible to Abel Keeling, and he knew not what it was in the tone of these last words that reminded him of the honour due to the *Mary of the Tower.* Blister-white and at the end of her life as she was, Abel Keeling was still jealous of her dignity; the voice had a youngish ring; and it was not fitting that young chins should be wagged about his galleon. He spoke curtly.

"You that spoke—are you the master of that ship?"

"Officer of the watch," the words floated back; *"the captain's below."*

"Then send for him. It is with masters that masters hold speech," Abel Keeling replied.

He could see the two shapes, flat and without relief, standing on a high narrow structure with rails. One of them gave a low whistle, and seemed to be fanning his face; but the other rumbled something into a sort of funnel. Presently the two shapes became three. There was a murmuring, as of a consultation, and then suddenly a new voice spoke. At its thrill and tone a sudden tremor ran through Abel Keeling's frame. He wondered what response it was that that voice found in the forgotten recesses of his memory.

"Ahoy!" seemed to call this new yet faintly remembered voice. *"What's all this about? Listen. We're His Majesty's destroyer* Seapink, *out of Devonfort last October, and nothing particular the matter with us. Now who are you?"*

"The *Mary of the Tower,* out of the Port of Rye on the day of Saint Anne, and only two men——"

A gasp interrupted him.

"Out of WHERE?" that voice that so strangely moved Abel Keeling said unsteadily, while Bligh broke into groans of renewed rapture.

"Out of the Port of Rye, in the County of Sussex . . . nay, give ear, else I cannot make you hear me while this man's spirit and flesh wrestle so together! . . . Ahoy! Are you gone?" For the voices had become a low murmur, and the ship-shape had faded before Abel Keeling's eyes. Again and again he called. He wished to be informed of the disposition and economy of the wind-chamber. . . .

"The wind-chamber!" he called, in an agony lest the knowledge almost within his grasp should be lost. "I would know about the wind-chamber . . ."

Like an echo, there came back the words, uncomprehendingly uttered, *"The wind-chamber? . . ."*

". . . that driveth the vessel—perchance 'tis not wind—a steel bow that is bent also conserveth force—the force you store, to move at will through calm and storm. . . ."

"Can you make out what it's driving at?"

"Oh, we shall all wake up in a minute. . . ."

"Quiet, I have it; the engines; it wants to know about our engines. It'll be wanting to see our papers presently. Rye Port! . . . Well, no harm in humouring it; let's see what it can make of this. Ahoy there!" came the voice to Abel Keeling, a little strongly, as if a shifting wind carried it, and speaking faster and faster as it went on. *"Not wind, but steam; d'you hear? Steam, steam. Steam, in eight Yarrow water-tube boilers. S-t-e-a-m, steam. Got it? And we've twin-screw triple expansion engines, indicated horse-power four thousand, and we can do* 430 *revolutions per minute; savvy? Is there any-*

thing your phantomhood would like to know about our armament? . . ."

Abel Keeling was muttering fretfully to himself. It annoyed him that words in his own vision should have no meaning for him. How did words come to him in a dream that he had no knowledge of when wide awake? The *Seapink*—that was the name of this ship; but a pink was long and narrow, low-carged and square-built aft. . . .

"*And as for our armament,*" the voice with the tones that so profoundly troubled Abel Keeling's memory continued, "*we've two revolving Whitehead torpedo-tubes, three six-pounders on the upper deck, and that's a twelve-pounder forward there by the conning-tower. I forgot to mention that we're nickel steel, with a coal capacity of sixty tons in most damnably placed bunkers, and that thirty and a quarter knots is about our top. Care to come aboard?*"

But the voice was speaking still more rapidly and feverishly, as if to fill a silence with no matter what, and the shape that was uttering it was straining forward anxiously over the rail.

"*Ugh! But I'm glad this happened in the daylight,*" another voice was muttering.

"*I wish I was sure it was happening at all. . . . Poor old spook!*"

"*I suppose it would keep its feet if her deck was quite vertical. Think she'll go down, or just melt?*"

"*Kind of go down . . . without wash . . .*"

"*Listen—here's the other one now—*"

For Bligh was singing again:

"*For, Lord, Thou know'st our nature such*
If we great things obtain,
And in the getting of the same
Do feel no grief or pain,

"*We little do esteem thereof;*
But, hardly brought to pass,
A thousand times we do esteem
More than the other was."

"*But oh, look—look—look at the other! . . . Oh, I say, wasn't he a grand old boy! Look!*"

For, transfiguring Abel Keeling's form as a prophet's form is transfigured in the instant of his rapture, flooding his brain with the white eureka-light of perfect knowledge, that for which he and his dream had been at a standstill had come. He knew her, this ship of the future, as if God's Finger had bitten her lines into his brain. He knew her as those already sinking into the grave know things, miraculously, completely, accepting Life's impossibilities with a nodded "Of course." From the ardent mouths of her eight furnaces to the last drip from her lubricators, from her bed-plates to the breeches of her quick-firers, he knew her—read her gauges, thumbed her bearings, gave the ranges from her range-finders, and lived the life he lived who was in command of her. And he would not forget on the morrow, as he had forgotten on many morrows, for at last he had seen the water about his feet, and knew that there would be no morrow for him in this world. . . .

And even in that moment, with but a sand or two to run in his glass, indomitable, insatiable, dreaming dream on dream, he could not die until he knew more. He had two questions to ask, and a master-question; and but a moment remained. Sharply his voice rang out.

"Ho, there! . . . This ancient ship, the *Mary of the Towers,* cannot steam thirty and a quarter knots, but yet she can sail the waters. What more does your ship? Can she soar above them, as the fowls of the air soar?"

"Lord, he thinks we're an aeroplane! . . . No, she can't. . . ."

"And can you dive, even as the fishes of the deep?"

"No. . . . Those are submarines . . . we aren't a submarine. . . ."

But Abel Keeling waited for no more. He gave an exulting chuckle.

"Oho, oho—thirty knots, and but on the face of the waters—no more than that? Oho! . . . Now *my* ship, the ship I see as a mother sees full-grown the child she has but conceived—*my* ship I say—oho!—*my* ship shall. . . . Below there—trip that gun!"

The cry came suddenly and alertly, as a muffled sound came from below and an ominous tremor shook the galleon.

"By Jove, her guns are breaking loose below—that's her finish—"

"Trip that gun, and double-breech the others!" Abel Keeling's voice rang out, as if there had been any to obey him. He had braced himself within the belfry frame; and then in the middle of the next order his voice suddenly failed him. His ship-shape, that for the moment he had forgotten, rode once more before his eyes. This was the end, and his master-question, apprehension for the answer to which was now torturing his face and well-nigh bursting his heart, was still unasked.

"Ho—he that spoke with me—the master," he cried in a voice that ran high, "is he there?"

"Yes, yes!" came the other voice across the water, sick with suspense. *"Oh, be quick!"*

There was a moment in which hoarse cries from many voices, a heavy thud and rumble on wood, and a crash of timbers and a gurgle and a splash were indescribably mingled; the sun under which Abel Keeling had lain had snapped her rotten breechings and plunged down the deck, carrying Bligh's unconscious form with it. The deck came up vertical, and for one instant longer Abel Keeling clung to the belfry.

"I cannot see your face," he screamed, "but meseems your voice is a voice I know. *What is your name?*"

In a torn sob the answer came across the water:

"Keeling—Abel Keeling. . . . Oh, my God!"

And Abel Keeling's cry of triumph, that mounted to a victorious "Huzza!" was lost in the downward plunge of the *Mary of the Tower,* that left the strait empty save for the sun's fiery blaze and the last smoke-like evaporation of the mists.

W. Somerset Maugham

English writer born in Paris in 1874, the author of innumerable novels, plays, and short stories. The selection below is taken from Here and There *published in 1948.*

LORD MOUNTDRAGO

Dr. Audlin looked at the clock on his desk. It was twenty minutes to six. He was surprised that his patient was late, for Lord Mountdrago prided himself on his punctuality; he had a sententious way of expressing himself which gave the air of an epigram to a commonplace remark, and he was in the habit of saying that punctuality is a compliment you pay to the intelligent and a rebuke you administer to the stupid. Lord Mountdrago's appointment was for five-thirty.

There was in Dr. Audlin's appearance nothing to attract attention. He was tall and spare, with narrow shoulders and something of a stoop; his hair was grey and thin; his long, sallow face deeply lined. He was not more than fifty, but he looked older. His eyes, pale blue and rather large, were weary. When you had been with him for a while you noticed that they moved very little; they remained fixed on your face, but so empty of expression were they that it was no discomfort. They seldom lit up. They gave no clue to his thoughts nor changed with the words he spoke. If you were of an observant turn it might have struck you that he blinked much less often than most of us. His hands were on the large side, with long, tapering fingers; they were soft but firm, cool but not clammy. You could never have said what Dr. Audlin wore unless you had made a point of looking. His clothes were dark. His tie was black. His dress made his sallow lined face paler and his pale eyes more wan. He gave you the impression of a very sick man.

Dr. Audlin was a psychoanalyst. He had adopted the profession by accident and practised it with misgiving. When the war broke out he had not been long qualified and was getting experience at various hospitals; he offered his services to the authorities, and after a time was sent out to France. It was then that he discovered his singular gift. He could allay certain pains by the touch of his cool, firm hands, and by talking to them often induce sleep in men who were suffering from sleeplessness. He spoke slowly. His voice had no particular colour, and its tone did not alter with the words he uttered, but it was musical, soft and lulling. He told the men that they must rest, that they mustn't worry, that they must sleep; and rest stole into their jaded bones, tranquillity pushed their anxieties away, like a man finding a place for himself on a crowded bench, and slumber fell on their tired eyelids like the light rain of spring upon the fresh-turned earth. Dr. Audlin found that by speaking to men with that low, monotonous voice of his, by looking at them with his pale, quiet eyes, by stroking their weary foreheads with his long firm hands, he could soothe their perturbations, resolve the conflicts that distracted them and banish the phobias that made their lives a torment. Sometimes he effected cures that seemed miraculous. He restored speech to a man who, after being buried under the earth by a bursting shell, had been struck dumb, and he gave back the use of his limbs to another who had been paralyzed after a crash in a plane. He could not understand his powers; he was of a sceptical turn, and though they say that in circumstances of this kind the first thing is to believe in yourself, he never quite succeeded in doing that; and it was only the outcome of his activities, patent to the most incredulous observer, that obliged him to admit that he had some faculty, coming from he knew not where, obscure and uncertain, that enabled him to do things for which he could offer no explanation. When the war was over he went to Vienna and studied there, and afterwards to Zurich; and then settled down in London to practise the art he had so strangely acquired. He had been practising now for fifteen years, and had attained, in the speciality he followed, a distinguished reputation. People told one another of the amazing things he had done, and though his fees were high, he had as many patients as he had time to see. Dr. Audlin knew that he had achieved some very extraordinary results; he had saved men from suicide, others from the lunatic asylum, he had assuaged griefs that embittered useful lives, he had turned unhappy marriages into happy ones, he had eradicated abnormal instincts and thus delivered not a few from a hateful bondage, he had given health to the sick in spirit; he had done all this, and yet at the back of his mind remained the suspicion that he was little more than a quack.

It went against his grain to exercise a power that he could not understand, and it offended his honesty to trade on the faith of the people he treated when he had no faith in himself. He was rich enough now to live without working, and the work exhausted him; a dozen times he had been on the point of giving up practice. He knew all that Freud and Jung and the rest of them had written. He was not satisfied; he had an intimate conviction that all their theory was hocus-pocus, and yet there the results were, incomprehensible, but manifest. And what had he not seen of human nature during the fifteen years that patients had been coming to his dingy back room in Wimpole Street? The revelations that had been poured into his ears, sometimes only too willingly, sometimes with shame, with reservations, with anger, had long ceased to surprise him. Nothing could shock him any longer. He knew by now that men were liars, he knew how extravagant was their vanity; he knew far worse than that about them; but he knew that it was not for him to judge or to condemn. But year by year as these terrible confidences were imparted to him his face grew a little greyer, its lines a little more marked and his pale eyes more weary. He seldom laughed, but now and again when for relaxation he read a novel he smiled. Did their authors really think the men and women they wrote of were like that? If they only knew how much more complicated they were, how much more unexpected, what irreconcilable elements co-existed within their souls and what dark and sinister contentions afflicted them!

It was a quarter to six. Of all the strange cases he had been called upon to deal with, Dr. Audlin could remember none stranger than that of Lord Mountdrago. For one thing the personality of his patient made it singular. Lord Mountdrago was an able and a distinguished man. Appointed Secretary for Foreign Affairs when still under forty, now after three years in office he had seen his policy prevail. It was generally acknowledged that he was the ablest politician in the Conservative Party, and only the fact that his father was a peer, on whose death he would no longer be able to sit in the House of Commons, made it impossible for him to aim at the premiership. But if in these democratic times it is out of the question for a Prime Minister of England to be in the House of Lords, there was nothing to prevent Lord Mountdrago from continuing to be Secretary for Foreign Affairs in successive Conservative administrations and so for long directing the foreign policy of his country.

Lord Mountdrago had many good qualities. He had intelligence and industry. He was widely travelled and spoke several languages fluently. From early youth he had specialized in foreign affairs and had conscientiously made himself acquainted with the political and economic circumstances of other countries. He had courage, insight and determination. He was a good speaker, both on the platform and in the House, clear, precise and often witty. He was a brilliant debater and his gift of repartee was celebrated. He had a fine presence: he was a tall, handsome man, rather bald and somewhat too stout, but this gave him solidity and an air of maturity that were of service to him. As a young man he had been something of an athlete and had rowed in the Oxford boat, and he was known to be one of the best shots in England. At twenty-four he had married a girl of eighteen whose father was a duke and her mother a great American heiress, so that she had both position and wealth, and by her he had had two sons. For several years they had lived privately apart, but in public united, so that appearances were saved, and no other attachment on either side had given the gossips occasion to whisper. Lord Mountdrago indeed was too ambitious, too hard-working, and it must be added too patriotic, to be tempted by any pleasures that might interfere with his career. He had in short a great deal to make him a popular and successful figure. He had unfortunately great defects.

He was a fearful snob. You would not have been surprised at this if his father had been the first holder of the title. That the son of an ennobled lawyer, manufacturer or distiller should attach an inordinate importance to his rank is understandable. The earldom held by Lord Mountdrago's father was created by Charles II, and the barony held by the first earl dated from the Wars of the Roses. For three hundred years the successive holders of the title had allied themselves with the noblest families of England. But Lord Mountdrago was as conscious of his birth as a *nouveau riche* is conscious of his money. He never missed an opportunity of impressing it upon others. He had beautiful manners when he chose to display them, but this he did only with people whom he regarded as his equals. He was coldly insolent to those whom he looked upon as his social inferiors. He was rude to his servants and insulting to his secretaries. The subordinate officials in the government offices to which he had been successively attached feared and hated him. His arrogance was horrible. He knew that he was a great deal cleverer than most of the persons he had to do with, and never hesitated to apprise them of the fact. He had no patience with the infirmities of human nature. He felt himself born to command and was irritated with people who expected him to listen to their arguments or wished to hear the reasons for his decisions. He was immeasurably selfish. He looked upon any service that was rendered him as a right due to his rank and intelligence and therefore deserving of no gratitude. It never entered his head that he was called upon to do anything for others. He had many enemies: he despised them. He knew no one who merited his assistance, his sympathy or his compassion. He had no friends. He was distrusted by his chiefs, because they doubted his loyalty; he was unpopular with his party, because he was overbearing and discourteous; and yet his merit was so great, his patriotism so evident, his intelligence so solid and his management of affairs so brilliant, that they had to put up with him. And what made it possible to do this was that on occasion he could be enchanting: when he was with persons whom he considered his equals, or whom he wished to captivate, in the company of foreign dignitaries or women of distinction, he could be gay, witty and debonair; his manners then reminded you that in his veins ran the same blood as had run in the veins of Lord Chesterfield; he could tell a story with point, he could be natural, sensible and even profound. You were surprised at the extent of his knowledge and the sensitiveness of his taste. You thought him the best company in the world; you forgot that he had insulted you the day before and was quite capable of cutting you dead the next.

Lord Mountdrago almost failed to become Dr. Audlin's patient. A secretary rang up the doctor and told him that his lordship, wishing to consult him, would be glad if he would come to his house at ten o'clock on the following morning. Dr. Audlin answered that he was unable to go to Lord Mountdrago's house, but would be pleased to give him an appointment at his consulting room at five o'clock on the next day but one. The secretary took the message and presently rang back to say that Lord Mountdrago insisted on seeing Dr. Audlin in his own house and the doctor could fix his own fee. Dr. Audlin replied that he saw patients only in his consulting room and expressed his regret that unless Lord Mountdrago was prepared to come to him he could not give him his attention. In a quarter of an hour a brief message was delivered to him that his lordship would come not next day but one, but next day, at five.

When Lord Mountdrago was then shown in he did not come forward, but stood at the door and insolently looked the doctor up and down. Dr. Audlin perceived that he was in a rage; he gazed at him, silently, with still eyes. He saw a big heavy man, with greying hair, receding on the forehead so that it gave nobility to his brow, a puffy face with bold regular features and an expression of haughtiness. He had somewhat the look of one of the Bourbon sovereigns of the eighteenth century.

"It seems that it is as difficult to see you as a Prime Minister, Dr. Audlin. I'm an extremely busy man."

"Won't you sit down?" said the doctor.

His face showed no sign that Lord Mountdrago's speech in any way affected him. Dr. Audlin sat in his chair at the desk. Lord Mountdrago still stood, and his frown darkened.

"I think I should tell you that I am His Majesty's Secretary for Foreign Affairs," he said acidly.

"Won't you sit down?" the doctor repeated.

Lord Mountdrago made a gesture, which might have suggested that he was about to turn on his heel and stalk out of the room; but if that was his intention he apparently thought better of it. He seated himself. Dr. Audlin opened a large book and took up his pen. He wrote without looking at his patient.

"How old are you?"

"Forty-two."

"Are you married?"

"Yes."

"How long have you been married?"

"Eighteen years."

"Have you any children?"

"I have two sons."

Dr. Audlin noted down the facts as Lord Mountdrago abruptly answered his questions. Then he leaned back in his chair and looked at him. He did not speak; he just looked, gravely, with pale eyes that did not move.

"Why have you come to see me?" he asked at length.

"I've heard about you. Lady Canute is a patient of yours, I understand. She tells me you've done her a certain amount of good."

Dr. Audlin did not reply. His eyes remained fixed on the other's face, but they were so empty of expression that you might have thought he did not even see him.

"I can't do miracles," he said at length. Not a smile, but the shadow of a smile flickered in his eyes. "The Royal College of Physicians would not approve of it if I did."

Lord Mountdrago gave a brief chuckle. It seemed to lessen his hostility. He spoke more amiably.

"You have a very remarkable reputation. People seem to believe in you."

"Why have you come to me?" repeated Dr. Audlin. Now it was Lord Mountdrago's turn to be silent. It looked as though he found it hard to answer. Dr. Audlin waited. At last Lord Mountdrago seemed to make an effort. He spoke.

"I'm in perfect health. Just as a matter of routine I had myself examined by my own doctor the other day, Sir Augustus Fitzherbert, I daresay you've heard of him, and he tells me I have the physique of a man of thirty. I work hard, but I'm never tired, and I enjoy my work. I smoke very little and I'm an extremely moderate drinker. I take a sufficiency of exercise and I lead a regular life. I am a perfectly sound, normal, healthy man. I quite expect you to think it very silly and childish of me to consult you.

Dr. Audlin saw that he must help him.

"I don't know if I can do anything to help you. I'll try. You're distressed?"

Lord Mountdrago frowned.

"The work that I'm engaged in is important. The decisions I am called upon to make can easily affect the welfare of the country and even the peace of the world. It is essential that my judgment should be balanced and my brain clear. I look upon it as my duty to eliminate any cause of worry that may interfere with my usefulness."

Dr. Audlin had never taken his eyes off him. He saw a great deal. He saw behind his patient's pompous manner and arrogant pride an anxiety that he could not dispel.

"I asked you to be good enough to come here because I know by experience that it's easier for someone to speak openly in the dingy surroundings of a doctor's consulting room than in his accustomed environment."

"They're certainly dingy," said Lord Mountdrago acidly. He paused. It was evident that this man who had so much self-assurance, so quick and decided a mind that he was never at a loss, at this moment was embarrassed. He smiled in order to show the doctor that he was at his ease, but his eyes betrayed his disquiet. When he spoke again it was with unnatural heartiness.

"The whole thing's so trivial that I can hardly bring myself to bother you with it. I'm afraid you'll just tell me not to be a fool and waste your valuable time."

"Even things that seem very trivial may have their importance. They can be a symptom of a deep-seated derangement. And my time is entirely at your disposal."

Dr. Audlin's voice was low and grave. The monotone in which he spoke was strangely soothing. Lord Mountdrago at length made up his mind to be frank.

"The fact is I've been having some very tiresome dreams lately. I know it's silly to pay any attention to them, but—well, the honest truth is that I'm afraid they've got on my nerves."

"Can you describe any of them to me?"

Lord Mountdrago smiled, but the smile that tried to be careless was only rueful.

"They're so idiotic, I can hardly bring myself to narrate them."

"Never mind."

"Well, the first I had was about a month ago. I dreamt that I was at a party at Connemara House. It was an official party. The King and Queen were to be there, and of course decorations were worn. I was wearing my ribbon and my star. I went into a sort of cloak-room they have to take off my coat. There was a little man there called Owen Griffiths, who's a Welsh member of Parliament, and to tell you the truth, I was surprised to see him. He's very common, and I said to myself: 'Really, Lydia Connemara is going too far, whom will she ask next?' I thought he looked at me rather curiously, but I didn't take any notice of him; in fact I cut the little bounder and walked upstairs. I suppose you've never been there?"

"Never."

"No, it's not the sort of house you'd ever be likely to go to. It's a rather vulgar house, but it's got a very fine marble staircase, and the Connemaras were at the top receiving their guests. Lady Connemara gave me a look of surprise when I shook hands with her, and began to giggle; I didn't pay much attention—she's a very silly, ill-bred woman, and her manners are no better than those of her ancestress whom King Charles II made a duchess. I must say the reception rooms at Connemara House are stately. I walked through, nodding to a number of people and shaking hands; then I saw the German Ambassador talking with one of the Austrian archdukes. I particularly wanted to have a word with him, so I went up and held out my hand. The moment the Archduke saw me he burst into a roar of laughter. I was deeply affronted. I looked him up and down sternly, but he only laughed the more. I was about to speak to him rather sharply, when there was a sudden hush, and I realized that the King and Queen had come. Turning my back on the Archduke, I stepped forward, and then, quite suddenly, I noticed that I hadn't got any trousers on. I was in short silk drawers, and I wore scarlet sock suspenders. No wonder Lady Connemara had giggled; no wonder the Archduke had laughed! I can't tell you what that moment was. An agony of shame. I awoke in a cold sweat. Oh, you don't know the relief I felt to find it was only a dream."

"It's the kind of dream that's not so very uncommon," said Dr. Audlin.

"I daresay not. But an odd thing happened next day. I was in the lobby of the House of Commons, when that fellow Griffiths walked slowly past me. He deliberately looked down at my legs, and then he looked me full in the face, and I was almost certain he winked. A ridiculous thought came to me. He'd been there the night before and seen me make that ghastly exhibition of myself and was enjoying the joke. But of course I knew that was impossible because it was only a dream. I gave him an icy glare, and he walked on. But he was grinning his head off."

Lord Mountdrago took his handkerchief out of his pocket and wiped the palms of his hands. He was making no attempt now to conceal his perturbation. Dr. Audlin never took his eyes off him.

"Tell me another dream."

"It was the night after, and it was even more absurd than the first one. I dreamt that I was in the House. There was a debate on foreign affairs which not only the country, but the world, had been looking forward to with the gravest concern. The government had decided on a change in their policy which vitally affected the future of the Empire. The occasion was historic. Of course the House was crowded. All the ambassadors were there. The galleries were packed. It fell to me to make the important speech of the evening. I had prepared it carefully. A man like me has enemies—there are a lot of people who resent my having achieved the position I have at an age when even the cleverest men are content with situations of relative obscurity—and I was determined that my speech should not only be worthy of the occasion, but should silence my detractors. It excited me to think that the whole world was hanging on my lips. I rose to my feet. If you've ever been in the House you'll know how members chat to one another during a debate, rustle papers and turn over reports. The silence was the silence of the grave when I began to speak. Suddenly I caught sight of that odious little bounder on one of the benches opposite, Griffiths, the Welsh member; he put out his tongue at me. I don't know if you've ever heard a vulgar music-hall song called 'A Bicycle Made for Two.' It was very popular a great many years ago. To show Griffiths how completely I despised him I began to sing it. I sang the first verse right through. There was a moment's surprise, and when I finished they cried 'Hear, hear,' on the opposite benches. I put up my hand to silence them and sang the second verse. The House listened to me in stony silence and I felt the song wasn't going down very well. I was vexed, for I have a good baritone voice, and I was determined that they should do me justice. When I started the third verse the members began to laugh; in an instant the laughter spread; the ambassadors, the strangers in the Distinguished Strangers' Gallery, the ladies in the Ladies' Gallery, the reporters, they shook, they bellowed, they held their sides, they rolled in their seats; everyone was overcome with laughter except the ministers on the Front Bench immediately behind me. In that incredible, in that unprecedented, uproar they sat petrified. I gave them a glance, and suddenly the enormity of what I had done fell upon me. I had made myself the laughing-stock of the whole world. With misery I realized that I should have to resign. I woke and knew it was only a dream."

Lord Mountrago's grand manner had deserted him as he narrated this, and now having finished he was pale and trembling. But with an effort he pulled himself together. He forced a laugh to his shaking lips.

"The whole thing was so fantastic that I couldn't help being amused. I didn't give it another thought, and when I went into the House on the following afternoon I was feeling in very good form. The debate was dull, but I had to be there, and I read some documents that required my attention. For some reason I chanced to look up, and I saw that Griffiths was speaking. He has an unpleasant Welsh accent and an unprepossessing appearance. I couldn't imagine that he had anything to say that it was worth my while to listen to, and I was about to return to my papers when he quoted two lines from 'A Bicycle Made for Two.' I couldn't help glancing at him, and I saw that his eyes were fixed on me with a grin of bitter mockery. I faintly shrugged my shoulders. It was comic that a scrubby little

Welsh member should look at me like that. It was an odd coincidence that he should quote two lines from that disastrous song that I'd sung all through in my dream. I began to read my papers again, but I don't mind telling you that I found it difficult to concentrate on them. I was a little puzzled. Owen Griffiths had been in my first dream, the one at Connemara House, and I'd received a very definite impression afterwards that he knew the sorry figure I'd cut. Was it a mere coincidence that he had just quoted those two lines? I asked myself if it was possible that he was dreaming the same dreams as I was. But of course the idea was preposterous, and I determined not to give it a second thought."

There was a silence. Dr. Audlin looked at Lord Mountdrago and Lord Mountdrago looked at Dr. Audlin.

"Other people's dreams are very boring. My wife used to dream occasionally and insist on telling me her dreams next day with circumstantial detail. I found it maddening."

Dr. Audlin faintly smiled.

"You're not boring me."

"I'll tell you one more dream I had a few days later. I dreamt that I went into a public house at Limehouse. I've never been to Limehouse in my life and I don't think I've ever been in a public house since I was at Oxford, and yet I saw the street and the place I went into as exactly as if I were at home there. I went into a room—I don't know whether they call it the saloon bar or the private bar; there was a fireplace and a large leather armchair on one side of it, and on the other a small sofa; a bar ran the whole length of the room, and over it you could see into the public bar. Near the door was a round marble-topped table and two armchairs beside it. It was a Saturday night, and the place was packed. It was brightly lit, but the smoke was so thick that it made my eyes smart. I was dressed like a rough, with a cap on my head and a handkerchief round my neck. It seemed to me that most of the people there were drunk. I thought it rather amusing. There was a gramophone going, or the radio, I don't know which, and in front of the fireplace two women were doing a grotesque dance. There was a little crowd round them, laughing, cheering and singing. I went up to have a look, and some man said to me: ''Ave a drink, Bill.' There were glasses on the table full of a dark liquid which I understand is called brown ale. He gave me a glass, and not wishing to be conspicuous I drank it. One of the women who were dancing broke away from the other and took hold of the glass. ''Ere, what's the idea?' she said. 'That's my beer you're putting away.' 'Oh, I'm so sorry,' I said, 'this gentleman offered it me, and I very naturally thought it was his to offer.' 'All right, mate,' she said, 'I don't mind.

You come an' 'ave a dance with me.' Before I could protest she'd caught hold of me and we were dancing together. And then I found myself sitting in the armchair with the woman on my lap and we were sharing a glass of beer. I should tell you that sex has never played any great part in my life. I married young because in my position it was desirable that I should marry, but also in order to settle once for all the question of sex. I had the two sons I had made up my mind to have, and then I put the whole matter on one side. I've always been too busy to give much thought to that kind of thing, and living so much in the public eye as I do, it would have been madness to do anything that might give rise to scandal. The greatest asset a politician can have is a blameless record as far as women are concerned. I have no patience with the men who smash up their careers for women. I only despise them. The woman I had on my knees was drunk; she wasn't pretty and she wasn't young: in fact, she was just a blowsy old prostitute. She filled me with disgust, and yet when she put her mouth to mine and kissed me, though her breath stank of beer and her teeth were decayed, though I loathed myself, I wanted her—I wanted her with all my soul. Suddenly I heard a voice: 'That's right, old boy, have a good time.' I looked up, and there was Owen Griffiths. I tried to spring out of the chair, but that horrible woman wouldn't let me. 'Don't you pay no attention to 'im,' she said, ' 'e's only one of them nosy parkers.' 'You go to it,' he said. 'I know Moll. She'll give you your money's worth all right.' You know, I wasn't so much annoyed at his seeing me in that absurd situation as angry that he should address me as old boy. I pushed the woman aside and stood up and faced him. 'I don't know you, and I don't want to know you,' I said. 'I know you all right,' he said. 'And my advice to you, Molly, is, see that you get your money, he'll bilk you if he can.' There was a bottle of beer standing on the table close by. Without a word I seized it by the neck and hit him over the head with it as hard as I could. I made such a violent gesture that it woke me up."

"A dream of that sort is not incomprehensible," said Dr. Audlin. "It is the revenge nature takes on persons of unimpeachable character."

"The story's idiotic. I haven't told it you for its own sake. I've told it you for what happened next day. I wanted to look up something in a hurry, and I went into the library of the House. I got the book and began reading. I hadn't noticed when I sat down that Griffiths was sitting in a chair close by me. Another of the Labour Members came in and went up to him. 'Hullo, Owen,' he said to him, 'you're looking pretty dicky today.' 'I've got an awful headache,' he answered, 'I feel as if I'd been cracked over the head with a bottle.' "

Now Lord Mountdrago's face was grey with anguish.

"I knew then that the idea I'd had and dismissed as preposterous was true. I knew that Griffiths was dreaming my dreams and that he remembered them as well as I did."

"It may also have been a coincidence."

"When he spoke he didn't speak to his friend, he deliberately spoke to me. He looked at me with sullen resentment."

"Can you offer any suggestion why this same man should come into your dreams?"

"None."

Dr. Audlin's eyes had not left his patient's face and he saw that he lied. He had a pencil in his hand, and he drew a straggling line or two on his blotting paper. It often took a long time to get people to tell the truth, and yet they knew that unless they told it he could do nothing for them.

"The dream you've just described to me took place just over three weeks ago. Have you had any since?"

"Every night."

"And does this man Griffiths come into them all?"

"Yes."

The doctor drew more lines on his blotting paper. He wanted the silence, the drabness, the dull light of that little room to have its effect on Lord Mountdrago's sensibility. Lord Mountdrago threw himself back in his chair and turned his head away so that he should not see the other's grave eyes.

"Dr. Audlin, you must do something for me. I'm at the end of my tether. I shall go mad if this goes on. I'm afraid to go to sleep. Two or three nights I haven't. I've sat up reading and when I felt drowsy put on my coat and walked till I was exhausted. But I must have sleep. With all the work I have to do I must be at concert pitch; I must be in complete control of all my faculties. I need rest; sleep brings me none. I no sooner fall asleep than my dreams begin, and he's always there, that vulgar little cad, grinning at me, mocking me, despising me. It's a monstrous persecution. I tell you, Doctor, I'm not the man of my dreams; it's not fair to judge me by them. Ask anyone you like. I'm an honest, upright, decent man. No one can say anything against my moral character either private or public. My whole ambition is to serve my country and maintain its greatness. I have money, I have rank, I'm not exposed to many of the temptations of lesser men, so that it's no credit to me to be incorruptible; but this I can claim, that no honour, no personal advantage, no thought of self would induce me to swerve by a hairsbreadth from my duty. I've sacrificed everything to become the man I am. Greatness is my aim. Greatness is within my reach, and I'm losing my nerve. I'm not that mean, despicable, cowardly, lewd creature that horrible little man sees. I've told you three of my dreams; they're nothing; that man has seen me do things that are so beastly, so horrible, so shameful, that even if my life depended on it I wouldn't tell them. And he remembers them. I can hardly meet the derision and disgust I see in his eyes, and I even hesitate to speak because I know my words can seem to him nothing but utter humbug. He's seen me do things that no man with any self-respect would do, things for which men are driven out of the society of their fellows and sentenced to long terms of imprisonment; he's heard the foulness of my speech; he's seen me not only ridiculous, but revolting. He despises me and he no longer pretends to conceal it. I tell you that if you can't do something to help me I shall either kill myself or kill him."

"I wouldn't kill him if I were you," said Dr. Audlin coolly, in that soothing voice of his. "In this country the consequences of killing a fellow creature are awkward."

"I shouldn't be hanged for it, if that's what you mean. Who would know that I'd killed him? That dream of mine has shown me how. I told you, the day after I'd hit him over the head with a beer bottle he had such a headache that he couldn't see straight. He said so himself. That shows that he can feel with his waking body what happens to his body asleep. It's not with a bottle I shall hit him next time. One night, when I'm dreaming, I shall find myself with a knife in my hand or a revolver in my pocket—I must because I want to so intensely—and then I shall seize my opportunity. I'll stick him like a pig; I'll shoot him like a dog. In the heart. And then I shall be free of this fiendish persecution."

Some people might have thought that Lord Mountdrago was mad; after all the years during which Dr. Audlin had been treating the diseased souls of men he knew how thin a line divides those whom we call sane from those whom we call insane. He knew how often in men who to all appearance were healthy and normal, who were seemingly devoid of imagination, and who fulfilled the duties of common life with credit to themselves and with benefit to their fellows, when you gained their confidence, when you tore away the mask they wore to the world, you found not only hideous abnormality, but kinks so strange, mental extravagances so fantastic, that in that respect you could only call them lunatic. If you put them in an asylum, not all the asylums in the world would be large enough. Anyhow, a man was not certifiable because he had strange dreams and they had shattered his nerve. The case was singular, but it was only an exaggeration of others that had come under Dr. Audlin's observation; he was doubtful, however, whether the methods of treatment that he had so often found efficacious would here avail.

"Have you consulted any other member of my profession?" he asked.

"Only Sir Augustus. I merely told him that I suffered from nightmares. He said I was overworked and recommended me to go for a cruise. That's absurd. I can't leave the Foreign Office just now when the international situation needs constant attention. I'm indispensable, and I know it. On my conduct at the present juncture my whole future depends. He gave me sedatives. They had no effect. He gave me tonics. They were worse than useless. He's an old fool."

"Can you give any reason why it should be this particular man who persists in coming into your dreams?"

"You asked me that question before. I answered it."

That was true. But Dr. Audlin had not been satisfied with the answer.

"Just now you talked of persecution. Why should Owen Griffiths want to persecute you?"

"I don't know."

Lord Mountdrago's eyes shifted a little. Dr. Audlin was sure that he was not speaking the truth.

"Have you ever done him an injury?"

"Never."

Lord Mountdrago made no movement, but Dr. Audlin had a queer feeling that he shrank into his skin. He saw before him a large, proud man who gave the impression that the questions put to him were an insolence, and yet for all that, behind that façade, was somcthing shifting and startled that made you think of a frightened animal in a trap. Dr. Audlin leaned forward and by the power of his eyes forced Lord Mountdrago to meet them.

"Are you quite sure?"

"Quite sure. You don't seem to understand that our ways lead along different paths. I don't wish to harp on it, but I must remind you that I am a Minister of the Crown and Griffiths is an obscure member of the Labour Party. Naturally there's no social connection between us; he's a man of very humble origin, he's not the sort of person I should be likely to meet at any of the houses I go to; and politically our respective stations are so far separated that we could not possibly have anything in common."

"I can do nothing for you unless you tell me the complete truth."

Lord Mountdrago raised his eyebrows. His voice was rasping.

"I'm not accustomed to having my word doubted, Dr. Audlin. If you're going to do that, I think to take up any more of your time can only be a waste of mine. If you will kindly let my secretary know what your fee is, he will see that a cheque is sent to you."

For all the expression that was to be seen on Dr. Audlin's face you might have thought that he simply had not heard what Lord Mountdrago said. He continued to look steadily into his eyes, and his voice was grave and low.

"Have you done anything to this man that *he* might look upon as an injury?"

Lord Mountdrago hesitated. He looked away, and then, as though there were in Dr. Audlin's eyes a compelling force that he could not resist, looked back. He answered sulkily:

"Only if he was a dirty, second-rate little cad."

"But that is exactly what you've described him to be."

Lord Mountdrago sighed. He was beaten. Dr. Audlin knew that the sigh meant he was going at last to say what he had till then held back. Now he had no longer to insist. He dropped his eyes and began again drawing vague geometrical figures on his blotting paper. The silence lasted two or three minutes.

"I'm anxious to tell you everything that can be of any use to you. If I didn't mention this before, its only because it was so unimportant that I didn't see how it could possibly have anything to do with the case. Griffiths won a seat at the last election, and he began to make a nuisance of himself almost at once. His father's a miner, and he worked in a mine himself when he was a boy; he's been a schoolmaster in the board schools and a journalist. He's that half baked, conceited intellectual, with inadequate knowledge, ill-considered ideas and impractical plans, that compulsory education has brought forth from the working classes. He's a scrawny, grey-faced man who looks half starved, and he's always very slovenly in appearance; heaven knows members nowadays don't bother much about their dress, but his clothes are an outrage to the dignity of the House. They're ostentatiously shabby, his collar's never clean, and his tie's never tied properly; he looks as if he hadn't had a bath for a month, and his hands are filthy. The Labour Party have two or three fellows on the Front Bench who've got a certain ability, but the rest of them don't amount to much. In the kingdom of the blind the one-eyed man is king: because Griffiths is glib and has a lot of superficial information on a number of subjects, the Whips on his side began to put him up to speak whenever there was a chance. It appeared that he fancied himself on foreign affairs, and he was continually asking me silly, tiresome questions. I don't mind telling you that I made a point of snubbing him as soundly as I thought he deserved. From the beginning I hated the way he talked, his whining voice and his vulgar accent; he had nervous mannerisms that intensely irritated me. He talked rather shyly, hesitatingly, as though it were torture to him to speak and yet he was forced to by some inner passion, and often he used to say some very disconcerting things. I'll admit that now and again he had a sort of tub-thumping eloquence. It had a certain influence over the ill-regulated minds of the members of his party. They were impressed by his earnestness, and they weren't, as I was, nauseated by his sentimentality. A certain sentimentality is the common coin of political debate. Nations are governed by self-interest, but they prefer to believe that their aims are altruistic, and the politician is justified if with fair words and fine phrases he can persuade the electorate that the hard bargain he is driving for his country's advantage tends to the good of humanity. The mistake people like Griffiths make is to take these fair words and fine phrases at their face value. He's a crank, and a noxious crank. He calls himself an idealist. He has at his tongue's end all the tedious blather that the intelligentsia have been boring us with for years. Nonresistance. The brotherhood of man. You know the hopeless rubbish. The worst of it was that it impressed not only his own party, it even shook some of the sillier, more sloppy-minded members of ours. I heard rumours that Griffiths was likely to get office when a Labour Government came in; I even heard it suggested that he might get the Foreign Office. The notion was grotesque but not impossible. One day I had occasion to wind up a debate on foreign affairs which Griffiths had opened. He'd spoken for an hour. I thought it a very good opportunity to cook his goose, and by God, sir, I cooked it. I tore his speech to pieces. I pointed out the faultiness of his reasoning and emphasized the deficiency of his knowledge. In the House of Commons the most devastating weapon is ridicule: I mocked him; I bantered him; I was in good form that day and the House rocked with laughter. Their laughter excited me, and I excelled myself. The Opposition sat glum and silent, but even some of them couldn't help laughing once or twice; it's not intolerable, you know, to see a colleague, perhaps a rival, made a fool of. And if ever a man was made a fool of, I made a fool of Griffiths. He shrank down in his seat; I saw his face go white, and presently he buried it in his hands. When I sat down I'd killed him. I'd destroyed his prestige for ever; he had no more chance of getting office when a Labour Government came in than the policeman at the door. I heard afterwards that his father, the old miner, and his mother had come up from Wales, with various supporters of his in the constituency, to watch the triumph they expected him to have. They had seen only his utter humiliation. He'd won the constituency by the narrowest margin. An incident like that might very easily lose him his seat. But that was no business of mine."

"Should I be putting it too strongly if I said you had ruined his career?" asked Dr. Audlin.

"I don't suppose you would."

"That is a very serious injury you've done him."

"He brought it on himself."

"Have you never felt any qualms about it?"

"I think perhaps if I'd known that his father and mother were there I might have let him down a little more gently."

There was nothing further for Dr. Audlin to say, and he set about treating his patient in such a manner as he thought might avail. He sought by suggestion to make him forget his dreams when he awoke; he sought to make him sleep so deeply that he would not dream. He found Lord Mountdrago's resistance impossible to break down. At the end of an hour he dismissed him.

Since then he had seen Lord Mountdrago half a dozen times. He had done him no good. The frightful dreams continued every night to harass the unfortunate man, and it was clear that his general condition was growing rapidly worse. He was worn out. His irritability was uncontrollable. Lord Mountdrago was angry because he received no benefit from his treatment, and yet continued it, not only because it seemed his only hope, but because it was a relief to him to have someone with whom he could talk openly. Dr. Audlin came to the conclusion at last that there was only one way in which Lord Mountdrago could achieve deliverance, but he knew him well enough to be assured that of his own free will he would never, never take it. If Lord Mountdrago was to be saved from the breakdown that was threatening, he must be induced to take a step that must be abhorrent to his pride of birth and his self-complacency. Dr. Audlin was convinced that to delay was impossible. He was treating his patient by suggestion, and after several visits found him more susceptible to it. At length he managed to get him into a condition of somnolence. With his low, soft, monotonous voice he soothed his tortured nerves. He repeated the same words over and over again. Lord Mountdrago lay quite still, his eyes closed; his breathing was regular, and his limbs were relaxed. Then Dr. Audlin in the same quiet tone spoke the words he had prepared.

"You will go to Owen Griffiths and say that you are sorry that you caused him that great injury. You will say that you will do whatever lies in your power to undo the harm that you have done him."

The words acted on Lord Mountdrago like the blow of a whip across his face. He shook himself out of his hypnotic state and sprang to his feet. His eyes blazed with passion, and he poured forth upon Dr. Audlin a stream of angry vituperation such as even he had never heard. He swore at him. He cursed him. He used language of such obscenity that Dr. Audlin, who had heard every sort of foul word, sometimes from the lips of chaste and distinguished women, was surprised that he knew it.

"Apologize to that filthy little Welshman? I'd rather kill myself."

"I believe it to be the only way in which you can regain your balance."

Dr. Audlin had not often seen a man presumably sane in such a condition of uncontrollable fury. Lord Mountdrago grew red in the face, and his eyes bulged out of his head. He did really foam at the mouth. Dr. Audlin watched him coolly, waiting for the storm to wear itself out, and presently he saw that Lord Mountdrago, weakened by the strain to which he had been subjected for so many weeks, was exhausted.

"Sit down," he said then, sharply.

Lord Mountdrago crumpled up into a chair.

"Christ, I feel all in. I must rest a minute and then I'll go."

For five minutes perhaps they sat in complete silence. Lord Mountdrago was a gross, blustering bully, but he was also a gentleman. When he broke the silence he had recovered his self-control.

"I'm afraid I've been very rude to you. I'm ashamed of the things I've said to you, and I can only say you'd be justified if you refused to have anything more to do with me. I hope you won't do that. I feel that my visits to you do help me. I think you're my only chance."

"You mustn't give another thought to what you said. It was of no consequence."

"But there's one thing you mustn't ask me to do, and that is to make excuses to Griffiths."

"I've thought a great deal about your case. I don't pretend to understand it, but I believe that your only chance of release is to do what I proposed. I have a notion that we're none of us one self, but many, and one of the selves in you has risen up against the injury you did Griffiths and has taken on the form of Griffiths in your mind and is punishing you for what you cruelly did. If I were a priest I should tell you that it is your conscience that has adopted the shape and lineaments of this man to scourge you to repentance and persuade you to reparation."

"My conscience is clear. It's not my fault if I smashed the man's career. I crushed him like a slug in my garden. I regret nothing."

It was on these words that Lord Mountdrago had left him. Reading through his notes, while he waited, Dr. Audlin considered how best he could bring his patient to the state of mind that, now that his usual methods of treatment had failed, he thought alone could help him. He glanced at his clock. It was six. It was strange that Lord Mountdrago did not come. He knew he had intended to because a secretary had rung up that morning to say that he would be with him at the usual hour. He must have been detained by pressing work. This notion gave Dr. Audlin something else to think of: Lord Mountdrago was quite unfit to work and in no condition to deal with important matters of state. Dr. Audlin wondered whether it behooved him to get in touch with someone in authority, the Prime Minister or the Permanent Under Secretary for Foreign Affairs, and impart to him his conviction that Lord Mountdrago's mind was so unbalanced that it was dangerous to leave affairs of moment in his hands. It was a ticklish thing to do. He might cause needless trouble and get roundly snubbed for his pains. He shrugged his shoulders.

"After all," he reflected, "the politicians have made such a mess of the world during the last five-and-twenty years, I don't suppose it makes much odds if they're mad or sane."

He rang the bell.

"If Lord Mountdrago comes now, will you tell him that I have another appointment at six-fifteen and so I'm afraid I can't see him."

"Very good, sir."

"Has the evening paper come yet?"

"I'll go and see."

In a moment the servant brought it in. A huge headline ran across the front page: Tragic Death of Foreign Minister.

"My God!" cried Dr. Audlin.

For once he was wrenched out of his wonted calm. He was shocked, horribly shocked, and yet he was not altogether surprised. The possibility that Lord Mountdrago might commit suicide had occurred to him several times, for that it was suicide he could not doubt. The paper said that Lord Mountdrago had been waiting in a tube station, standing on the edge of the platform, and as the train came in was seen to fall on the rail. It was supposed that he had had a sudden attack of faintness. The paper went on to say that Lord Mountdrago had been suffering for some weeks from the effects of overwork, but had felt it impossible to absent himself while the foreign situation demanded his unremitting attention. Lord Mountdrago was another victim of the strain that modern politics placed upon those who played the more important parts in it. There was a neat little piece about the talents and industry, the patriotism and vision, of the deceased statesman, followed by various surmises upon the Prime Minister's choice of his successor. Dr. Audlin read all this. He had not liked Lord Mountdrago. The chief emotion that his death caused in him was dissatisfaction with himself because he had been able to do nothing for him.

Perhaps he had done wrong in not getting into touch with Lord Mountdrago's doctor. He was discouraged, as always when failure frustrated his conscientious efforts, and repulsion seized him for the theory and practice of this empiric doctrine by which he earned his living. He was dealing with dark and mysterious forces that it was perhaps beyond the powers of the human mind to understand. He was like a man blindfold trying to feel his way to he knew not whither. Listlessly he turned the pages of the paper. Suddenly he gave a great start, and an exclamation once more was forced from his lips. His eyes had fallen on a small paragraph near the bottom of a column. Sudden Death of an M.P., he read. Mr. Owen Griffiths, member for so-and-so, had been taken ill in Fleet Street that afternoon and when he was brought to Charing Cross Hospital life was found to be extinct. It was supposed that death was due to natural causes, but an inquest would be held. Dr. Audlin could hardly believe his eyes. Was it possible that the night before Lord Mountdrago had at last in his dream found himself possessed of the weapon, knife or gun, that he had wanted, and had killed his tormentor, and had that ghostly murder, in the same way as the blow with the bottle had given him a racking headache on the following day, taken effect a certain number of hours later on the waking man? Or was it, more mysterious and more frightful, that when Lord Mountdrago sought relief in death, the enemy he had so cruelly wronged, unappeased, escaping from his own mortality, had pursued him to some other sphere, there to torment him still? It was strange. The sensible thing was to look upon it merely as an odd coincidence. Dr. Audlin rang the bell.

"Tell Mrs. Milton that I'm sorry I can't see her this evening, I'm not well."

It was true; he shivered as though of an ague. With some kind of spiritual sense he seemed to envisage a bleak, a horrible void. The dark night of the soul engulfed him, and he felt a strange, primeval terror of he knew not what.

Vladimir Nabokov

Born in 1899 in Russia, an American citizen since 1945. His first novels were published under the pseudonym of V. Sirine. Recent works are Lolita *and* Pale Fire. The Visit to the Museum *appeared for the first time in a Russian language periodical in Paris in 1939.*

THE VISIT TO THE MUSEUM

Several years ago a friend of mine in Paris—a person with oddities, to put it mildly—learning that I was going to spend two or three days at Montisert, asked me to drop in at the local museum where there hung, he was told, a portrait of his grandfather by Leroy. Smiling and spreading out his hands, he related a rather vague story to which I confess I paid little attention, partly because I do not like other people's obtrusive affairs, but chiefly because I had always had doubts about my friend's capacity to remain on this side of fantasy. It went more or less as follows: after the grandfather died in their St. Petersburg house back at the time of the Russo-Japanese War, the contents of his apartment in Paris were sold at auction. The portrait, after some obscure peregrinations, was acquired by the museum of Leroy's native town. My friend wished to know if the portrait was really there; if there, if it could be ransomed; and if it could, for what price. When I asked why he did not get in touch with the museum he replied that he had written several times already but had never received an answer.

I made an inward resolution not to carry out the request—I could always tell him I had fallen ill or changed my itinerary. The very notion of seeing sights, whether they be museums or ancient buildings, is loathsome to me; and besides, the good freak's commission seemed absolute nonsense. It so happened, however, that, while wandering about Montisert's empty streets in search of a stationery store, and cursing the spire of a long-necked cathedral, always the same one, that kept popping up at the end of every street, I was caught in a violent downpour, which immediately went about accelerating the fall of the maple leaves, for the fair weather of a southern October was holding on by a mere thread. I dashed for cover and found myself on the steps of the museum.

It was a building of modest proportions, constructed of many-colored stones, with columns, a gilt inscription over the frescoes of the pediment, and a lion-legged stone bench on either side of the bronze door. One of its leaves stood open, and the interior seemed dark against the shimmer of the shower. I stood for a while on the steps, but, despite the overhanging roof, they were gradually growing speckled. I saw that the rain had set in for good, and so, having nothing better to do, I decided to go inside. No sooner had I trod on the smooth, resonant flagstones of the vestibule than the clatter of a moved stool came from a distant corner, and the custodian—a banal pensioner with an empty sleeve—rose to meet me, laying aside his newspaper and peering at me over his spectacles. I paid my franc and, trying not to look at some statues at the entrance (which were as traditional and as insignificant as the first number in a circus programme), I entered the main hall.

Everything was as it should be: gray tints, the sleep of substance, matter dematerialized. There was the usual case of old worn coins, resting on the inclined velvet of their compartments. There was, on top of the case, a pair of owls, Eagle Owl and Long-eared, with their French names reading Grand Duke and Middle Duke if translated. Venerable minerals lay in their open graves of dusty papier-mâché; a photograph of an astonished gentleman with a pointed beard dominated an assortment of strange black lumps of various sizes. They bore a great resemblance to frozen frass, and I paused involuntarily over them for I was quite at a loss to guess their nature, composition and function. The custodian had been following me with felted steps, always keeping a respectful distance; now, however, he came up, with one hand behind his back and the ghost of the other in his pocket, and gulping if one judged by his Adam's apple.

"What are they?" I asked.

"Science has not yet determined," he replied, undoubtedly having learned the phrase by rote. "They were found," he continued in the same phony tone, "in 1895, by Louis Pradier, Municipal Councilor and Knight of the Legion of Honor," and his trembling finger indicated the photograph.

"Well and good," I said, "but who decided, and why, that they merited a place in the museum?"

"And now I call your attention to this skull!" the old man cried energetically, obviously changing the subject.

"Still, I would be interested to know what they are made of," I interrupted.

"Science . . ." he began anew, but stopped short and looked crossly at his fingers which were soiled with dust from the glass.

I proceeded to examine a Chinese vase, probably brought back by a naval officer; a group of porous fossils; a pale worm in clouded alcohol; a red-and-green map of Montisert in the seventeenth century; and a trio of rusted tools, bound by a funereal ribbon—a spade, a mattock, and a pick. "To dig the past," I thought absent-mindedly, but this time did not seek clarification from the custodian, who was following me noiselessly and meekly, weaving in and out among the display cases. Beyond the first hall there was another, apparently the last, and in its center a large sarcophagus stood like a dirty bathtub, while the walls were hung with paintings.

At once my eye was caught by the portrait of a man, between two abominable landscapes (with cattle and "atmosphere"). I moved closer, and, to my considerable amazement, found the very object whose existence had hitherto seemed to me but the figment of an unstable mind. The man depicted in wretched oils wore a frock coat, whiskers and a large pince-nez on a cord; he bore a likeness to Offenbach, but, in spite of the work's vile conventionality, I had the feeling one could make out in his features the horizon of a resemblance, as it were, to my friend. In one corner, meticulously traced in carmine against a black background, was the signature Leroy in a hand as commonplace as the work itself.

I felt a vinegarish breath near my shoulder, and turned to meet the custodian's kindly gaze.

"Tell me," I asked, "supposing someone wished to buy one of these paintings, whom should he see?"

"The treasures of the museum are the pride of the city," replied the old man, "and pride is not for sale."

Fearing his eloquence, I hastily concurred, but nevertheless asked for the name of the museum's director. He tried to distract me with the story of the sarcophagus but I insisted. Finally he gave me the name of one M. Godard, and explained where I could find him.

Frankly, I enjoyed the thought that the portrait existed. It is fun to be present at the coming true of a dream, even if it is not one's own. I decided to settle the matter without delay. When I get in the spirit, no one can hold me back. I left the museum with a brisk, resonant step, and found that the rain had stopped, blueness had spread across the sky, a woman in besplattered stockings was spinning along on a silver-shining bicycle, and only over the surrounding hills did clouds still hang. Once again the cathedral began playing hide-and-seek with me, but I outwitted it. Barely escaping the onrushing tires of a furious red bus packed with singing youths, I crossed the asphalt thoroughfare, and a minute later was ringing at the garden gate of M. Godard. He turned out to be a thin middle-aged gentleman in high collar and dickey, with a pearl in the knot of his tie, and a face very much resembling a Russian wolfhound; as if that were not enough, he was licking his chops in a most dog-like manner while sticking a stamp on an envelope, when I entered his small but lavishly furnished room, with its malachite inkstand on the desk and a strangely familiar Chinese vase on the mantel. A pair of fencing foils hung crossed over the mirror which reflected the narrow gray back of his head. Photographs of a warship pleasantly broke up here and there the blue flora of the wallpaper.

"What can I do for you?" he asked, throwing the letter he had just sealed into the wastebasket. This action seemed unusual to me; however, I did not see fit to interfere. I explained in brief my reason for coming, even naming the substantial sum with which my friend was willing to part, though he had asked me not to mention it, and wait instead for the museum's terms.

"All this is delightful," said M. Godard. "The only thing is, you are mistaken—there is no such picture in our museum."

"What do you mean there is no such picture?" I exclaimed, "I have just seen it! 'Portrait of a Russian Nobleman,' by Gustave Leroy."

"We do have one Leroy," said M. Godard when he had leafed through an oilcloth notebook and his black fingernail had stopped at the entry in question. "However, it is not a portrait but a rural landscape: The Return of the Herd."

I repeated that I had seen the picture with my own eyes five minutes before, and that no power on earth could make me doubt its existence.

"Agreed," said M. Godard, "but I am not crazy either. I have been curator of our museum for almost twenty years now and know this catalog as well as I know the Lord's Prayer. It says here 'Return of the Herd' and that means the herd is returning, and, unless perhaps your friend's grandfather is depicted as a shepherd, I cannot conceive of his portrait's existence in our museum."

"He is wearing a frock coat," I cried, "I swear he is wearing a frock coat!"

"And how did you like our museum in general?" M. Godard asked suspiciously. "Did you appreciate the sarcophagus?"

"Listen," I said (and I think there was already a tremor in my voice), "do me a favor—let's go there this minute, and let's make an agreement that if the portrait is there you will sell it."

"And if not?" inquired M. Godard.

"I shall pay you the sum anyway."

"All right," he said. "Here, take this red-and-blue pencil and using the red—the red, please—put it in writing for me."

In my excitement I carried out his demand. Upon glancing at my signature, he deplored the difficult pronunciation of Russian names. Then he appended his own signature and, quickly folding the sheet, thrust it into his waistcoat pocket.

"Let's go," he said freeing a cuff.

On the way he stepped into a shop and bought a bag of sticky-looking caramels which he began offering me insistently; when I flatly refused, he tried to shake out a couple of them into my hand. I pulled my hand away. Several caramels fell on the sidewalk; he stopped to pick them up and then overtook me at a trot. When we drew near the museum, we saw the red tourist bus (now empty) parked outside.

"Aha," said M. Godard, pleased, "I see we have many visitors today."

He doffed his hat and, holding it in front of him, walked decorously up the steps.

All was not well at the museum. From within issued rowdy cries, lewd laughter, and even what seemed like the sound of a scuffle. We entered the first hall; there the elderly custodian was restraining two sacrilegists who wore some kind of festive emblems in their lapels and were altogether very purple-faced and full of pep as they tried to extract the municipal councilor's merds from beneath the glass. The rest of the youths, members of some rural athletic organization, were making noisy fun, some of the worm in alcohol, others of the skull. One joker was in rapture over the pipes of the steam radiator, which he pretended to take for an exhibit; another was taking aim at an owl with his fist and forefinger. There were about thirty of them in all, and their motion and voices created a condition of crush and thick noise.

M. Godard clapped his hands and pointed at a sign reading "Visitors to the museum must be decently attired." Then he pushed his way, with me following, into the second hall. The whole company immediately swarmed after us. I steered Godard to the portrait; he froze before it, chest inflated, and then stepped back a bit, as if admiring it, and his feminine heel trod on somebody's foot.

"Splendid picture," he exclaimed with genuine sincerity. "Well, let's not be petty about this. You were right, and there must be an error in the catalog."

As he spoke, his fingers, moving as it were on their own, tore up our agreement into little bits which fell like snowflakes into a massive spittoon.

"Who's the old ape?" asked an individual in a striped jersey, and, as my friend's grandfather was depicted holding a glowing cigar, another funster took out a cigarette and prepared to borrow a light from the portrait.

"All right, let us settle on the price," I said, "and, in any case, let's get out of here."

"Make way, please!" shouted M. Godard, pushing aside the curious.

There was an exit, which I had not noticed previously, at the end of the hall, and we thrust our way through to it.

"I can make no decision," M. Godard was shouting above the din. "Decisiveness is a good thing only when supported by law. I must first discuss the matter with the mayor, who has just died and has not yet been elected. I doubt that you will be able to purchase the portrait, but nonetheless I would like to show you still other treasures of ours."

We found ourselves in a hall of considerable dimensions. Brown books, with a half-baked look and coarse foxed pages, lay open under glass on a long table. Along the walls stood dummy soldiers in jackboots with flared tops.

"Come, let's talk it over," I cried out in desperation, trying to direct M. Godard's evolutions to a plush-covered sofa in a corner. But in this I was prevented by the custodian. Flailing his one arm, he came running after us, pursued by a merry crowd of youths, one of whom had put on his head a copper helmet with a Rembrandtesque gleam.

"Take it off, take it off!" shouted M. Godard, and someone's shove made the helmet fly off the hooligan's head with a clatter.

"Let us move on," said M. Godard, tugging at my sleeve, and we passed into the Section of Ancient Sculpture.

I lost my way for a moment among some enormous marble legs and twice ran around a giant knee, before I again caught sight of M. Godard who was looking for me behind the white ankle of a neighboring giantess. Here a person in a bowler, who must have clambered up her, suddenly fell from a great height to the stone floor. One of his companions began helping him up, but they were both drunk, and, dismissing them with a wave of the hand, M. Godard rushed on to the next room, radiant with oriental fabrics; here hounds raced across azure carpets, and a bow and quiver lay on a tiger skin.

Strangely, though, the expanse and motley only gave me a feeling of oppressiveness and imprecision, and, perhaps because new visitors kept dashing by, or perhaps because I was impatient to leave the unnecessarily spreading museum and amid calm and freedom conclude my business negotiations with M. Godard, I began to experience a vague sense of alarm. Meanwhile we had transported ourselves into yet another hall, which must have been really enormous, judging by the fact that it housed the entire skeleton of a whale resembling a frigate's frame; beyond were visible still other halls, with the oblique sheen of large paintings, full of storm clouds, among which floated the delicate idols of religious art in blue and pink vestments; and all this resolved itself in an abrupt turbulence of misty draperies, and chandeliers came aglitter, and fish with translucent frills meandered through illuminated aquariums. Racing up a staircase, we saw, from the gallery above, a crowd of gray-haired people with umbrellas examining a gigantic mock-up of the universe.

At last, in a somber but magnificent room dedicated to the history of steam machines, I managed to halt my carefree guide for an instant.

"Enough!" I shouted. "I'm leaving. We'll talk tomorrow."

He had already vanished. I turned and saw, scarcely an inch from me, the lofty wheels of a sweaty locomotive. For a long time I tried to find the way back among models of railroad stations. How strangely glowed the violet signals in the gloom beyond the fan of wet tracks, and what spasms shook my poor heart! Suddenly everything changed again: in front of me stretched an infinitely long passage, containing numerous office cabinets and elusive, scurrying people. Taking a sharp turn, I found myself amid a thousand musical instruments; the wall, all mirror, reflected an enfilade of grand pianos, while in the center there was a pool with a bronze Orpheus atop a green rock. The acquatic theme did not end here, as, racing back, I ended up in the Section of Fountains and Brooks, and it was difficult to walk along the winding, slimy edges of those waters.

Now and then, on one side or the other, stone stairs, with puddles on the steps which gave me a strange sensation of fear, would descend into misty abysses, whence issued whistles, the rattle of dishes, the clatter of typewriters, the ring of hammers and many other sounds, as if, down there, were exposition halls of some kind or other, already closing or not yet completed. Then I found myself in darkness and kept bumping into unknown furniture until I finally saw a red light and walked out onto a platform that clanged under me—and suddenly, beyond it, there was a bright parlor, tastefully furnished in Empire style, but not a living soul, not a living soul . . . By this time I was indescribably terrified, but every time I turned and tried to retrace my steps along the passages, I found myself in hitherto unseen places—a greenhouse with hydrangeas and broken windowpanes, with the darkness of artificial night showing through beyond; or a deserted laboratory with dusty alembics on its tables. Finally I ran into a room of some sort with coat racks, monstrously loaded down with black coats and astrakhan furs; from beyond a door came a burst of applause but when I flung the door open, there was no theater, but only a soft opacity and splendidly counterfeited fog with the perfectly convincing blotches of indistinct street lights. More than convincing! I advanced, and immediately a joyous and unmistakable sensation of reality at last replaced all the unreal trash amid which I had just been dashing to and fro. The stone beneath my feet was real sidewalk, powdered with wonderfully fragrant newly fallen snow in which the infrequent pedestrians had already left fresh black tracks. At first the quiet and the snowy coolness of the night, somehow strikingly familiar, gave me a pleasant feeling after my feverish wanderings. Trustfully, I started to conjecture just where I had come out, and why the snow, and what were those lights exaggeratedly but indistinctly beaming here and there in the brown darkness. I examined, and, stooping, even touched a round spur stone on the curb, then glanced at the palm of my hand, full of wet granular cold, as if hoping to read an explanation there. I felt how lightly, how naïvely I was clothed, but the distinct realization that I had escaped from the museum's maze was still so strong that, for the first two or three minutes, I experienced neither surprise nor fear. Continuing my leisurely examination, I looked up at the house beside which I was standing and was immediately struck by the sight of iron steps and railings that descended into the snow on their way to the cellar. There was a twinge in my heart, and it was with a new, alarmed, curiosity that I glanced at the pavement, at its white cover along which stretched black lines, at the brown sky, across which there kept sweeping a mysterious light, and at the massive parapet some distance away. I sensed that there was a drop beyond it, something was creaking and gurgling down there. Further on, beyond the murky cavity, stretched a chain of fuzzy lights. Scuffling along the snow in my soaked shoes, I walked a few paces, all the time glancing at the dark house on my right; only in a single window did a lamp glow softly under its green glass shade. Here, a locked wooden gate. . . . There, what must be the shutters of a sleeping shop . . . And by the light of a street lamp whose shape had long been shouting to me its impossible message, I made out the ending of a sign: "*. . . . inka Sapog*" ("*. . . oe Repair*"), but no, it was not the snow that had obliterated the "hard sign" at the end.* "No, no, in a minute I shall wake up," I said aloud, and, trembling, my heart pounding, I turned, walked on, stopped again. From somewhere came the receding sound of hooves, cushioned, lazy and even; the snow sat like a skullcap on a slightly leaning spur stone, and indistinctly showed white on the wood pile on the other side of the fence, and already I knew, irrevocably, where I was. Alas, it was not the Russia I remembered, but the factual Russia of today, forbidden to me, hopelessly slavish, and hopelessly my own native land. A semi-phantom in a light foreign suit, I stood on the impassive snow of an October night, somewhere on the Moyka or the Fontanka Canal, or perhaps on the Obvodny, and I had to do something, go somewhere, to desperately protect my fragile, my illegal life. Oh, how many times, in my sleep, I had experienced a similar sensation! Now, though, it was reality. Everything was real —the air that seemed to mingle with scattered snowflakes, the still unfrozen canal, the floating fish house, and that peculiar squareness of the darkened and the yellow windows. A man in fur cap, with a

* After the Revolution, the "hard sign," appearing after consonants at the end of the word, was eliminated from the alphabet.

briefcase under his arm, came toward me out of the fog, gave me a startled glance, and turned to look again when he had passed me. I waited for him to disappear and then, with tremendous haste, began pulling out everything I had in my pockets, ripping up papers, throwing them into the snow and stamping them down. There were some documents, a letter from my sister in Paris, five hundred francs, a handkerchief, cigarettes—however, in order to shed all the integument of exile, I would have to tear off and destroy my clothes, my linen, my shoes, everything, and remain ideally naked; and, even though I was already shivering from my anguish and from the cold, I did what I could.

But enough. I shall not recount how I was arrested, nor tell of my subsequent ordeals. Suffice it to say that it cost me incredible patience and effort to get back abroad, and that, ever since, I have foresworn carrying out commissions entrusted one by the insanity of others.

Paris, 1938

Translated from the Russian
by Dmitri Nabokov

Louis Golding

1895-1958

English poet and novelist, born in Manchester. His best-known works are Magnolia Street, The Pursuer, Five Silver Daughters, The Dance Goes On, The World I Knew, *and* The Dangerous Places.

PALE BLUE NIGHTGOWN

Mr. Dofferty was tall and thin and had big hands and feet. The small boys called him 'Lampy,' which was an abbreviation of 'Lamp-post.' He hated the small boys calling him 'Lampy,' not only because he was sensitive about his appearance, but because he hated small boys. He would rather have taken the top form in a refined girls' school and would have got on very well there. He could have talked about Swinburne with the girls, and about his foreign travels. 'Was there ever really a Dolores, Mr. Dofferty?' 'Do the young warriors in Kashmir still go out to battle with roses behind their ears?' He would have been very happy with a top form at a refined girls' school.

But it had not worked out that way. He was getting on in years by the time he got his teacher's certificate, and he could not pick and choose. He became a pupil-teacher at a boys' school in Doomington. They were common boys.

In the course of time he became headmaster.

He knew that he deserved better things. He let it be known that he had travelled about the East quite a lot in his young days; and it was true, for he had been the son of a non-commissioned officer out in India. Later, he was employed on a tea plantation in Ceylon. When that failed, he came to England to take up teaching.

He was very proud of having travelled in the East. His 'sanctum,' as he called it, was cluttered with eastern curios. There were prayer wheels and fly whisks, curtains and cushions, elephants carved in ebony, ash trays and pen trays of Benares ware, a Malay kris he used as a paper knife, a soapstone Buddha he used as a paper weight. It was not very suitable furniture for a headmaster's room in a poor boys' school in Doomington, but it put people in their place. It put him in his place, too. He was a traveller, an empire-builder.

He did not feel so sure of himself when he went out into the playground. He would have preferred to stay in his sanctum, but he had a feeling that the small boys took to talking and laughing about him when they got together. He would stand for a long time, quite still, behind the windows of one of the classrooms, and then, all of a sudden, he was a few inches behind you. For a person with such large feet, he moved very quickly and quietly over the gravel.

The school day came to an end at half-past four. It was bad enough when the boys collected in the play-intervals between lessons, but when the last lesson was over there was absolutely no excuse for them to be hanging about, whispering, and pointing with their thumbs over their shoulders.

On the day in Mr. Dofferty's history with which this tale is concerned, there was an unusually large troop of boys assembled near the wood-work room, at the bottom end of the playground.

Mr. Dofferty happened to be at the top end of the playground. He observed that only one of the boys was talking, a small, pale boy named Albert Hewitt. The rest were listening. At least, they were listening in the intervals of laughing. The narrative with which Albert Hewitt was regaling them seemed to entertain them mightily, though Albert himself seemed not at all amused. On the contrary, his spotty little face seemed paler than usual; his eyes seemed to stand quite a long way out of his head.

Mr. Dofferty did not like Albert Hewitt; he thought him a soapy, sneaky sort of boy. He had had occasion more than once to take him into his sanctum and use the cane on him.

What was the boy doing, holding forth at this time of day, when well-behaved boys should be making tracks for home, with their heads filled with the night's homework? What and who was there to talk about that was so frightfully funny?

Of course; Mr. Dofferty could swear to it . . . 'Lampy,' and once again, 'Lampy.' It was a long way from the bottom end to the top end of the playground, but Mr. Dofferty had extraordinarily acute hearing. 'Lampy' again, and a roar of laughter. The boy was talking about his headmaster; he was making jokes about his headmaster. Mr. Dofferty's lips set thin and hard.

Mr. Dofferty made a sort of sideways movement on a segment of a wide circle towards the group of boys. He looked a bit like a huntsman keeping to windward of his quarry. The maneuver was successful. He had come up to within a few yards of them, always in the rear of Albert Hewitt, before the boys became aware of him. Then, suddenly, the boys caught sight of him: all but Albert Hewitt. One moment later, they had scuttled away, like a warren-full of rabbits shocked into a hedge by a footstep.

A hand came down heavily on Albert Hewitt's shoulder.

'You were talking about me, I think,' said Mr. Dofferty. His voice was gentle.

Albert Hewitt's body quivered under the great hand. He did not dare to turn round.

'No, sir, Mr. Dofferty, I wasn't,' said the small boy.

'You were referring to me by another name,' pointed out Mr. Dofferty.

'No, sir, Mr. Dofferty, I wasn't,' the small boy said again. His voice was hardly more than a whisper.

Mr. Dofferty removed his hand from Albert Hewitt's shoulder.

'Perhaps you'll turn round, Albert,' he suggested.

Albert turned round. He did not dare to look up into Mr. Dofferty's face, cold and remote. The thin thighs of the headmaster seemed to soar into space, like trees. The playground was appallingly empty, but for himself and the soft voice that came down from so high.

'I would like you to look into my face,' requested Mr. Dofferty. 'Will you?'

The small boy did as he was told. Mr. Dofferty continued 'Excellent, Albert. Now, I feel quite certain you won't lie to me. You *were* referring to me by a name which I have forbidden the school to use. Is that not so, Albert?'

'Yes sir,' whispered the small boy.

His lips started quivering. He found it as difficult not to lower his eyes from Mr. Dofferty's eyes as it had been difficult a moment ago to raise them.

'Now, now,' Mr. Dofferty wagged his finger almost playfully. 'Don't make an exhibition of yourself. No harm will come to you, so long as you're a good boy and speak up. What was it you were saying to those boys, Albert? Come, come, Albert, what was it?'

The boy said not a word. He stared up into Mr. Dofferty's eyes, as if he had neither ears nor tongue.

'What are you staring at me like that for?' barked Mr. Dofferty. 'Is there anything wrong with me?'

The boy's head sagged suddenly towards his chest.

'Well, Albert!' The headmaster's voice had become gentle as a dove's again. 'Are you going to tell me what it was you were saying about me?'

'I wasn't saying nothing,' Albert said. His lower lip projected a little. He looked sullen.

'Obstinate, eh?' said Mr. Dofferty, quite gaily now. 'You know, Albert,' he almost wheedled, 'it will be a lot better for you if you tell me what you were saying.'

'I wasn't saying nothing,' Albert repeated.

'I see,' Mr. Dofferty said shortly. He raised his eyes to roof-level and joined his hands behind his back. He seemed to be communing with himself. Then he spoke again. His tone was very matter-of-fact. 'If you go on disobeying me, I'll take you into the sanctum and thrash you. Do you hear?'

The boy said nothing.

'Do you hear?' he asked again, more grimly.

'Yes, sir,' the boy mumbled.

'Very well, then. Are you going to tell me what you were saying to the boys?'

'No, sir.'

'I'll take you into the sanctum and thrash you within an inch of your life. Are you going to tell me?'

Again silence.

'Are you going to tell me?' Mr. Dofferty reached down and got his fingers round the boy's arm.

With a quick involuntary gesture the boy wrenched his arm free.

'It was only a dream!' he cried. 'Let me go home!'

'Oh, it was only a dream?' said Mr. Dofferty, easily. 'Why didn't you say so before, you silly boy?' His heart felt curiously lighter. He took his watch out of his waistcoat pocket. 'You're right!' he exclaimed. 'It's time we were both going home!' His voice was quite genial.

'Oh, thank you, thank you very much, sir!' cried Albert. 'Good afternoon, Mr. Dofferty.' The boy was already scampering off.

'Oh, by the way!' the headmaster called after him.

The boy turned. 'Yes, sir?' he asked fearfully.

Mr. Dofferty did not say anything for a moment or two. He realized, in fact, he had nothing to say. He was merely aware that he did not like the boy going off like that, as if he had not used the forbidden nickname, as if he were innocent as the shorn lamb. Then he found his lips uttering a question concerning which his mind had no curiosity at all. For, after all, what interest was it to Mr. Dofferty, headmaster, Mr. Dofferty, world-traveller, what dream a snivelling, little elementary schoolboy might dream?

'What did you dream about, Albert?'

The boy's jaw fell. The faint flush of colour that had come up into his face went out completely.

'Nothing,' he muttered.

'Nonsense!' said Mr. Dofferty. 'You were dreaming about me, weren't you?'

Then, suddenly, Mr. Dofferty remembered how amused all the small boys had been while Albert Hewitt had been holding forth. He had been telling them his dream, of course, a dream about their headmaster.

Mr. Dofferty blushed. It was in the last degree undignified for a person in his position to insist on ferreting out a small boy's dream, whatever the dream was about. But he could not bear the way the boy was lying to him. If the boy would only own up simply and honestly, they could go home, both of them. He was beginning to want his tea.

'Well, are you going to say something?' asked Mr. Dofferty.

The boy was as silent as a lump of wood.

Mr. Dofferty, suddenly, lost patience. 'Very well, then. You will please come along with me.'

He strode forward towards the big door in the middle of the building. The boy hesitated for one moment. He looked round wildly. It was impossible to get away from those long legs. And there would be a tomorrow, and a tomorrow after that.

The sanctum was a room on the right-hand side of the main corridor. Mr. Dofferty took out his bunch of keys and unlocked the door.

'This way,' he said frigidly.

The boy followed. He knew the way well enough. There was a faint smell in the air which turned his stomach, as it had been turned once or twice before. Mr. Dofferty burned joss-sticks, now and again, when his nostalgia for the East got him badly.

The headmaster went over to the table in the middle of the room and carefully removed two or three of his oriental knickknacks—the soapstone Buddha he used as a paper weight, the ivory-handled Malay kris he used as a paper knife, the heavy brass Chinese seal. He sat down in the space thus cleared and reached casually along the table for his cane.

'Stand here,' he ordered the boy. The boy came and stood beside him. 'What was your dream about?'

The boy stood obdurate.

'You're not going to tell me?' Mr. Dofferty roared. 'So, you're not going to tell me?' He lifted the cane high in air, ready to strike.

'I'll tell you!' the boy shouted suddenly. 'Please, sir, I'll tell you!'

Mr. Dofferty's face was as white as a tablecloth, his lips were almost as white. 'Very well, then! Go on!'

'I—I—dreamed'—the boy whimpered. 'I—I—dreamed—that I—' Then he looked up beseechingly. 'I *can't* tell you, sir!' he wailed.

'I think you can,' said the other.

The boy swallowed hard. 'I dreamed in my dream, sir, you was wearing—you was wearing——'

'Go on!'

'You was wearing a long nightgown, sir. It was a silk one, sir, pale blue silk. And—and——' Again the words stuck in the boy's throat. The sweat poured down his cheeks. His fists shut and opened as if they were catching at something that eluded them.

Mr. Dofferty was not aware of the boy's discomfort. He was aware only of his own. He knew he had never felt so ridiculous in all his life before. He had never felt so humiliated. His face was as red as a cock's comb. His ears blazed.

'Go on!' he said thickly. 'Anything more?' He wanted to get through with it, to get it behind him, to kick the miserable little brat into the gutter he came from.

'Yes sir!' blubbered the boy. 'You was wearing a wreath of daisies round your head!'

'I see,' whispered Mr. Dofferty.

But he did not mean that he himself saw. He meant that the small boys saw, the small boys who had laughed uproariously when Albert had told them his dream. He saw with their eyes his own unspeakable grotesqueness—pale blue nightgown and wreath of daisies.

Why didn't the small boy get to hell out of it? What was the blob of dirt hanging about for? He must take himself in hand. He must not let the boy realize how naked he had left him, shivering in the whistling blackness, with only a pale blue nightgown round his skinny body, a wreath of daisies for headgear.

'Is that all?' he asked, with a deadly attempt at casualness.

Then the boy gave tongue, with a voice so shrill and terrible that it seemed to pierce the eardrums.

'That's all!' he screamed. 'I tell you that's all! I didn't dream nothing more! Nothing at all!'

The eyes glared. The jaw was so rigid that the words came through with the effect of ventriloquy.

For the first time in the encounter Mr. Dofferty's intellectual interest was aroused. He forgot his anger with the boy and his shame of himself. He was conscious only of an exceeding curiosity. What more was it the boy had dreamed, the terror of which made him a gibbering idiot? What on earth could it be? He licked his lips, appreciatively. The whole thing really was extraordinarily interesting.

'Listen, Albert,' he said coaxingly. 'Don't be frightened. I know you dreamed something more. I'd like to know what it was. Won't you tell me?'

'Nothing more! I didn't dream nothing more!' The boy stamped his feet.

'I assure you, you're going to tell me!' Mr. Dofferty said. 'You might as well tell me now as later.'

He was not going to have the struggle start all over again. He was feeling completely worn out. He got down from the table. The cane had fallen to the floor. He reached down and lifted it. He swished it through the air.

'Won't you tell me, Albert?' he asked once again.

The boy said nothing.

'Won't you tell me, Albert?' he repeated.

The boy still said nothing.

Then the man's patience snapped. The cane went hissing into the air and came screaming down again. He did not know where it landed, on the boy's hands, body, or face.

The boy did not know, either. He knew nothing more excepting that the whole world was a blackness with a great wind roaring in it. Then, at last, the wind ceased roaring and there was light in the world again.

He became aware that he was in the sanctum of Mr. Dofferty, his headmaster. He became aware of Mr. Dofferty's body extended interminably between his own legs and the legs of the table. The Malay kris that Mr. Dofferty used as a paper knife stuck out from between his ribs.

The boy leaned forward, pointing towards the ivory handle, where the blood gushed above the blade.

'That's what I dreamed!' his lips went. 'That's what I dreamed!'

Henry Kuttner 1914-1958 and Catherine L. Moore

American writers who, in collaboration, have written many science-fiction stories. Henry Kuttner wrote under numerous pseudonyms (Lawrence O'Donnell, C. H. Liddell, etc.).

"Do you feel that you are dreaming now, Mr. Hooten?" Dr. Scott asked gently.

Timothy Hooten evaded the psychiatrist's eyes. He fingered the smooth leather of the chair arms, found the sensation unsatisfactory, and turned his head to gaze out the window at the Empire State's tower.

"It's like a dream, isn't it?" he said evasively.

"What is?"

"That." Hooten nodded at the needle-like mooring mast on the top of the tower. "Imagine mooring a dirigible to that thing. They never did, did they? It's just the sort of thing that would happen in a dream. You know. Big plans, and then somehow everybody forgets about it and starts something new. Oh, I don't know. Things get unreal."

Solipsism, Dr. Scott thought, but suspended judgment.

"What things?" he murmured.

"You, for example," Hooten said. "You've got the wrong shape."

"Can you amplify that, Mr. Hooten?"

"Well, I don't know that I can," Hooten said, looking with faint alarm at his own hands. "I've got the wrong shape too, you see."

"Do you know what the right shape is?"

Hooten closed his eyes and thought hard. A look of astonishment passed fleetingly across his face. He scowled. Dr. Scott, studying him closely, made a note on a desk pad.

"No," Hooten said, opening his eyes very wide and assuming a negativistic attitude. "I haven't the least idea."

"Don't you want to tell me?"

"I—ah—I don't know. I simply don't know."

"Why did you come to see me, Mr. Hooten?"

"My doctor said I should. So did my wife."

"Do you feel they were right?"

"Personally," Hooten said, with an air of quiet triumph, "I don't feel that it makes the least difference what I do in a dream. Imagine walking on two legs!" He paused, startled. "Maybe I shouldn't have said that," he added.

Dr. Scott smiled slightly.

"Suppose you tell me a little more about the dream."

"About now, you mean? It's just that everything's wrong. Even talking. Wiggling the tongue this way." Hooten fingered his jaw exploringly, and Dr. Scott made another note. "I'm dreaming, that's all."

"Are you ever awake?"

"Only when I'm asleep," Hooten said. "How strange that sounds. I wonder what I mean."

"This is the dream world?" Dr. Scott asked.

"Of course."

"Can you tell me what your problem is, Mr. Hooten?"

"I haven't any problems," Hooten said, surprised. "If I had, they'd just be dream problems, wouldn't they?"

"Do you have problems when you're—awake?"

"I'm sure I must have," the patient said. He looked thoughtful. "It seems to me I've got a psychiatrist in the real world, too. That's where my conscious mind is. This, of course, is my unconscious."

"Can you tell me a little more about that?"

Hooten closed his eyes again.

"I'll try," he said. "When I'm asleep, you see, when I'm dreaming, the conscious mind is unconscious. That's here and now. Well, in the real, waking world—the other world—I think my psychiatrist is trying to probe into my unconscious. What seems to you like my waking mind."

"Very interesting," Dr. Scott said. "This other psychiatrist, now, could you describe him? What kind of a man is he?"

"Man?" Hooten said, opening his eyes again. He hesitated. Then he shook his head. "I don't know, exactly. I can't remember what things are like in the real world. Different. That I know. Quite, quite different." He spread out his hand and regarded it thoughtfully. He turned it over and looked at the lines of his palm. "My, my," he murmured. "What won't they think of next."

"Try to remember," Dr. Scott urged.

"I have tried. You dream-people keep telling me to try. But it's no use. I must have a block in my mind," he finished triumphantly.

"We must try to find out what this block is, then. I'd like to try a little test, Mr. Hooten, if you don't mind. I'm going to show you a picture, and I want you to tell me a story about it."

"Make up a story, you mean?"

"Exactly," Dr. Scott said, and handed Hooten a large card, on which were inartistically depicted two ambiguous and semi-shapeless figures.

"How strange," Hooten said. "Their bones are inside them."

"Go on."

"They're two psychiatrists," Hooten murmured. "Anyone could see that. One's awake and one's asleep. One's real and one isn't. They're both treating me. One is named Scott and the other—the other—"

"Go on," Scott said.

"—is named—"

"What is his name?"

"Rasp," Hooten said faintly. "Dr. Rasp. I have an appointment with him at two o'clock in the morning, when I'm awake."

"Do you feel that you are dreaming now?" Dr. Rasp telepathized gently.

Timothy Hooten evaded the psychiatrist's faceted gaze. He swung his oval body around to stare out the sky-slit at the distant polyhedron of the Quatt Wunkery. Then he waved his antennae gently and clicked his mandibles.

"It's like a dream, isn't it?" he said evasively, though naturally not audibly. "Imagine building a Wunkery simply to pleat Quatts. Of course they never showed up. That sort of thing could happen only in a dream. Oh, you can't convince me. This *is* a dream. Imagine walking around on all sixes."

Dr. Rasp scratched a memorandum on his left wing-case.

"How do you think you should walk?" he asked.

"I wonder," Hooten said. "I do it all the time when I'm awake, but this is one of those recurrent dreams where I seem to get amnesia. I've tried and tried to remember what it's like, but it's no use. It's like trying to pleat Quatts in a Wunkery. Oh, how idiotic."

"Just what is your problem, Mr. Hooten?"

"Well, this absurd body I'm wearing, for one thing. My bones are in the wrong place." Hooten's faceted eyes glittered in a startled fashion. "Did I just say that? A minute ago, I mean? It reminds me of something."

"No," Dr. Rasp said. "What does it remind you of?"

Hooten irritably scratched his belly with a hind foot. There was a sharp, scraping sound.

"I've forgotten," he said.

"I would like to try a little test," Dr. Rasp said. "I'm going to project a thought, and I would like you to tell me what it makes you think of. Are you ready?"

"I suppose so," Hooten said.

Dr. Rasp projected a curly nebular thought. Hooten studied it.

"That's my conscious mind," he pointed out presently. "It might be an Angry Curler—the kind that live in the Antipodes, I mean—but what it reminds me of is my conscious mind, because of the psychiatrist swimming around in the middle of it."

"Psychiatrist?" Dr. Rasp inquired, surprised.

"He's treating my conscious mind—I think," Hooten explained uncertainly. "He lives in the waking world with my conscious. You and I, Dr. Rasp, inhabit my unconscious, here and now. This other doctor—he's treating both of us."

"This other doctor does not exist," Dr. Rasp telepathized rather sourly. Then he caught himself and went on in a more professional tone, "Tell me about him, Mr. Hooten. What does this psychiatrist look like?"

"Tartuffe," said Hooten, to the surprise of Dr. Rasp, who had never heard the name. "No, Tartan. No, Scott. That's it. A psychiatrist named Dr. Scott who lives in my conscious mind. I have an appointment with him at two P.M. tomorrow, when I'm awake."

Timothy Hooten looked out the window at the Empire State Building. He was taking a word association test.

"Home," Dr. Scott said.

"Estivate," Hooten replied.

"Sex."

"Eggs."

"Mother."

"Larva."

"Psychiatrist."

"Bugs," Hooten said.

Dr. Scott paused. "Larva," he said.

"Clouds of glory," Hooten said briskly. "Trailing."

"Bugs," Dr. Scott said.

"Awake."

"Glory."

"Nuptial flight," Hooten said rather dreamily.

Dr. Scott made a note.

"Bugs," he said.

"Appointment. Two A.M. Dr. Rasp."

"This word *man,*" Dr. Rasp said. "It keeps cropping up in your mind. Exactly what does it mean?"

"I haven't the least idea," Hooten told him, looking through the sky-slit at the Quatt Wunkery.

"What does it make you think of?"

"Being awake," Hooten said.

Dr. Rasp rubbed his right mandible.

"I'd like to try a little experiment," he said. "You've been coming here for nearly twelve glitters, and we still haven't got past that block in your mind. You're resisting me, you know."

"I can't help it if I'm dreaming, can I?" Hooten demanded.

"That's the exact point. Are you trying to evade responsibility?"

"Certainly not," Hooten said with dignity. "Not when I'm awake. But I'm not awake now. You're not real. *I'm* not real—at least, this ridiculous body of mine isn't. And as for the Quatt Wunkery—!"

"The experiment I'd like to try," Dr. Rasp said, "is a matter of quasi-estivation. Do you know what that is?"

"Certainly," Hooten said glibly. "Hypnosis."

"I don't think I know the word," Dr. Rasp said. "What does it mean?"

"Quasi-estivation. My conscious mind blanks out and my unconscious mind cuts in."

Dr. Rasp suppressed whatever reaction he might have had to this lucid explanation. "Very well," he said, extending his antennae. "Shall we try it? Just relax. Let your wing-cases hang. Open your mandibles just a little. That's right." He crossed antennae with Hooten and looked fixedly into the patient's faceted eyes with his own. "Now you are estivating. You are in a burrow. It is warm and delightfully musty. You are curled up and estivating. Are you estivating?"

"Yes," Hooten telepathized dully.

"There is a block in your mind. Something in your mind is fighting me. Something keeps insisting that you are dreaming. In a short time I shall order you to wake up. Will you obey me?"

"Yes."

"Will you be awake then?"

"No."

"Why not?"

"Because you're a dream," the estivated Hooten said languidly.

"Who says so?"

"Dr. Scott."

"There is no Dr. Scott," Dr. Rasp said with great firmness. "Dr. Scott is imaginary. Your unconscious mind has created Dr. Scott, to protect itself. You do not want to find out what is really troubling you, and so you have created another psychiatrist to fight me. But he does not really exist. There are no such creatures as *men*. Their world is imaginary. Dr. Scott is just a censor in your mind. He is not real. Do you understand that?"

Hooten's antennae twiddled.

"Y-yes," he said reluctantly.

"Is Dr. Scott real?"

"Certainly," Hooten said. "I've got an appointment with him at two P.M. He's going to give me narcosynthesis." He added kindly, "That is a form of estivation."

There was a pause.

Then Dr. Rasp said, "You will return to *this* office at two P.M. You will not keep your appointment with Dr. Scott. You will undergo quasi-estivation again. Do you understand?"

"But I . . . yes."

"When I count to minus one you will wake up. Minus ten, minus nine. . . ."

At minus one Hooten woke up. He looked uneasily at Dr. Rasp.

"What happened?" he inquired.

"We are making progress," the psychiatrist said. "I think it wise that we continue the treatment as soon as possible. Suppose you meet me here at two P.M.

"Two P.M.?" Hooten said. "What an unearthly hour."

"I have a reason," Dr. Rasp said.

"I'm sorry to be late," Hooten said, coming into Dr. Scott's office. "I guess I was daydreaming or something."

"That's all right," Dr. Scott said. "Are you ready for the narcosynthesis?"

"Oh, I suppose so," Hooten said. "But I've got a funny feeling."

"What kind of a feeling?"

"That I'm beginning to wake up."

Dr. Scott looked pleased.

"Well, suppose you take off your coat and roll up your left sleeve. Lie on the couch there, that's right. Now I'm going to give you an injection, and you'll begin to feel sleepy. Simply relax. That's all you have to do."

"Ouch," Hooten said.

"That's all there is to it," Dr. Scott said, withdrawing the hypodermic. "Suppose you look at something and tell me when it begins to look blurry."

"All right," Hooten said obediently, staring out the window. "The Empire State—you know, it doesn't look right even now. It's got the wrong shape. Not like a Wunkery at all."

"Like a what?" Dr. Scott asked.

"A Wunkery. Dr. Rasp's sky-slit has a fine view of a—"

"You know there is no such thing as a Wunkery, don't you?" Dr. Scott broke in with a slight touch of undoctorly impatience. "Dr. Rasp is a creation of your unconscious mind. When you go to sleep you simply dream like anyone else. There is no world full of Wunkeries and Rasps. All that is just a defense against me, isn't it?"

"No," Hooten said drowsily.

Dr. Scott sighed. "Do things begin to look blurry yet?"

"No, but I'm . . . I'm beginning to. . . ."

"To what?"

"To wake up," Hooten said indistinctly, and closed his eyes. "Hello, Dr. Rasp."

"There is no Dr. Rasp," Dr. Scott said in an impatient voice. "Dr. Rasp is imaginary."

"Dr. Rasp says you don't exist," Hooten murmured, his eyes shut. "Yes, Dr. Rasp. . . ."

Hooten opened his faceted eyes and stared through the sky-slit at the Quatt Wunkery. He shook his head dizzily.

"What's the matter?" Dr. Rasp asked.

"Dr. Scott just gave me an injection of sodium pentothal," Hooten said.

The psychiatrist made a quick note on his wing-case. Then he crossed his antennae with Hooten's again and turned on the juice.

"Dr. Scott is simply a defense," he pointed out. "There is no Dr. Scott. There is no such thing as sodium pentothal. You are going to estivate now, do you hear me? You will be deeply asleep, so deeply that Dr. Scott cannot wake you up. You will obey *me,* not Dr. Scott. I tell you to estivate. Do you hear me?"

"Yes . . . but I'm afraid it isn't going to work very well. You see, if I estivate I'll just wake up in Dr. Scott's—"

"There is no Dr. Scott. Forget Dr. Scott."

"But—"

"Estivate. Estivate."

"All right. Now I'm . . . oh, hello, Dr. Scott."

Dr. Scott reached for another hypodermic and used it.

"Just relax," he said gently.

"I'm beginning to hate this," Hooten said pettishly. "I'm caught right in the middle. Something's going to give if we keep on. I don't know what, but—can't we postpone it till tomorrow and let Dr. Rasp have his innings?"

"I am your doctor," Scott pointed out. "Not Dr. Rasp. You refer Dr. Rasp to me if he tries to—"

"Oh, those antennae," Hooten murmured. "I can't—I—"

"Just relax," Dr. Scott said. "There is no Dr. Rasp."

Hooten struggled feebly. "This can't go on," he protested in a drowsy voice. "I tell you, something will have to give. I—oh, for God's sake, Dr. Rasp keeps telling me to estivate."

"Hush," Dr. Scott said, looking thoughtfully toward the hypodermics.

"Estivate," said Dr. Rasp.

"Look out!" Hooten said wildly, struggling. "He's going to give me another shot."

Dr. Rasp curled his antennae tightly around Hooten's and poured on more juice.

"Estivate," he said, and then had a sudden idea. "You too, Dr. Scott. Do you hear me? You're going to estivate, Dr. Scott. Relax. Stop struggling. You're in a warm, comfortable, musty burrow. You're beginning to estivate, Dr. Scott. . . ."

"Now he's trying to make you estivate," Hooten said, squirming on the couch.

Dr. Scott smiled grimly. He bent forward and fixed Hooten with a compelling gaze.

"Relax," he said. "I'm talking to you, Dr. Rasp. Relax and sleep. I'm going to give you another shot of pentothal in a moment, and that will put you to sleep. Do you hear me, Dr. Rasp?"

"Oh, God," Hooten said, blinking his eyes very rapidly indeed. "I feel as though I'm on an alternating current. What's going to happen? I warn you—we'd better stop this before—"

He squealed faintly as Dr. Scott punctured his skin with a hypodermic, filled, however, with nothing but a harmless and ineffective solution designed for psychosomatic purposes only. Hooten was already at the brink of tolerance for sodium pentothal and should have been fathoms deep long ago.

"Go to sleep, Dr. Rasp," Dr. Scott commanded in a firm, confident voice.

"Estivate, Dr. Scott," Dr. Rasp ordered.

"Sleep."

"Estivate."

"Sleep!"

"Wow!" cried Timothy Hooten, springing to his feet with the certain conviction that something had at last, quite resoundingly, given.

In the middle of Dr. Scott's office the air was still quivering around a buglike form that staggered on all sixes. Dr. Rasp's antennae vibrated almost to invisibility as he fixed his faceted stare in dazed disbelief upon the window, the Empire State Building, and the absurdly bipedal form of Timothy Hooten.

Dr. Scott in a shimmer of disturbed space-time gazed in wild surmise at the figure reclining before him, all six legs curled in comfortable relaxation, faceted eyes staring. "Hallucination, of course," he told himself dizzily. "Of course, of course, of course. . . ."

He turned his head for the reassuring sight of his own office around him and his eyes fell upon the sky-slit and the view beyond. The first glimmers of awful conviction began to dawn. He had never seen a Quatt Wunkery before.

Luisa Mercedes Levinson

Argentinian writer best known for La Casa de los Felipes *and* Concierto en mi. *In 1959* La Palida Rosa de Soho *appeared, an important collection of shorter works, from which the selection that follows is taken.*

THE DREAM THAT WAS VIOLATED

We have to hurry with this story because it depends solely on the time it takes to tell it. And on you.

Elsa Grau found it necessary to see, for the second time, *The Fog on Pier 77*. It was playing at a small movie house near the docks. It was about three-thirty in the afternoon and a sallow, sodden sun made one want to stretch and yawn. The river prowled past that part of town.

Elsa entered the darkness. Two other films on the bill slaked her expectations and surfeited her capacity for surprise. In the second film, the camera, as though caught in a trap, lingered over a cot that was used in shifts, by a stevedore at night and by a woman during the day. At dusk the woman would leave for work and the man would return; at dawn she would arrive and he would leave. Always the same desperation and battle, and the same compulsion to stretch out on that cot. Their sleep was a respite, to all appearances, between two disconnected drinking bouts, but Elsa thought that the camera, despite the doggedness of its focus, had not been able to capture the essential; the dream that had to continue without a pause, that could never be broken off, the infinite dream. She was certain that that man and that woman who, at the birth and death of day (or at the birth and death of night) cursed and beat one another for the possession of a cot, were no more than the means the dream had availed itself of in order to continue, which it had to do at all costs. Before the film she had come to see, *The Fog on Pier 77*, came on, Elsa felt too tired to be able to focus her attention. It seemed as though her living self had been swallowed up in the darkness by the story, and that the rest, perhaps the essential, was floating in the dusty air and was in danger of being devoured by the audience. Chocolate vendors stared at her too fixedly: she ran out.

It was night. A few drops of rain glanced off her cheeks. It turned out she felt it strange to have sensations: like being dead and feeling life.

The everyday things appeared new and hallucinating: the river, the port itself, a light. At that moment it was natural to descend a small set of steps to a boat, to stand there on the deck, to look at and approach slowly and look at again, a little more closely, a man sleeping. Meanwhile the drops of rain kept running off her hair: she felt a sensual pleasure at the little cold threads of water against her neck.

Elsa took one step and paused: then another: and saw what she had always hoped for, dreamed about: she saw a man's dream, a real living dream with figures that moved, acted, obeyed a law. Elsa wanted to know, to know. What destiny, what pattern did the dream figures obey? Suddenly they were motionless. Their stares knew something about her, too much. Then one figure waved an arm; it was a signal. The others copied it. They were calling her; why? Elsa recognized that bloody figure which struggled among them. That bloodied form was hers, it belonged to her, it had been torn from her own dreams.

That gesticulating group was not serious, now it verged on the ridiculous, it appeared as though it were acting especially for her. She dropped her guard for a moment and took one step more. It was the definitive one: she had penetrated the circle of a dream.

Now the figures no longer occupied themselves with her. The bloodied form turned into a wolf. Elsa stood there, not knowing what to do. She had lost her previous destiny and did not yet know how to submit to the other.

Suddenly an empty contour described itself, becoming more and more familiar. It was she, Elsa Grau, the form of Elsa Grau, her exact dimension, and the contour closed around her, snaring her, capturing her. And it was swelling with her anxiety and dread.

Elsa wanted to scream but had no voice. The contour was choking her, or her lethargy was accumulating . . . Elsa Grau knew that now she could not leave the circle of the dream.

And if the man who was sleeping woke up? Maybe the other forms in the dream could continue their destinies without asking questions, maybe they'd evaporate. But Elsa Grau, Elsa Grau . . .

She's there, in that circle of dream she has violated; she is there, as though caught in a snare, inside the contour of a dream figure, squeezed in, not knowing what can happen, afterward.

The man who is sleeping is moving now, he is ready to wake up. Someone is needed to relieve him, someone who will fall asleep immediately, immediately and keep on with that dream.

Elsa is afraid. An interruption, that might carry her off to—where? Please, you continue the dream. Consider that this violating a dream is something that might happen to anyone, even you.

Translated from the Spanish by Paul Blackburn

Jorge Luis Borges

Argentinian writer born in 1899, the author of poems, critical studies, and short stories of an abstract, fantastic nature. He is principally known in this country for Ficciones *and* Labyrinth and Other Writings. *The selection below appeared in* El Hacedor, *published in 1960.*

EVERYTHING AND NOTHING

There was no one in him; behind his face (which even in the poor paintings of the period is unlike any other) and his words, which were copious, imaginative, and excited, there was nothing but a little chill, a dream not dreamed by anyone. At first he thought everyone was like him, but the puzzled look on a friend's face when he remarked on that emptiness told him he was mistaken and convinced him forever that an individual must not differ from his species. Occasionally he thought he would find in books the cure for his ill, and so he learned the small Latin and less Greek of which a contemporary was to speak. Later he thought that in the exercise of an elemental human rite he might well find what he sought, and he let himself be initiated by Anne Hathaway one long June afternoon. At twenty-odd he went to London. Instinctively, he had already trained himself in the habit of pretending that he was someone, so it would not be discovered that he was no one. In London he hit upon the profession to which he was predestined, that of actor, who plays on stage at being someone else, before a gathering of persons who play at taking him for that someone else. His playacting taught him a singular happiness, perhaps the first he had known; but when the last line was applauded and the last corpse removed from the stage, the hated sense of unreality came over him again. He ceased to be Ferrex or Tamburlaine and again became a nobody. Trapped, he fell to imagining other heroes and other tragic tales. Thus, while in London's bawdyhouses and taverns his body fulfilled its destiny as body, the soul that dwelled in it was Caesar, who fails to heed the augurer's admonition, and Juliet, who detests the lark, and Macbeth, who converses on the heath with the witches who are also the fates. Nobody was ever as many men as that man, who like the Egyptian Proteus managed to exhaust all the possible shapes of being. At times he slipped into some corner of his work a confession, certain that it would not be deciphered; Richard affirms that in his single person he plays many parts, and Iago says with strange words, "I am not what I am." His passages on the fundamental identity of existing, dreaming, and acting are famous.

Twenty years he persisted in that controlled hallucination, but one morning he was overcome by the surfeit and the horror of being so many kings who die by the sword and so many unhappy lovers who converge, diverge, and melodiously agonize. That same day he disposed of his theater. Before a week was out he had returned to the village of his birth, where he recovered the trees and the river of his childhood; and he did not bind them to those others his muse had celebrated, those made illustrious by mythological allusions and

Latin phrases. He had to be someone; he became a retired impresario who has made his fortune and who interests himself in loans, lawsuits, and petty usury. In this character he dictated the arid final will and testament that we know, deliberately excluding from it every trace of emotion and of literature. Friends from London used to visit his retreat, and for them he would take on again the role of poet.

The story goes that, before or after he died, he found himself before God and he said: "I, who have been so many men in vain, want to be one, myself." The voice of God replied from a whirlwind: "Neither do I exist; I dreamed the world as you dreamed your work, my Shakespeare, and among the shapes of my dream are you, who, like me, are many persons and none."

Translated from the Spanish by Mildred Boyer

Julio Cortazar

Argentinian author born in 1914 in Belgium. He is known for a dramatic poem, Los Reyes, *published in 1949, two short-story collections,* Bestiario *and* Final del Juego, *and his novel,* Los Premios. *The selection that follows is taken from* Bestiario.

THE DISTANCES

The Diary of Alina Reyes:

January 12.

Last night it happened again, I so tired of bracelets and cajoleries, of pink champagne and Renato Viñes' face, oh that face like a spluttering seal, that picture of Dorian Gray in the last stages. It was a pleasure to go to bed to the Red Bank Boogie, with a chocolate mint, mama ashen-faced and yawning (as she always comes back from parties, ashen and half-asleep, an enormous fish and not even that).

Nora who says to fall asleep when it's light, the hubbub already starting in the street in the middle of the urgent chronicles her sister tells half-undressed. How happy they are, I turn off the lights and the hands, take all my clothes off to the cries of daytime and stirring, I want to sleep and I'm a terrible sounding bell, a wave, the chain the dog trails all night against the privet hedges. Now I lay me down to sleep . . . I have to recite verses, or the system of looking for words with *a,* then with *a* and *e,* with five vowels, with four. With two and one consonant (obo, emu), with four consonants and a vowel (crass, dross), then the poems again, The moon came down to the forge/ in its crinoline of tuberoses./ The boy looks and looks./ The boy is looking at it. With three and three in alternate order, cabala, bolero, animal; pavane, Canada, repose, regale.

So hours pass: with four, with three and two, then later palindromes: easy ones like hah, bob, mom, did, dad, gag, radar; then more complicated or nice silly ones like oho Eve oho, or the Napoleon joke, "able was I ere I saw Elba." Or the beautiful anagrams: Salvador Dalí, *avida dollars*; Alina Reyes, *es la reina y* . . . That one's so nice because it opens a path, because it does not close. Because the queen and . . . *la reina y* . . .

No, horrible. Horrible because it opens a path to this one who is not the queen and whom I hate again at night. To her who is Alina Reyes but not the queen of the anagram; let her be anything, a Budapest beggar, a beginner at a house of prostitution in Jujuy, a servant in Quetzaltenango, any place that's far away and not the queen. But yes Alina Reyes and because of that last night it happened again, to feel her and the hate.

January 20.

At times I know that she's cold, that she suffers, that they beat her. I can only hate her so much, detest the hands that throw her to the ground and her as well, her even more because they beat her, because I am I and they beat her. Oh, I'm not so despondent when I'm sleeping or when I cut a suit or it's the hours mama receives and I'm serving tea to the Señora Regules or to the boy from the Rivas'. Then it's less important to me, it's a little more like something personal, I with myself; I feel she is more mistress of her adversity, far away and alone, but the mistress. Let her suffer, let her freeze; I endure it from here, and I believe that then I help her a little. Like making bandages for a soldier who hasn't been wounded yet, and to feel that's acceptable, that one is soothing him beforehand, providentially.

Let her suffer. I give a kiss to the Señora Regules, tea to the boy from the Rivas', and I keep myself for that inner resistance. I say to myself: "Now I'm crossing a bridge, it's all frozen, now the snow's coming in through my shoes. They're broken." It's not that she's feeling nothing. I only know it's like that, that on one side I'm crossing a bridge at the same instant (but I don't know if it is at the same instant) as the boy from the Rivas' accepts the cup of tea from me and puts on his best spoiled face. And I stand it all right because I'm alone among all these people without sensitivity and I'm not so despondent. Nora was petrified last night, and asked: "But what's happening to you?" It was happening to that one, to me far off. Something horrible must have happened to her, they were beating her or she was feeling sick and just when Nora was going to sing Fauré and I at the piano gazing happily at Luis María leaning with his elbows on the back of it which made him look like a model, he gazing at me with his puppy-look, the two of us so close and loving one another so much. It's worse when that happens, when I know something about her just at the moment I'm dancing with Luis María, kissing him, or just near him. Because in the distances they do not love me—her. That's the part they don't like and as it doesn't suit me to be rent to pieces inside and to feel they are beating me or that the snow is coming in through my shoes when Luis María is dancing with me and his hand on my waist makes the strong odor of oranges, or of cut hay, rise in me like heat at midday, and they are beating her and it's impossible to fight back, and I have to tell Luis María that I don't feel well, it's the humidity, humidity in all that snow which I do not feel, which I do not feel and it's coming in through my shoes.

January 25.

Sure enough, Nora came to see me and made a scene. "Look, doll, that's the last time I ask you to play piano for me. We were quite an act." What did I know about acts, I accompanied her as best I could, I remember hearing her as though she were muted. *Votre âme est un paysage choisi* . . . but I watched my hands on the keys and it seemed to me they were playing all right, that they accompanied Nora decently. Luis María also was watching my hands. Poor thing, I think that was because it didn't cheer him up particularly to look at my face. I must look pretty strange.

Poor little Nora. Let someone else accompany her. (Each time this seems more of a punishment, now I know myself there only when I'm about to be happy, when I am happy, when Nora is singing Fauré I know myself there and only the hate is left.)

Night.

At times it's tenderness, a sudden and necessary tenderness toward her who is not queen and walks there. I would like to send her a telegram, my respects, to know that her sons are well or that she does not have sons—because I don't think there I have sons—and could use consolation, compassion, candy. Last night I fell asleep thinking up messages, places to meet. WILL ARRIVE THURSDAY STOP MEET ME AT BRIDGE. What bridge? An idea that recurs just as Budapest always recurs, to believe in the beggar in Budapest where they'll have lots of bridges and percolating snow. Then I sat straight up in bed and almost bawling, I almost run and wake mama, bite her to make her wake up. I keep on thinking about it. It is still not easy to say it. I keep on thinking that if I really wanted to, if it struck my fancy, I would be able to go to Budapest right away. Or to Jujuy or Quetzaltenango. (I went back to look up those names, pages back.) Useless, it would be the same as saying Tres Arroyos, Kobe, Florida Street in the 400-block. Budapest just stays because *there* it's cold, there they beat me and abuse me. There (I dreamed it, it's only a dream, but as it sticks and works itself into my wakefulness) there's someone called Rod—or Erod, or Rodo—and he beats me and I love him, I don't know if I love him but I let him beat me, that comes back day after day, so I guess I do love him.

Later.

A lie. I dreamed of Rod or made him from some dream figure already worn out or to hand. There's no Rod, they're punishing me there, but who knows whether it's a man, an angry mother, a solitude.

Come find me. To say to Luis María: "We're getting married and you're taking me to Budapest, to a bridge where there's snow and someone." I say: and if I am? (Because I think all that from the secret vantage point of not seriously believing it. And if I am?) All right, if I am . . . But plain crazy, plain. . . ? What a honeymoon!

January 28.

I thought of something odd. It's been three days now that nothing has come to me from the distances. Maybe they don't beat her now, or she could have come by a coat. To send her a telegram, some stockings . . . I thought of something odd. I arrived in the terrible city and it was afternoon, a green watery afternoon as afternoons never are if one does not help out by thinking of them. Beside the Dobrina Stana, on the Skorda Prospect equestrian statues bristling with stalagmites of hoarfrost and stiff policemen, great smoking loaves of coarse bread and flounces of wind puffing in the windows. At a tourist's pace, walking by the Dobrina, the map in the pocket of my blue suit (in this freezing weather and to leave my coat in the Burglos), until I come to a plaza next to the river, nearly in the river thundering with broken ice floes and barges and some kingfisher which is called there *sbundia tjéno* or something worse.

I supposed that the bridge came after the plaza. I thought that and did not want go on. It was the afternoon of Elsa Piaggio de Tarelli's concert at the Odeón, I fussed over getting dressed, unwilling, suspecting that afterwards only insomnia would be waiting for me. This thought of the night, so much of night . . . Who knows if I would not get lost. One invents names while traveling, thinking, remembers them at the moment: Dobrina Stana, *sbundia tjéno,* The Burglos. But I don't know the name of the square, it is a little as though one had really walked into a plaza in Budapest and was lost because one did not know its name; if there's no name, how can there be a plaza?

I'm coming, mama. We'll get to your Bach all right, and your Brahms. The way there is easy. No plaza, no Hotel Burglos. We are here, Elsa Piaggio there. Sad to have to interrupt this, to know that I'm in a plaza (but that's not sure yet, I only think so and that's nothing, less than nothing). And that at the end of the plaza the bridge begins.

Night.

Begins, goes on. Between the end of the concert and the first piece I found the name and the route. Vladas Square and the Market Bridge. I crossed Vladas Square to where the bridge started, going along slowly and wanting to stop at times, to stay in the houses or store windows, in small boys all bundled up and the fountains with tall heroes with their long cloaks all white, Tadeo Alanko and Vladislas Néroy, tokay drinkers and cymbalists. I saw Elsa Piaggio acclaimed between one Chopin and another Chopin, poor thing, and my orchestra seat gave directly onto the plaza, with the beginning of the bridge between the most immense columns. But I was thinking this, notice, it's the same as making the anagram *es la reina y . . .* in place of Alina Reyes, or imagining mama at the Suarez' house instead of beside me. Better not to fall for that nonsense; that's something very strictly my own, to give in to the desire, the real desire. Real because Alina, well, let's go— Not the other thing, not feeling her being cold or that they mistreat her. I long for this and follow it by choice, by knowing where it's going, to find out if Luis María is going to take me to Budapest, if we get married and I ask him to take me to Budapest. Easier to go out and look for that bridge, to go out on my own search and find myself, as now, because now I've walked to the middle of the bridge amid shouts and applause, between "Albéniz!" and more applause and "The Polonaise!" as if that had any meaning amid the whipping snow which pushes against my back with the wind-force, hands like a thick towel around my waist drawing me to the center of the bridge.

(It's more convenient to speak in the present tense. This was at eight o'clock when Elsa Piaggio was playing the third piece, I think it was Julián Aguirre or Carlos Guastavino, something with pastures and little birds.) I have grown coarse with time, I have no respect for her now. I remember I thought one day: "There they beat me, there the snow comes in through my shoes and I know it at that moment, when it is happening to me there I know it at the same time. But why at the same time? Probably I'm coming late, probably it hasn't happened yet. Probably they will beat her within fourteen years or she's already a cross and an epitaph in the St. Ursule cemetery." And that seemed to me pleasant, possible, quite idiotic. Because behind that, one falls always into the matching time. If now she were really starting over the bridge, I know I would feel it myself, from here. I remember that I stopped to look at the river which was like spoiled mayonnaise thrashing against the abutments, furiously as possible, noisy and lashing. (This last I was thinking.) It was worth it to lean over the parapet of the bridge and to hear in my ears the grinding of the ice there below. It was worth it to stop a little bit for the view, a little bit from fear too which came from inside—or it was being without a coat, the light snowfall melting and my topcoat at the hotel—And after all, for I am an unassuming girl, a girl without petty prides, but let them come tell me that the same thing could have happened to anyone else, that she could have journeyed to Hungary in the middle of the Odeón. Say, that would give anyone the shivers!

But mama was pulling at my sleeve, there was hardly anyone left in the orchestra section. I'm writing to that point, not wishing to go on remembering what I thought. I'm going to get sick if I go on remembering. But it's certain, certain; I thought of an odd thing.

January 30.

Poor Luis María, what an idiot to get married to me. He doesn't know what he'll get on top of that. Or underneath that Nora says, posing as an emancipated intellectual.

January 31.

We'll be going there. He was so agreeable about it I almost screamed. I was afraid, it seemed to me that he entered into this game too easily. And he doesn't know anything, he's like a queen's pawn that sews up the game without even suspecting it. The little pawn Luis María beside his queen. Beside the queen and—

February 7.

What's important now is to get better. I won't write the end of what I had thought at the concert. Last night again I sensed her suffering. I know that they're beating me there again. I can't avoid knowing it, but enough chronicle. If I had limited myself to setting this down regularly just as a whim, as alleviation . . . It was worse, a desire to understand in reading it over; to find keys in each word set to paper after those nights. Like when I thought of the plaza, the torn river and the noises and afterwards . . . But I'm not writing that, I'll never, ever, write that.

To go there to convince myself that celibacy has been no good for me, that it's nothing more than that, to be twenty-seven years old and never to have had a man. Now he will be my puppy, my penguin, enough to think and to be, to be finally and for good.

Nevertheless, now that I shall close this diary, for one gets married or one keeps a diary, the two things don't go well together—even now I don't want to finish it up without saying this with the happiness of hope, with hope for happiness. We will go there but it doesn't have to be what I thought the night of the concert. (I'll write it, and enough of the diary as far as I'm concerned.) I will find her on the bridge and we will look at one another. The night of the concert I felt echo in my ears the grinding of the ice there below. And it will be the queen's victory over that malignant relationship, that soundless and unlawful encroachment. If I am really I, she will yield, she will join my radiant *zone,* my lovelier and surer life; I have only to go to her side and lay a hand on her shoulder.

Alina Reyes de Aráoz and her husband arrived in Budapest April sixth, and took accommodations at the Ritz. That was two months before their divorce. On the afternoon of the second day, Alina went out to get to know the city and enjoy the thaw. As it pleased her to walk alone—she was brisk and curious—she went in twenty different directions looking vaguely for something, but without thinking about it too much, content to let her desire choose, that it express itself in abrupt changes of direction which led her from one store window to another, crossing streets, moving from one showcase to another.

She came to the bridge and crossed it as far as the middle, walking now with some difficulty because the snow hindered her and from the Danube a wind comes up from below, a difficult wind which hooks and lashes. She felt as though her skirt were glued to her thighs (she was not dressed properly for the weather) and suddenly a desire to turn around, to go back to the familiar city. At the center of the desolate bridge the ragged woman with black straight hair waited with something fixed and anxious in the lined face, in the folding of the hands, a little closed but already outstretched. Alina was close to her, repeating, now she knew, facial expressions and distances as if after a dress rehearsal. Without foreboding, liberating herself at last—she believed it in one terrible, jubilant, cold leap—she was beside her and also stretched out her hands, refusing to think, and the woman on the bridge hugged her against her chest and the two, stiff and silent, embraced one another on the bridge with the crumbling river hammering against the abutments.

Alina ached: it was the clasp of the pocketbook, the strength of the embrace had run it in between her breasts with a sweet, bearable laceration. She surrounded the slender woman, feeling her complete and absolute within her arms, with a springing up of happiness equal to a hymn, to loosing a cloud of pigeons, to the river singing. She shut her eyes in the total fusion, declining the sensations from outside, the evening light; suddenly very tired but sure of her victory, without celebrating it as so much her own and at last.

It seemed to her that one of the two of them was weeping softly. It should have been her because she felt her cheeks wet, and even the cheekbone aching as though she had been struck there. Also the throat, and then suddenly the shoulders, weighed down by innumerable hardships. Opening her eyes (perhaps now she screamed) she saw that they had separated. Now she did scream. From the cold, because the snow was coming in through her broken shoes, because making her way along the roadway to the plaza went Alina Reyes, very lovely in her grey suit, her hair a little loose against the wind, not turning her face. Going off.

Translated from the Spanish by Paul Blackburn

Conclusion

Bernard Groethuysen

1880-1946

Philosopher, essayist, and literary critic, Groethuysen was the author of various semi-historical, semi-philosophic works. The selection that follows was first published in the French magazine, Mesures, *in 1938.*

THE EPISTEMOLOGY OF THE DREAM

I. A MEETING BETWEEN A READER AND AN UNKNOWN AUTHOR

AUTHOR: Let's have a talk.

READER: But I don't know you.

AUTHOR: But why do you have to know me? What I say should be enough.

READER: But what if you should later take back what you say?

AUTHOR: I promise you I won't.

READER: But do we know what we say?

AUTHOR: I must admit I don't understand you.

READER: Look. . . The other day I met a madman who believed he was Christ. He told me he had given the *Sermon on the Mount*.

AUTHOR: And did you ever hear him give a sermon?

READER: Yes, I saw him preach.

AUTHOR: And you heard his words?

READER: I could repeat them for you.

AUTHOR: What for? The word of a madman is enough for me.

READER: But he didn't speak on the Mount.

AUTHOR: Obviously.

READER: And he wasn't Christ.

AUTHOR: How can you say the contrary? But what he said, he said.

READER: How can this interest you, since everything he said is false?

AUTHOR: It's up to you to judge if what I say is true or false. But listen to me first.

READER: Gladly. But promise me you won't later disavow what you say.

AUTHOR: Of course.

II. THE AUTHOR SPEAKS OF HORRIBLE THINGS, BUT IT'S ONLY A DREAM

AUTHOR: At last we can begin our discussion.

READER: Wait a second; I must tell you a story. The other night I saw you in a dream. We met, just like today, and you spoke to me.

AUTHOR: What did I say?

READER: You spoke of horrible things.

AUTHOR: Horrible things?

READER: Horrible things.

AUTHOR: And what happened next?

READER: I woke up and called Eulalia who sleeps in the next room.

AUTHOR: And what did she tell you?

READER: To go back to sleep.
AUTHOR: And is that what you did?
READER: No, I began reading a novel. Maybe you know it.
AUTHOR: What's the title?
READER: *Theodore and Sophie.*
AUTHOR: And what did you do next?
READER: That's all.
AUTHOR: But can't you repeat to me the horrible things I told you?
READER: You'd blush.
AUTHOR: Why should I be ashamed, since I never said anything of the sort?
READER: I wish I could believe you.

III. WRITING NOVELS ISN'T THE SAME THING AS SPEAKING IN DREAMS

AUTHOR: Don't you want to discuss things with me?
READER: You know very well why.
AUTHOR: Tell me anyway.
READER: You don't keep your promises.
AUTHOR: Well, what was it I promised?
READER: You don't even remember it any more. Never to take back what you say
AUTHOR: And what have I disclaimed?
READER: Your horrible things of the other night.
AUTHOR: But you were dreaming.
READER: Prove to me right now that, listening to you, I'm not dreaming.
AUTHOR: I wouldn't know how to do it. But, tell me, haven't you ever spoken in a dream?
READER: Yes, from time to time I have. In fact, the other night I distinctly said, "Go away!"
AUTHOR: And was this addressed to me?
READER: Yes, you had spoken of horrible things.
AUTHOR: And you really uttered those words?
READER: Certainly. In the morning at breakfast Eulalia repeated them to me. But what are you trying to get at?
AUTHOR: That everything in a dream isn't dreamed.
READER: Would you by chance maintain that these horrible things had really been said?
AUTHOR: I ask you that.
READER: That isn't the case here. I don't think I'm capable of anything like that.
AUTHOR: Maybe that's why you had me say them. But let's talk

about something else. What about that novel you started the other night?

READER: I only read a few pages.

AUTHOR: And what does Theodore have to say?

READER: Silly things.

AUTHOR: Are you holding that against him?

READER: Why should I want to do that, since he doesn't exist?

AUTHOR: Then who said these silly things?

READER: The author, obviously.

AUTHOR: It's lucky you're not an author.

READER: Why?

AUTHOR: I would have suspected you of having said the horrible things which you attribute to me.

READER: But as a reader?

AUTHOR: You aren't responsible.

READER: Then everything depends on one's knowing if one is an author or a reader.

AUTHOR: Perhaps.

READER: It's late and I'm in a hurry to get on with my novel.

IV. IN WHAT WAY DOES A CHARACTER IN A NOVEL EXIST? WE ONLY MEET AUTHORS AND READERS

AUTHOR: What have you been doing with yourself since last time?

READER: I've been reading my novel.

AUTHOR: And what's becoming of Theodore?

READER: He speaks.

AUTHOR: Won't you tell me what he said?

READER: What for? He's speaking of a Sophie who doesn't exist any more than he does.

AUTHOR: But how do you know what he says?

READER: I read it.

AUTHOR: *You* did—then you exist?

READER: Certainly. I read, therefore I am.

AUTHOR: Ah, if Theodore could only read what he says!

READER: Don't put words into my mouth. I don't exist by myself. Every reader has his author.

AUTHOR: So there would always be a reader and an author. And Theodore, who doesn't exist.

READER: Yes, of the three he's the one who doesn't exist.

AUTHOR: Well, then: you and I, we exist.

READER: You? How do you exist?

AUTHOR: I'll have to acknowledge it finally: I'm the novel's author.

READER: I thought as much.

AUTHOR: And the two of us communicate in a nonexistent Theodore, you as a reader and I as the author. Does that make sense to you?

READER: Let me think about it.

V. THAT WHAT YOU HEAR SAID IN A DREAM IS WHAT SOMEONE MUST HAVE SAID

AUTHOR: You seem preoccupied.

READER: Theodore came to me in the night.

AUTHOR: And what did he say to you?

READER: No one spoke. I was all alone in bed.

AUTHOR: But what seems to be on your mind?

READER: I heard Theodore speak.

AUTHOR: You must have had a dream.

READER: Obviously. But then who uttered the words that I heard in my dream?

AUTHOR: I'd like to know myself.

READER: Are you suggesting, by any chance, that your Theodore was me?

AUTHOR: I wouldn't want to affirm anything.

READER: Now listen: I wasn't Theodore; I was what he said.

AUTHOR: I'm not following you too well now.

READER: I am the voice of this nonexistent person.

AUTHOR: You'll have to explain yourself better.

READER: That's what I'm going to try to do. The other night I dreamed of you. You remember that still.

AUTHOR: Very well.

READER: And when you came to me we embraced. Now I don't pretend that you embraced me, nor that, you not being there, I embraced myself in your place, nor that. . .

AUTHOR: Evidently.

READER: You've confused me. Where was I?

AUTHOR: You didn't to me, I didn't to you, you aren't you, I'm not . . .

READER: Stop! You've made your point. On the other hand, when I then told you to go away—you remember that?—it was me all right who said it.

AUTHOR: Eulalia confirms it.

READER: I don't need her to know that. The only truth is what is said. Every word in my dream was really uttered.

AUTHOR: But by whom?

READER: By me, obviously, since we're discussing my dream. But it's getting dark. We've got to quit for now.

VI. THE READER DOESN'T WANT TO BE A FICTIONAL CHARACTER: HE WANTS TO BE, TOO

AUTHOR: You've come early. I have a question for you.

READER: All right.

AUTHOR: I'd like to know how what you told me about your dream applies to my novel.

READER: I'll explain. In my dream, I alone speak. Does that make sense?

AUTHOR: There was no one there who could speak for you.

READER: But there were characters in my dream.

AUTHOR: Myself among others.

READER: And still others I haven't mentioned. Everything to do with these characters is my invention.

AUTHOR: Otherwise you wouldn't have been dreaming.

READER: But what about their words?

AUTHOR: They didn't say them.

READER: But what they said, someone said.

AUTHOR: And that someone. . .is you?

READER: Yes, me.

AUTHOR: But you didn't invent yourself.

READER: At least as far as my speech goes. For I imagined myself doing things I didn't do.

AUTHOR: One speaks while dreaming, but one doesn't dream of speaking. Right?

READER: Yes, we don't dream our words, not even the words we hear spoken by other people. We say them.

AUTHOR: Then everything that is said is your own.

READER: Whatever was said, I said.

AUTHOR: Even the horrible things you attributed to me?

READER: Don't interrupt me. In our dreams we conduct monologues with the help of interposed characters. Are you in agreement with that?

AUTHOR: But how will you apply this to my novel?

READER: Nothing could be easier. You have done none of the things Theodore is supposed to have done. It isn't you who pursued Sophie with your attentions. But you are saying what Theodore is supposed to say.

AUTHOR: And also everything that Sophie replies to Theodore.

READER: Naturally.

AUTHOR: To write a novel is, I conclude, to be speaking alone.

READER: Every novel is an interior dialogue.

AUTHOR: And our conversation now—wouldn't that be an exterior dialogue?

READER: Yes, for fortunately I'm not your Theodore.
AUTHOR: Nor yours? Are you quite sure of that?

VII. THE READER IS WILLING TO READ THE NOVEL OUT LOUD, BUT HE WON'T PUT HIS NAME TO IT

READER: It seemed to me that last time you weren't quite serious. I'd like to have your views.
AUTHOR: It is to discover them that I came to see you. Have you gone on reading my novel?
READER: I'm at the place now where Theodore has gone to see Sophie.
AUTHOR: Can you repeat what Theodore said to her?
READER: He says: "I beg your forgiveness, Sophie, for having thought you unfaithful." And she was, for that matter.
AUTHOR: Poor Theodore! But you just said something.
READER: Then you must not have been listening. I just said to you what Theodore said to Sophie.
AUTHOR: May I ask you to repeat it for me?
READER: All right: "I beg your forgiveness, Sophie, for having thought you unfaithful."
AUTHOR: I thank you.
READER: But why have me repeat it?
AUTHOR: I like to hear you say it.
READER: But it isn't me who said it, but Theodore.
AUTHOR: Then Theodore is able to speak?
READER: If it isn't him, it's you.
AUTHOR: Me? But wouldn't I have said to Sophie: "You have betrayed me, faithless one . . ." or something to that effect?
READER: You didn't say it to Sophie, but to . . . it doesn't matter to whom. To the readers, to me, for example.
AUTHOR: I would have said to you: "Sophie. . ." But let's go on. And next you said what I said to you.
READER: I repeated what you had said.
AUTHOR: And in repeating it, you said it.
READER: How would I have been able to say it, without repeating it?
AUTHOR: Then we both must have said it.
READER: But you said it first.
AUTHOR: What does that prove?

VIII. THAT ONE MUST NOT CONFUSE THE AUTHOR WITH HIS CHARACTER

READER: I don't know what to speak to you about.
AUTHOR: Tell me about my novel.
READER: I'll be careful not to do that.
AUTHOR: Why?
READER: You make me say things I haven't said.
AUTHOR: By making you repeat Theodore's words?
READER: Precisely. Theodore is you; Theodore isn't me.
AUTHOR: You're mistaken. I'm not Theodore.
READER: Don't you want to have said what he said, either?
AUTHOR: I don't believe in Sophie's innocence.
READER: You know what Theodore doesn't know.
AUTHOR: He doesn't know about Sophie.
READER: That's also why he wouldn't have been able to write your novel.
AUTHOR: Theodore must have an author.
READER: And a reader.
AUTHOR: He could scarcely get along without them.
READER: But where does that bring you?
AUTHOR: To this: Theodore and I. . . are two.
READER: And with me, three. That's one too many. May I express a request?
AUTHOR: Go right ahead.
READER: That there'll be only two of us next time.
AUTHOR: I promise you.

IX. WHAT IS REPEATED IS NOT SAID

AUTHOR: Do you want to hear me out?
READER: Listening is my role, just as yours is to speak.
AUTHOR: But it seems to me that you don't succeed in defining where my role ends and where yours begins.
READER: Nevertheless, it's very simple. You're on one phone and I'm on the other.
AUTHOR: And you're willing to listen to me.
READER: Perfectly willing. Go on and ring me. I'll take the call.
AUTHOR: And would you be willing to take a message?
READER: Certainly. In fact, just the other day a gentleman told me some pretty unpleasant things about his wife.
AUTHOR: A bad type, I'm sure.
READER: And to please him, I immediately phoned his wife and told her what he had said.

AUTHOR: Did the lady get angry?

READER: Yes, she became furious.

AUTHOR: With good reason.

READER: But not at me, since I didn't say anything.

AUTHOR: Then one can say something without having said anything.

READER: Exactly. And there's the difference between us. You speak all the time, and I say nothing, even when I'm repeating what you say. That's my revelation for the day!

AUTHOR: What admirable philosophers telephone operators must be!

READER: What are you trying to say?

AUTHOR: They take calls and suspend their judgment.

READER: I'll go on. Readers don't ever argue with one another.

AUTHOR: It's a readers' paradise.

READER: And no author will ever enter it.

AUTHOR: Why not?

READER: An author always wants to say something.

AUTHOR: That's what makes him original.

READER: And that's his damnation.

AUTHOR: You—you avoid this pitfall.

READER: I only listen.

AUTHOR: But sometimes you speak in your dreams.

READER: I suppose Eulalia told you that? But let's go back to my dream. What you said to me the other day about it no longer holds.

AUTHOR: Tell me why.

READER: I'll tell you next time.

X. *EVERYONE IS A READER. ON THE VANITY OF AUTHORS*

AUTHOR: You owe me an explanation.

READER: About my dream?

AUTHOR: On the subject of the horrible things in your dream.

READER: Well, all right! Do you agree that an essential difference must be made between the person who gives a message and he who receives one?

AUTHOR: Quite.

READER: Well, I was on the receiver when the horrible things were said.

AUTHOR: But who called you? I didn't, I swear.

READER: And I didn't either, since I was listening.

AUTHOR: But who were you listening to?

READER: If it wasn't you, then someone else.

AUTHOR: Well, then, perhaps it was Theodore.
READER: You promised me you wouldn't say that name any more.
AUTHOR: Then it couldn't be anyone.
READER: No one is responsible for the horrible things in my dream.
AUTHOR: Neither the dreamer nor his character.
READER: Neither I nor you.
AUTHOR: Still, you attributed them to me.
READER: I was in error there.
AUTHOR: I don't hold it against you. But, tell me, isn't there anyone on the other end of the line?
READER: No one. The word is anonymous.
AUTHOR: But don't I sign my books?
READER: You sign what isn't yours.
AUTHOR: That would make literature only plagiarism.
READER: The true author hides himself.
AUTHOR: We listen then without knowing to whom we listen. And each of us repeats only what he hears said. And what is said, no one has said.
READER: Which makes you a reader just as I am one.
AUTHOR: And ready for paradise.

XI. HOW TO RECOGNIZE ONE'S OWN VOICE AMONG OTHERS

AUTHOR: You hardly seem like you want to listen to me.
READER: I hear voices.
AUTHOR: And among these voices, your own is there.
READER: And yours.
AUTHOR: And that of someone else.
READER: The voices of many others.
AUTHOR: Isn't Theodore's voice also there?
READER: I don't like Theodore.
AUTHOR: But what is it then you want to know?
READER: I want to know what *I* said.
AUTHOR: Eulalia will tell you.
READER: There's Eulalia again!
AUTHOR: She and Theodore. But, tell me, are you still a reader?
READER: A reader I am and a reader I'll remain.
AUTHOR: And I, an author?
READER: You certainly give me that impression.
AUTHOR: And you don't want me as a reader?
READER: Would you agree to give up writing novels?
AUTHOR: Last night I reread my novel.
READER: And were you pleased to have written it?

AUTHOR: I didn't remember it any more.
READER: But you're the author of the novel, aren't you?
AUTHOR: And its reader.
READER: And what am I?
AUTHOR: My reader.
READER: And not my own?
AUTHOR: Since you're not an author.
READER: Would you reproach me for that?
AUTHOR: I'll avoid doing that. But why are you so interested in having your own words attributed to you?
READER: Because if I want to read you, I can't be your creation.
AUTHOR: How could you be that?
READER: In order to exist, one must speak.
AUTHOR: I speak, therefore I am.
READER: Exactly.
AUTHOR: But explain yourself better.
READER: Theodore can't speak. That's why you speak for him. Therefore you exist and he doesn't.
AUTHOR: And you insist on your own existence.
READER: Right. And I must know exactly what I'm saying.
AUTHOR: Even if you're only repeating what someone else has said.
READER: What's that to me? I don't insist on having said it first; I'm not an author.
AUTHOR: Then it's enough for you to speak.
READER: And to recognize my voice. But I'm too tired to go on with this discussion.

XII. THE ANONYMITY OF THE WORD

AUTHOR: You look like you got up on the wrong side of bed.
READER: I dreamed all night.
AUTHOR: Try not to think about it any more.
READER: But if it was only a dream?
AUTHOR: Speak, and you'll see that, at least for you, it wasn't anything of the kind.
READER: That's what I'm going to do.
AUTHOR: But did you dream of me? Did I again tell you horrible things?
READER: No, this time you said nothing to me. But someone spoke to me.
AUTHOR: Someone you didn't know?
READER: He resembled you.
AUTHOR: And what did you say to him?
READER: I said: "And who are you?"

AUTHOR: You're most inquisitive. And what did he answer?
READER: He disappeared.
AUTHOR: That's surely your fault.
READER: What could I have done?
AUTHOR: Remain silent or only reply.
READER: But where does this person who speaks hide himself?
AUTHOR: Neither you nor I have met him.
READER: However, he was just there.
AUTHOR: In the Beginning was the Word.
READER: And then nothing?
AUTHOR: That's all I can say.

Translated from the French by Peter Mayer